IMPORTANT BIRD AREAS
IN THE
UNITED KINGDOM
INCLUDING THE
CHANNEL ISLANDS AND
THE ISLE OF MAN

Cover illustration: golden plover *Pluvialis apricaria* by Stephen Message
Other illustrations: John Busby, Darren Rees

© RSPB/JNCC 1992

ISBN : 0 903 138 46 8

Published by The Royal Society for the Protection of Birds, The Lodge, Sandy,
Bedfordshire SG19 2DL

RSPB Reference No 22/370/92

Typesetting by Bedford Typesetters Limited
Printed by The KPC Group, Ashford, Kent

Important Bird Areas in the United Kingdom including the Channel Islands and the Isle of Man

Editors: D E Pritchard, S D Housden (RSPB)
G P Mudge, C A Galbraith, M W Pienkowski (JNCC)

Compiled by: A M Dodd, A J Stones

Principal Contributors: A Henderson, T M Reed

This book should be cited as: D E Pritchard, S D Housden, G P Mudge, C A Galbraith and M W Pienkowski (Eds.). 1992 *Important Bird Areas in the UK including the Channel Islands and the Isle of Man*. Published by RSPB.

'Important Bird Areas' includes sites designated or identified for designation as Special Protection Areas under European Community Directive 79/409 on the Conservation of Wild Birds. Many of these will also be designated or candidate Wetlands of International Importance under the Ramsar Convention. They are given effect through sympathetic land management, with core areas notified as Sites of Special Scientific Interest, (or Areas of Special Scientific Interest in Northern Ireland).

The Royal Society for the Protection of Birds
The Lodge, Sandy, Bedfordshire SG19 2DL

English Nature
Northminster House, Peterborough PE1 1UA

Countryside Council for Wales
Plas Penrhos, Ffordd Penrhos, Bangor, Gwynedd LL57 2LQ

Scottish Natural Heritage
12 Hope Terrace, Edinburgh EH9 2AS

Joint Nature Conservation Committee
Monkstone House, City Road, Peterborough PE1 1JY

ABOUT THE PUBLISHERS

The Royal Society for the Protection of Birds is Europe's largest wildlife conservation charity, with nearly a million members. The support of this huge and growing membership is a result of the Society's positive ideas, vision for the future and record of achievement. Too often, environmentalists are accused of idealism. The RSPB's approach is practical, realistic and informed. It exists to safeguard our natural heritage by:

- buying special areas of land to manage as nature reserves for the benefit of wildlife and people;
- researching conservation issues, proposing and implementing solutions to the problems;
- developing programmes of action to safeguard our rarest species;
- campaigning for government and planning decisions sympathetic to wildlife;
- acting to promote the conservation of migratory birds and threatened species worldwide;
- placing a strong emphasis on youth and education;
- working with landowners, industry and the public to provide a better future for wildlife.

English Nature advises the Government on policies relating to and affecting nature conservation in England, and is responsible for the conservation of flora, fauna and geological features, for scheduling Sites of Special Scientific Interest and for establishing and managing National Nature Reserves and Marine Nature Reserves. It also has powers to commission research and to make grants available.

The Countryside Council for Wales is the organisation which deals with countryside matters in Wales on behalf of the Government. The Council is responsible for conserving the natural features and wildlife of Wales and the intrinsic quality of our landscape. It also promotes opportunities for access to the countryside so that we can all enjoy it. It provides advice on countryside matters to Ministers and Government departments as well as enabling others including local authorities, voluntary organisations and interested individuals to pursue countryside management projects through grant aid. The Council is accountable to the Secretary of State for Wales.

Scottish Natural Heritage is an independent government agency established by Parliament in 1992 and responsible to the Secretary of State for Scotland. Its task is to secure the conservation and enhancement of Scotland's unique and precious natural heritage. It will advise on policies and promote projects that aim to improve this heritage and support its sustainable utilisation. SNH's aim is to help people to enjoy Scotland's natural heritage responsibly, understand it more fully and use it wisely so that it can be sustained for future generations.

The UK **Joint Nature Conservation Committee** (JNCC) was established by the Environmental Protection Act 1990 'for the purposes of nature conservation, and fostering the understanding thereof' in Great Britain as a whole and outside Great Britain. JNCC is a committee of the three country councils (English Nature, Scottish Natural Heritage and the Countryside Council for Wales), together with independent members and representatives from Northern Ireland and the Countryside Commission. It is supported by specialist staff. Its statutory responsibilities include:

- the establishment of common scientific standards;
- the undertaking and commissioning of research;
- advising Ministers on the development and implementation of policies for or affecting nature conservation in Great Britain as a whole, nature conservation outside Great Britain, or European and international matters affecting nature conservation;
- the provision of advice and the dissemination of knowledge to any persons about nature conservation.

Contents

Foreword by HRH The Duke Of Edinburgh

The pressure of human population and the demands it makes on the natural environment have been gradually eroding or disturbing wildlife habitats of all kinds in all parts of the world. In this country, with its very rich wild bird heritage, the threats to coastal, wetland and migratory bird habitats are particularly severe. Drainage, pollution, disturbance and fishing pressure have already caused serious problems and I hope that the timely publication of this important book will help to ensure that the most valuable bird areas in the United Kingdom, the Channel Islands and the Isle of Man are given the effective and permanent protection that they urgently need.

The United Kingdom is a signatory to the Ramsar Convention on Wetlands of International Importance and it is also bound by the European Community Directive on the Conservation of Wild Birds. I think it is significant, and much to be welcomed, that the Royal Society for the Protection of Birds, as a voluntary body, and the four statutory nature conservation bodies, are co-operating to meet the intentions of those two international agreements. In a democratic society, things only get done when public pressure and administrative willingness coincide. The publication of this book, and the purpose it is intended to serve, augurs well for the future of our resident and migratory birds.

1992

Preface

The conservation of wild birds is an international responsibility. The great migrations of birds, their range and their diversity, have been a source of wonder and inspiration for centuries.

In the modern world, we have acquired the ability to change their distribution and numbers in many ways. The drainage of wetlands, agricultural intensification and the afforestation of open moorlands all generate significant impacts on native flora and fauna, including birds.

In the United Kingdom, birdwatching has become an enormously popular pursuit and as a result many thousands of skilled volunteers take part in regular surveys and bird monitoring studies. This effort, coupled with the professional work of the official agencies and leading voluntary conservation bodies, has generated a widely-based understanding of our birds and their habitats.

Throughout the countryside we have been able to identify specially favoured sites which support vulnerable species, or particularly large numbers of birds, or both. These important bird areas are cornerstones of conservation. The proper protection of these areas is an essential link in the conservation of viable bird populations in the United Kingdom and Europe, as required under international directives and conventions.

In this book are listed 256 such areas. They are all of international importance and qualify for protection under the European Communities Directive on the Conservation of Wild Birds, and many also under the Ramsar Convention on Wetlands of International Importance. They are maintained wherever possible through sympathetic land management, with core areas notified as Sites of Special Scientific Interest (or Areas of Special Scientific Interest in Northern Ireland).

This list is not the last word: new sites of importance could be added as survey work progresses. All the areas in this book have been carefully validated to confirm that they do support internationally important bird populations, and this assessment must continue to be kept under review.

This volume follows the earlier work entitled *Important Bird Areas in Europe*, which was published in 1989. Similar national inventories are also being produced in the other European countries. It is our hope that this book will advance the conservation of these areas, and will assist owners and managers of land, decision-makers in central and local Government, in other statutory bodies, and in conservation organisations to be more aware of the significance of the list as a whole, and of their responsibilities in safeguarding our heritage of birds.

Adrian Darby, Chairman RSPB 1986-1993
Earl of Cranbrook, Chairman EN 1991-
Michael Griffith, Chairman CCW 1991-
Magnus Magnusson, Chairman NCCS/SNH 1991-
Earl of Selborne, Chairman JNCC 1991-

ACKNOWLEDGMENTS

This book represents a massive act of collaboration by scores of busy people, without whose help and patience it could not have been completed. We are indebted to all those listed below. Unless otherwise indicated, named individuals are employees of the publishing organisations.

The project was funded by RSPB and by grant-aid from the former Nature Conservancy Council, which is gratefully acknowledged.

The editors throughout were assisted by other members of a project steering group including J Finnie, E C Hammond, S Payne, T M Reed, D Stroud, P Stuttard and S Ward.

Senior individuals in all the publishing organisations are thanked for helping to make this collaborative project possible: we are grateful to Professor Sir Frederick Holliday, Timothy Hornsby, Derek Langslow, Ian Mercer, Ian Prestt, Sir William Wilkinson, Graham Wynne and Barbara Young.

The substantial task of coordinating contributions for the site accounts was ably undertaken by A M Dodd and A J Stones, who also originated many of the accounts themselves.

The other principal originator of site accounts was A Henderson. I K Dawson and S Sankey compiled additional accounts. The text for Northern Ireland was compiled by K Partridge with assistance from P Bradley. The Channel Islands section was written by N Milton, J Waldon and G Williams, and that for the Isle of Man was written by J P Cullen (Manx Ornithological Society) and G Williams.

In Scotland, help in drafting or coordinating site accounts was provided by L Austin, M V Bell, S Benn, J Boyle, L Brain, R Broad, E Cameron, G Christer, C Crooke, R Dennis, J Dunbar, A Duncan, P Ellis, R Evans, W Mattingley, E Meek, D Minns, S Moyes, G W Rebecca, M Robinson, S Sankey, C Seymour, K Shaw, J Stevenson, B Thomas and A Webb.

In England, help in drafting or coordinating site accounts was provided by J Armitage, C Bain, T Barfield, K Bayes, T Bines, C Carson, M Clark, T R Cleeves, C Corrigan, M Davies, C Durdin, A R Farrar, P Gotham, R J Hornby, P Lambley, R Land, F Lucas, M Robins, J Shackles, L Street, D Townshend, C Tubbs, F Ulf-Hansen, J Waldon, G Welch, J Wilson and P Wisniewski (Wildfowl and Wetlands Trust).

In Wales, help in drafting or coordinating site accounts was provided by C Fuller, G Howells, P Stuttard, S J Tyler and P Williams.

In Northern Ireland help in drafting site accounts was provided by P Bradley and C Mellon; additional comments were provided by J Furphy of the Department of Environment (Northern Ireland).

Help in drafting the Channel Islands section was provided by J Bishop, T Bourgaize, I J Buxton, N Hammond, R Long, La Société Guernsaise Ornithological Section and la

Société Jersiaise Ornithology Section, and M Mendham. Special acknowledgment is due to M Freeman and M Romeril of the States of Jersey Island Development Committee for additional assistance.

Help in drafting the Isle of Man section was provided by I Armstrong, G Elliott and A del Nevo.

In various other ways significant help was provided by L H Campbell, D Dick, A B Gammell, R F Grimmett (ICBP), S Lambton, M Langeveld (ICBP), A Pillay, N Pillow, R F Porter, H Riley, L Rose, M L Tasker, G J Thomas, P Walsh, L Way and J M Wilbraham. Many others in regional, country and headquarters offices of the publishing organisations also contributed.

Finally, a special mention is due to the thousands of volunteer ornithologists throughout the United Kingdom, Channel Islands and Isle of Man, on whose freely given hard work in field data collection much of the information in this book is based. Through scientific counting and survey schemes run by organisations such as the British Trust for Ornithology, Wildfowl and Wetlands Trust and numerous local bird clubs, an invaluable body of detailed data has been built up over many years. This, as much as any other factor, is what has enabled such a complete picture of these important places for birds to be presented in this volume.

D E Pritchard, S D Housden, G P Mudge, C A Galbraith, M W Pienkowski (Eds).

LIST OF ABBREVIATIONS USED

AOS	Apparently Occupied Sites
ASSI	Area of Special Scientific Interest
BOU	British Ornithologists' Union
BTO	British Trust for Ornithology
c.	Circa
CCW	Countryside Council for Wales
CI	Channel Islands
CSD	(NCC) Chief Scientist Directorate
DAFF	Department of Agriculture, Fisheries and Forestry (IoM)
DoE	Department of the Environment
DoE(NI)	Department of the Environment (Northern Ireland)
EAF	East Atlantic Flyway
EC/EEC	European Community
EN	English Nature
ESA	Environmentally Sensitive Area
GB	Great Britain
ha	Hectares
IBA	Important Bird Area
ICBP	International Council for Bird Preservation
IoM	Isle of Man
ITE	Institute of Terrestrial Ecology
IUCN	International Union for Conservation of Nature and Natural Resources
IWRB	International Waterfowl and Wetlands Research Bureau
km	Kilometres
LNR	Local Nature Reserve
LWOST	Low Water Ordinary Spring Tides
m	Metres
MAFF	Ministry of Agriculture, Fisheries and Food
Max	Maximum
Min	Minimum
MNR	Marine Nature Reserve
MoD	Ministry of Defence
N/A	Not applicable
NCC	Nature Conservancy Council
NCCE	Nature Conservancy Council England
NCCS	Nature Conservancy Council for Scotland
NGO	Non-Government Organisation
NI	Northern Ireland
NNR	National Nature Reserve
NW	North-West
NYMNP	North York Moors National Park
OS	Ordnance Survey
Prs	Pairs
RDB	*Red Data Birds in Britain*
RSPB	Royal Society for the Protection of Birds
SNH	Scottish Natural Heritage
SPA	Special Protection Area

SSI	Site of Special Interest (CI)
SSSI	Site of Special Scientific Interest
SW	South-West
UK	United Kingdom
WO	Welsh Office
WSG	Wader Study Group
WWA	Wessex Water Authority
WWT	Wildfowl and Wetlands Trust
>	Greater than
<	Less than

1. The Significance of 'Important Bird Areas'

1.1 INTRODUCTION

Birds are our common heritage. Their popularity with the public, as well as spectacular migrations, has led to international commitments being made by governments to conserve populations throughout their range. Indeed, in many cases we should strive to restore the distribution of those species that have suffered at the hand of man in the past. The increasing rate of habitat loss in recent years coupled with declines in numbers of some bird species has stimulated the current worldwide concern, first to stop, and where possible to reverse that decline. This book lists those sites in the United Kingdom[1] that are known to support internationally important assemblages of birds. The protection of these areas is of paramount importance for bird conservation both within the UK and elsewhere.

For the conservation of most bird species, international cooperation is essential. For many species this is due to their migratory habits, and their dependence on different countries at different times of the year. For some species, even when habitat is available, populations are so low that urgent international conservation action is essential if the risk of major losses of range and numbers is to be avoided. This stresses the need for coordination of conservation science and policy at as wide a scale as possible. Birds show little respect for country or other administrative boundaries, and we need to plan accordingly.

This book is an inventory of those special areas in the UK that, under present knowledge, are regarded as of international importance for birds. Each area qualifies for designation

[1]Unless the context dictates otherwise, references to the 'United Kingdom' for the purposes of this book generally should be taken to include the Channel Islands and Isle of Man.

as a Special Protection Area or SPA in the context of the EC Directive 79/409 on the Conservation of Wild Birds (the 'Birds Directive') and many also qualify for designation as 'Ramsar sites' under the Convention on Wetlands of International Importance Especially as Waterfowl Habitat (see Section 1.7). The inventory builds on the ICBP/ IWRB's book entitled *Important Bird Areas in Europe* (Grimmett and Jones 1989) and is designed to provide more extensive and up-to-date information for the UK. This book is also part of a series of country gazetteers across Europe designed for decision makers, to provide them with the essential facts needed to discharge their obligations under the EC Directive on the Conservation of Wild Birds and their responsibilities under the Ramsar Convention. These obligations bear on the actions of local authorities in discharging their planning functions, as well as other statutory bodies and Government Departments. This is clearly explained in DoE/WO Circular 27/87 (1992 Planning Policy Guidance in press), and Scottish Office Circular 13/1991, which gives explicit guidance on how to treat development proposals on *all* sites qualifying for protection under the Wild Birds Directive, *ie* the areas described in this book.

The United Kingdom

In common with most countries, the countryside of the United Kingdom has undergone considerable change in recent years, much of which has been to the detriment of nature conservation. The gradual changes of land use that have occurred since the prehistoric clearance of the wildwood, have been replaced by those of modern times where high speed and large scale are the dominant values. This is largely as a result of technological and chemical advances in agriculture. Farming of one sort or another is the primary land use over 79% of the UK, and thus has a major impact on nature conservation.

Change in farming practice has in many areas done away with traditional farming methods, which have helped sustain the semi-natural landscape, rich in flora and fauna, and has resulted in intensively managed land of low value to wildlife. Improvements in technology and transport coupled with fiscal incentives have also led farmers to specialise their farming operations, with cereal growing dominating in eastern Britain and stock rearing in the west and in Northern Ireland. Hedgerows have been lost, land drained, moorlands ploughed and agricultural activity generally intensified. Consequently, in many areas, valuable bird habitats dependent on an intimate mix of land-use types have been lost. This has led to a more uniform avifauna over the country as a whole, and the disappearance of the characteristic regional patterns of land-use and bird distribution.

The UK, due to its geographic location and great variety of landscapes, holds internationally important numbers[2] of many birds. Sometimes the importance of certain areas is obvious from the vast numbers of birds that occur there. For example, many of our estuaries hold internationally important numbers of waterfowl. Their dramatic flights are a wildlife spectacle. Similarly the great seabird 'cities' of the northern isles of Orkney and Shetland impress the observer with their numbers, sound and activity. The international importance of other areas is sometimes less immediately apparent. For example, the global importance of the 'Flow Country' of Caithness and Sutherland was not fully realised until fairly recently, when comparisons with data from other countries

[2]See pages 16-21 for definitions of 'importance'

indicated that this area was possibly the largest single expanse of blanket bog in the world. These peat bogs support the majority of Britain's breeding greenshanks, as well as internationally important populations of other birds such as dunlin (Stroud *et al* 1987; Bainbridge *et al* 1987).

Many sites that are internationally important for birds are also of conservation value for a variety of other fauna and flora. For example, seasonally flooded grasslands provide nesting habitat for a variety of breeding waders and wildfowl. In addition, such wet meadows also support important populations of wetland invertebrates and plants, which, like wet grassland birds, are becoming increasingly scarce owing to the fragmentation and loss of this once extensive habitat. Losses of wet grassland, as with many other habitats, have not been restricted to the UK but have occurred throughout Europe, making those which remain even more important.

International Obligations

We have a moral duty to conserve the best wildlife areas for posterity; but also a legislative requirement to do so. The EC Directive on the Conservation of Wild Birds (79/409/EEC) requires Member States to safeguard the habitats of migratory birds and certain particularly threatened birds (listed on Annex 1 to the Directive). In 1976 the UK Government ratified The Convention on Wetlands of International Importance especially as Waterfowl Habitat which was drafted at Ramsar, Iran in 1971. The Ramsar Convention, as it is commonly known, aims to conserve wetlands and promote their wise (sustainable) use. Many of the concepts of the Ramsar Convention have been further developed and extended to all bird habitats.

Both of these international commitments require measures not only to classify and protect sites, but also to promote the incorporation of conservation measures in land-use policy making generally. This is essential for the maintenance of many populations of birds, particularly widely dispersed species, whose conservation is dependent upon the sympathetic management of large areas of land, the primary economic use of which is sporting, agricultural or silvicultural.

As some species migrate long distances through many countries, all of which must contribute to their conservation for it to be successful, it is essential that we in the UK play our part and give particular attention to our international conservation responsibilities. The UK's soft coasts and estuaries, for example, gather wintering waterfowl and seabirds from a large part of the northern hemisphere; the fate of birds that nest in Greenland, Iceland, Scandinavia and large parts of Canada and central Siberia depends on how we treat our coastline. In addition, we have obligations to protect many other rare or vulnerable birds. For example, the birds of our upland moors are of special significance in European terms.

Species Requirements

Each species has particular requirements with respect to feeding, breeding and shelter, which can only be met in certain locations. There are also advantages to individuals in returning to areas with which they are familiar; for example, many wading birds are now known to frequent the same part of an estuary year after year. The loss of key sites that

3

regularly support substantial numbers is likely, therefore, to have adverse effects on total populations (Goss-Custard 1985). Birds cannot just 'squeeze up' and survive as easily on the remaining habitat. Competition for food and nest sites, for example, means that wintering survival or reproductive success is limited, thus reducing the population to a new (lower) equilibrium. A site does not have to hold large numbers of birds every year or at all times of the year to be of importance (see pages 13–14).

Migratory Birds

Some bird species migrate on a 'broad front', concentrating at natural bottle-necks like mountain passes or short sea crossings. Others use a series of 'stepping stones' for flights across areas where they are unable to land and feed. For example, some waders, such as knot, breed in the Taimyr Peninsula of the former Soviet arctic, winter in South Africa and depend on British estuaries as 'refuelling' areas on their journeys between the two. Each stopover area is an essential link in a chain. Conservation efforts in one country can be rendered ineffective by the loss of a critically important area in another; thus there is a need to create international networks of protected sites. The loss of any one of these may damage the total conservation effort and so reduce the overall species' population.

The UK has a major responsibility in international bird conservation. It lies where the migration paths of waders and wildfowl from arctic Canada, Greenland and Iceland meet those from northern Europe and Siberia. Birds from a vast breeding range in the arctic depend on estuaries and other wetlands in Britain and western Europe. Some stay here to over-winter; others may moult and feed before moving on as far as southern Africa, to return once more in spring.

The UK also holds substantial numbers of breeding waders and wildfowl. Some species of wader, for example, the dunlin, breed at very high densities in places such as the Western Isles (Fuller *et al* 1986); often at much higher densities than other populations breeding in the arctic (Watson 1963; Meltofte 1985; Fox 1987).

The UK is also the breeding area for many species of seabird, some of which may travel as far as the Antarctic and Australia on their migrations. For example nearly 60% of the world's gannets breed around our shores, 30% of the world's storm petrels, and 20% of the world's razorbills. The UK's cliffs, islands and offshore stacks form some of the most important seabird breeding areas in the north Atlantic (Lloyd *et al* 1991).

Vulnerable Species

Many migratory and non-migratory species are considered 'vulnerable' and require conservation measures to maintain their range and numbers. It is important to maintain not only total numbers of each species of bird but also its traditional geographical range. Fragmented populations are much more vulnerable to future losses, and even extinction, than more widespread ones which occur over a more or less continuous range. Unfortunately, the present-day distributions of many birds are much fragmented and greatly reduced compared with previous years, making them more vulnerable than ever to inappropriate development, pollution and natural catastrophes. Species confined to rare and vulnerable habitats such as reedbeds or lowland heaths are a cause of special concern, and many of them, such as the bittern and Dartford warbler, are listed on Annex 1 of the EC Directive.

Some other species, for example, some terns, are considered vulnerable due to their concentration on a few small breeding sites. The loss of just one or two sites would be a major blow to their conservation. Networks of protected areas are thus vitally important in maintaining both the size and genetic variability of populations of birds (Soulé 1987).

1.2 THE IBA CONCEPT AND THE DYNAMIC NATURE OF THE LIST OF SITES

The list of Important Bird Areas described in this book for England, Scotland and Wales corresponds with the Government's statutory advisers' (Joint Nature Conservation Committee-JNCC) list of designated and proposed SPAs and Ramsar sites (bird-based Ramsars only) as published in Hansard (17 July 1991 columns 203–208 and 219–224 and 18 July 1991 columns 256–257). These lists of sites are the subject of regular consultation within the forum of the Joint Working Party on SPAs and Ramsar sites chaired by JNCC. This Working Party includes representatives from the three Country Conservation Agencies (EN, CCW and SNH), Government Departments and non-government organisations such as the RSPB (see also 2.4 below).

The list of areas given in this book should not be regarded as fixed. It is a reflection of current status and knowledge and may change as the years pass. It is a matter of pride that the UK is one of the best surveyed countries in the world for the numbers and distribution of birds. Nevertheless, new facts regularly come to light and change the interpretation to be placed on existing information. Thus the special interest of some existing sites may decline in relative terms and cause them eventually to be deleted from the list. Other sites, which do not currently reach international thresholds, may increase in importance and be added to the list, while other new sites may be found to qualify as a result of further field surveys. Regular updates to the list to reflect such changes will be made by JNCC, in consultation with the statutory country conservation agencies.

Dispersed Species

It should be made clear that a site-based approach is not always well suited to cater for the wide ranging needs of vulnerable and dispersed bird species. For example, many extensive areas in northern England and in Scotland support important populations of birds such as merlin, golden eagle, and golden plover and pose particular problems. This is discussed further in section 1.5 below.

1.3 INTERNATIONAL TREATIES

The need for international treaties to protect migratory species is accepted by many countries (IUCN 1986). The more recent international measures relevant to birds, to which the United Kingdom is a party, are outlined below.

EEC Directive 79/409 on the Conservation of Wild Birds

The full text of this Directive is presented in Appendix III.

Under the EC Council Directive on the Conservation of Wild Birds of 1979, the United Kingdom is committed to taking **'the requisite measures to preserve, maintain or re-establish a sufficient diversity and area of habitat'** for **'all species of naturally occurring birds in the wild state.'** Over and above this, the UK is committed to taking special conservation measures, concerning their habitat, for two groups of birds. These are certain listed **threatened and vulnerable species** ('Annex 1') as well as **all regularly occurring migratory species**. Among the measures to be taken for both the 'Annex 1' list and the migratory species is the designation of Special Protection Areas (SPAs).

The Council of Ministers adopted the Directive on the Conservation of Wild Birds (Directive 79/409) on 2 April 1979 and required Member States to introduce legislation to implement the Directive within two years. In Great Britain this was done with the passing of the Wildlife and Countryside Act 1981. The Directive concerns the urgent need for European-wide cooperation in bird conservation policies and action. For example some bird populations move from one Member State to another. Birds which range widely and use habitats and areas in different Member States will benefit from a coordinated positive approach to conservation.

Like all such Directives under the Treaty of Rome, the Birds Directive describes what needs to be achieved; but the manner in which these objectives are to be attained is left to individual Member States. The European Commission has a monitoring role and can initiate court proceedings against Member States for failure to comply with the Directive.

The conservation measures required by the Directive include prohibitions on killing or taking birds, including standardisation of seasons in which gamebirds are protected, and restrictions on certain non-specific methods of killing, for example, poisoning. Monitoring of bird populations is also stipulated.

Emphasis is placed in the Directive on the need to conserve bird habitats as a means of maintaining populations. In part, such habitat protection is to be achieved by the establishment of a network of protected areas for birds throughout the Community: the Special Protection Areas. As well as stating the need for SPAs, the Birds Directive also indicates that other means of protecting populations are necessary, especially where these populations are vulnerable and dispersed. These 'wider countryside' conservation measures, as they are often termed, are a necessary complement to site-based conservation.

Article 2 of the Directive states that in respect of SPAs, economic and recreational requirements must be considered only after ecological, scientific and cultural requirements. Article 3 requires Member States to take requisite measures to preserve, maintain or re-establish a sufficient diversity and area of habitats for all the species of birds referred to in Article 1 (ie all species of birds naturally occurring in the wild state in the European Community).

Article 4 is concerned with applying special conservation measures, including the classification of Special Protection Areas, to two groups of birds. These are, firstly, vulnerable species which are listed in Annex 1 (amended with some additions by Directives 81/854/EEC, 85/411/EEC, 86/122/EEC and 91/244/EEC); and secondly, all other regularly occurring migratory bird species.

An EC Council Resolution of 2 April 1979 concerning the Birds Directive also made it clear that the Directive, and Special Protection Areas designated under it, should be used to further the conservation of biotopes wherever possible. The Resolution further called upon Member States to notify the Commission within two years of the Directive (that is by 1981) of the list of SPAs to be notified, progress that had been made and progress which was intended.

In Great Britain, the domestic legislation intended to allow implementation of the Birds Directive is incorporated into the Wildlife and Countryside Act 1981. The Northern Ireland equivalent is the Nature Conservation and Amenity Lands Order 1985. The UK Government has stated that in order for it to be able to comply with the Directive all sites of international importance are, or will be, notified as Sites of Special Scientific Interest (SSSIs) (or Areas of Special Scientific Interest in Northern Ireland) (House of Commons Official Report 11 May 1987 c. 85). This may work well where birds aggregate within clearly defined boundaries, for example, an estuary or a discrete area of lowland heathland. However, where upland ecosystems are involved, sites tend to be larger than the average SSSI.

Some EC States have chosen to implement the Birds Directive in other ways, through different forms of domestic legislation or by direct incorporation of the Birds Directive into domestic law. Consequently, compared with the UK, they have designated markedly differing proportions of their territory as SPAs. Denmark leads the way at the time of writing, having designated over 22% of its territory as Special Protection Areas, and is actively evaluating other sites for SPA status. In contrast, the UK has so far designated less than 1% of its territory as SPAs, and many species lack the SPA protection they require.

Public statements by Government ministers and officials at the time of the passage of the Wildlife and Countryside Act gave the impression that a fairly rapid listing of appropriate SSSIs as SPAs and Ramsar sites would follow, allowing the UK to meet its obligations soon after the specified date of 1981. In practice, progress has been slow, on average four sites being listed per annum.

As at January 1992, a total of 43 sites had been designated in the UK as Special Protection Areas under the Directive and a total of 50 internationally important wetlands designated under the Ramsar Convention. (Many of these sites are designated under both the Directive and the Convention).

It would be open to the UK Government to declare SPAs or Ramsar sites without first notifying them as SSSI or ASSI, *provided* the Government had some means of preventing the deterioration of the habitats and species populations on the site. This could be achieved, for example, via the declaration of Environmentally Sensitive Areas (ESAs), or perhaps in Scotland by using the new designation of Natural Heritage Areas enacted by the Natural Heritage (Scotland) Act 1991. For the time being, however, the areas in this book, subject to evaluation against the SSSI selection criteria and definition of precise boundaries, must first be notified/declared SSSI/ASSI before their international status can be formalised by SPA or Ramsar classification.

Ramsar Convention

Wetland areas are extremely important for their biological value and for the maintenance of systems on which humans depend, but are intensely threatened throughout the world (Maltby 1986). The importance of wetlands, and the need for international perspectives in encouraging their conservation, was recognised by the adoption of the Convention on Wetlands of International Importance especially as Waterfowl Habitat at a meeting of countries concerned with wetland and waterfowl conservation held at Ramsar, Iran, in 1971 (Carp 1972). The preamble to the Convention refers to the contracting parties' desire 'to stem the progressive encroachment on and loss of wetlands now and in the future'. The UK Government signed the Convention in 1973 and Parliament ratified it in 1976. The Ramsar Convention has proved extremely successful in focussing attention on the need for wetland conservation, especially as habitat for waterfowl (Smart 1987), and many countries have made important contributions to the international network of protected Ramsar sites. The full text of the Convention is given in Appendix IV.

Article 2 requires each Contracting Party to designate suitable wetlands within its territory for inclusion in a list of wetlands of international importance. At present the UK Government is unable to meet the terms of the Convention satisfactorily where coastal zones or marine waters are involved.

Article 3 requires Contracting Parties to formulate and implement their planning so as to promote the conservation of wetlands included in the list and also, as far as possible, the 'wise use' of all wetlands in their territory. If the ecological character of any wetland in the list has changed or is changing, or is likely to change as the result of technological developments, pollution, or other human interference, the relevant Party must notify the Ramsar Bureau.

Article 4 requires Contracting Parties to promote the conservation of wetlands and waterfowl. It also requires that where a Contracting Party, in its own urgent national interest, deletes or restricts the boundaries of wetlands included in the list, it should compensate for any loss of wetland resources.

Among the other provisions of the Ramsar Convention, Article 6 requires Contracting Parties to convene conferences to consider matters relating to the Convention. The most recent of these was held at Montreux in Switzerland in 1990. The 1987 Conference at Regina in Canada (Ramsar Convention Bureau 1988) defined the 'wise use' specified in Article 3 thus: 'The wise use of wetlands is their sustainable utilisation for the benefit of humankind in a way compatible with the maintenance of the natural properties of the ecosystem'. Natural properties of the ecosystem were defined as its 'physical, biological or chemical components, such as soil, water, plants, animals and nutrients, and the interactions between them'. Further expansion of this is provided in Appendix IV. The criteria for selecting sites under this Convention are also set out in Appendix IV.

The Convention on the Conservation of European Wildlife and Natural Habitats (The 'Berne Convention')

This encourages in particular the promotion of cooperation between European countries in their conservation efforts, especially with respect to migratory species. Article 4(3) of the Convention states that Parties should: 'undertake to give special attention to the protection of areas that are of importance for the migratory species specified in Appendices II and III (including most birds) and which are appropriately situated in relation to migration routes as wintering, staging, feeding, breeding or moulting areas.'

The UK is a party to this Convention, having ratified its provisions in May 1982.

The Convention parties have taken a particular interest in the conservation of lowland heathlands, and their threatened flora and fauna. Many such sites in the UK also meet the criteria for protection under the EC Birds Directive.

The Convention on the Conservation of Migratory Species of Wild Animals (the 'Bonn Convention')

This is specifically concerned with migratory species. It provides for their conservation by giving strict protection to a number of endangered animals listed in its Appendix I, whilst also providing the framework for a series of 'AGREEMENTS' between 'Range States' (ie States exercising jurisdiction over any part of the range of relevant migratory species) for the conservation and management of Appendix II species. Currently, an AGREEMENT on the conservation of migratory populations of *Anatidae* (ducks and geese) is being drawn up under the terms of the Convention. The UK is a party to this Convention also, having signed it in June 1979 and ratified its provisions in July 1985.

1.4   WHY HABITAT PROTECTION IS IMPORTANT FOR BIRDS

Importance of Maintaining Geographic Range

There are fundamental biological reasons for sustaining the geographical range of populations as well as their numerical size.

Recent research into the relationship between species viability and population size has shown the importance of maintaining as wide a range as possible for the long-term well-being of populations (for example, Salwasser *et al* 1983; Gilpin 1987; Marcot and Holthausen 1987). There is a lower probability of chance extinction when a species occurs over a wide geographic range. This is because those environmental fluctuations (including those caused by man) which may be detrimental to populations will not generally occur synchronously across wide areas. Even though environmental variation (such as extreme winter cold) may cause some of a population to suffer depressed productivity, or even local extinctions, this is very unlikely to occur in all the areas occupied by a wide-ranging population (Goodman 1987). When large populations occur over wide geographic areas this also leads to the conservation of broader genetic variation through reduced inbreeding, and hence to enhanced long-term population viability (Salwasser *et al* 1983; Lande and Barrowclough 1987; Harris 1988).

The present day distributions of many bird species are greatly reduced and fragmented compared with their former state. Usually this is due to man-induced habitat changes or other impacts (such as persecution). Present distributions are unlikely therefore to be indicative of 'natural' range in many cases. For example, species such as red kite and corncrake, two of the three globally threatened UK species, now occupy a very small part of their known former range owing to persecution and habitat change. Declines have occurred throughout their range in Europe. Lowland breeding waders such as ruff, black-tailed godwit, snipe and redshank are much reduced in distribution and numbers, both in Britain and elsewhere, owing to the loss or modification of their wet grassland habitat through drainage and intensive agriculture (Beintema 1983; Smith 1983; O'Brien and Smith in press).

Even in cases where overall geographical range is sustained, the fragmentation of prime habitat by land use or other changes can lead to local populations becoming more isolated and hence being more vulnerable to chance processes of extinction (Alexandersson 1987; Temple and Cary 1988). In these cases, immigration into the isolated populations is difficult. Although isolated populations can sometimes become extinct without human interference (MacArthur and Wilson 1967), such events are normally redressed by eventual immigration from neighbouring populations. In situations where fragmentation of habitats and reduction of population sizes continue, a point is reached where there are no further sources of immigrants likely to re-colonise an area destroyed by natural catastrophes (Soulé and Simberloff 1986), resulting in permanent local extinction. The logical long-term consequence of continued fragmentation is the extinction of the species.

Some Threatened Birds in the UK

The following species provide examples where fragmentation and reduction have occurred.

1. Light-bellied brent goose.
The breeding population of light-bellied brent geese in Svalbard winters in Denmark and on Lindisfarne in England. With a total of only 3,000–4,000 birds, it is one of the smallest and most threatened goose stocks in the world (Madsen 1984, 1987). Formerly however, it totalled in excess of 50,000 geese and bred in many areas of the Svalbard archipelago. However, the population declined rapidly at the beginning of this century due to a combination of factors on both breeding and wintering grounds. The birds' staple winter food of *Zostera* (eel-grass) died out along most North Atlantic coasts and many geese died of starvation or from excessive hunting pressure during winter. In addition, hunting pressure was also excessive in summer.

The present restricted breeding distribution of light-bellied brent geese is centred on a small group of islands in the extreme south of Svalbard. Here productivity is consistently low, with an average proportion of only 12% young in the autumn flocks each year, and with many years of almost complete breeding failure. Recently, it has been established that this is due to nest predation by polar bears, which can reach these islands when there is a lot of pack-ice (Madsen *et al* 1989; Madsen and Mehlum unpublished).

The population is consequently threatened to a much greater extent by this 'natural' predation than it would previously have been. When the population was much larger, the geese would also have nested in many places inaccessible to polar bears, and thus production by these other birds in years of dense pack-ice would have offset losses to polar bears elsewhere. In this case a combination of both natural (*Zostera* disease) and human (over-shooting) factors have reduced and restricted the population. Now, even with complete protection, the population is highly vulnerable to extinction.

2. Red Kite

The red kite, a raptor that was once widespread throughout Britain, is now restricted to a limited area in mid-Wales. This non-migratory population has not naturally re-colonised other areas in which it once occurred, because of low breeding productivity exacerbated by human persecution and habitat fragmentation in surrounding areas. This relict population is now much more vulnerable to possible catastrophes such as disease, poisoning and egg collecting than when it was more widespread and numerous. For this and other reasons, the JNCC statutory agencies and RSPB are attempting to re-establish the kite in other areas of Britain.

3. Dartford Warbler

Dartford warblers have been adversely affected by the fragmentation of heathland habitats in southern England (Moore 1962). Small blocks of heathland hold lower densities of Dartford warblers than more extensive areas (Bibby and Tubbs 1975). Small and isolated groups of birds are more likely to become extinct following high mortality in severe winters. Fragmentation of heathland also increases the significance of adverse edge-effects from neighbouring non-heathland habitats, such as nutrient enrichment from adjacent farmland, and vegetation change following grazing by rabbits (Bibby and Tubbs 1975).

Review of General Changes in Bird Populations

The present day distribution and abundance of bird species and their habitats is often the result of extensive and long-term human influence.

Only a very few generalist species, for example, some common farmland birds such as the yellowhammer, have benefited from some of the landscape modifications introduced by man's activities (Laursen 1980; O'Connor and Shrubb 1986). However, even within agricultural landscapes, change has been occurring at increasing speed with a variety of adverse consequences even for these adaptable species. Birds such as the lapwing occur in both agricultural and non-agricultural habitats, and although they have benefited to some extent from increased grassland in pastoral areas, they have declined markedly in lowland agricultural landscapes where grasslands have been lost and cereal production has predominated. In these areas, changing patterns of cereal production have had deleterious consequences for both the lapwing's breeding density and its productive success (O'Connor and Shrubb 1986). Where agricultural modification has occurred slowly and over long periods of time, it has sometimes interacted with natural and semi-natural habitats to produce areas of considerable value for wildlife. This is in marked contrast to the effects of the rapid change which has been so typical of agriculture in the latter part of this century. Examples of beneficial agricultural types include the crofting landscapes of the Hebrides and northern isles (Fuller *et al* 1986; Bignal *et al* 1988; Stroud 1989; Campbell 1989), and lowland wet grasslands throughout the country (Green and Cadbury 1987). Areas with low-intensity pastoral farmland, particularly where there has been traditional emphasis on extensive stock-rearing have generally produced habitats of significant conservation value.

Wetlands and coastal habitats have been drastically reduced. Prater (1981) gives examples of the reduction in extent of estuarine and saltmarsh habitats; extensive areas of saltmarsh such as those at the Wash have been 'claimed' for agriculture (Doody and Barnett 1987; Cadbury 1987a; Hill 1988). Lowland grasslands have been severely modified by intensive agriculture, with the loss of their characteristic breeding waders (Smith 1983; Green and Cadbury 1987; Fuller 1987; Williams and Bowers 1987). Freshwater coastal grasslands, in particular, have been lost at a rapid rate as a result of deep drainage and conversion to arable agriculture (Williams and Hall 1987). A study of lowland raised mires demonstrates that in some areas there has been up to 95% loss since 1948 (NCC 1984; Lindsay in prep.), and lowland English heaths have been much fragmented (Moore 1962) with adverse consequences for their characteristic birds (Bibby 1978; Tubbs 1985; Webb 1990). Populations of upland waders such as golden plover, dunlin and greenshank have been much reduced by recent afforestation and other land-use changes (Cadbury 1987b; Stroud *et al* 1987; Thompson *et al* 1988).

Thus the present day status and distribution of some birds cannot be regarded as the 'natural' status quo, and not necessarily as desirable. For many species, conservation planning needs to halt these losses and set targets to increase presently diminished population sizes and ranges. A network of protected internationally important 'core' areas is one way to ensure that further attrition is minimised, while other sympathetic land-use policies are devised and promoted in the 'wider countryside' to encourage expansion of these restricted populations.

The book *Red Data Birds in Britain,* published by the NCC and RSPB (Batten *et al* 1990), lists 117 species whose populations or status merit special conservation attention. Of these 117, 80 are threatened by land-use changes, ie loss or degradation of habitats, and some of these are considered to be at serious risk (Bibby *et al* 1989).

Importance of Site Networks for Migratory Birds

By definition, migratory birds depend on a number of areas which are used at different times of the year. The ecological requirements and the use made of different sites are perhaps best understood for well-studied groups of birds such as waders (for example, Pienkowski and Pienkowski 1983; Davidson and Pienkowski 1987; Prokosch 1988; Smit and Piersma 1989), and wildfowl (for example, Owen 1980; Patterson 1982; Prokosch 1984; Owen *et al* 1986; Pirot *et al* 1989). Some points important in planning site networks to conserve migratory populations are considered below.

Birds do not use sites randomly. Most have specialised requirements that can only be met in certain locations. Generally, birds tend to use sites at which their chances of survival and future reproduction are enhanced; perhaps those with which they are familiar – in terms of food resources, predation risk, nesting habitat, etc. Consequently, such sites are used regularly, with important numbers of birds returning each year. Loss of these areas is likely to have an adverse effect on bird populations. This 'site fidelity' at each season and over the years has been proven for an increasing number of birds (eg Pienkowski and Evans 1985; Hudson 1985; Diefenbach *et al* 1988; Thompson *et al* 1988).

Some sites are not of numerical importance every year, nor at all times of the year, yet can still be of crucial importance to the conservation of a population. For example, at times of severe winter weather, birds are displaced from 'normal' wintering areas (Baillie 1984) to more favourable sites, and at these times such sites can be crucial for population survival. For example, individual grey plovers each use particular sites on different sides of the North Sea according to the severity of the winter (Townshend 1982; Pienkowski and Evans 1984); as does the endangered population of light-bellied brent geese. These geese move from Denmark to Lindisfarne according to Danish winter weather conditions (Madsen 1984a). Bewick's swans are known to make rapid and extensive relocations, not only within Britain, but also to sites in Holland, Germany and Denmark, in response to severe winter weather (Evans 1982).

Clearly then, sites which hold important populations in these irregularly occurring conditions are of key importance for population viability, even if they may not achieve numerical criteria of 'importance' in every year. Similar arguments pertain to the use of certain important component parts of a 'site', which may not be used regularly but are vitally important overall. Examples would include parts of estuarine sites which are used by roosting waders when exceptional tidal conditions make more usual roosts unavailable. Such areas may be needed only infrequently, although at those times they are of critical importance.

The loss of sites will force birds to try to use other areas, which may be sub-optimal. The increasing density of birds forced onto smaller areas will adversely affect those birds through competition and other interference (Goss-Custard and Moser 1988; Thompson *et al* 1988) with the inevitable consequence of greater mortality and a decline in numbers.

The conservation of staging areas is of the utmost importance for populations of migrants, even if they are only used by birds for short periods each year. Such areas need to be adequately represented in the UK network of IBAs. For example, arctic breeding birds have a very short potential breeding period, and nesting is critically timed (Green *et al* 1977; Meltofte 1985). Failure to arrive on the nesting grounds in suitable condition, or at the right time, may mean not only that breeding is not possible, but also that the individual may not survive. Timing of migration by arctic birds therefore reflects their need to arrive on the breeding grounds with adequate body-fat reserves at a precisely determined time in spring.

All these factors argue for an approach to site protection which is not founded on disparate, piecemeal initiatives, but demands a coordinated international network of protected areas.

Providing for the Full Requirements of Birds

The ways in which birds use land or water areas is of great importance in determining their conservation requirements. An aim of conservation is the long-term maintenance, and in many cases enhancement, of bird populations. Protected sites should therefore include all areas necessary for the survival and reproduction of birds, where such habitats can be effectively influenced through site-based conservation. Some birds have complex ecological niches and conservation needs to take the full range of ecological requirements into consideration.

Nesting areas and feeding areas are obvious considerations, but other areas, such as refuges to which birds may retreat when disturbed, are also important. For example, the viability of some flocks of Greenland white-fronted geese (a sub-species listed on Annex 1 of the EC 'Birds' Directive) has been adversely affected when such 'retreat' areas have been lost either through afforestation or through disturbance following agricultural intensification (Ruttledge and Ogilvie 1979; Norriss and Wilson 1988). Likewise, large areas are necessary to support populations of many species, for example, chough. In such cases, it is necessary to protect not only the sites used by breeding pairs, but also the unimproved agricultural areas used for feeding by flocks of sub-adult birds (Bignal and Curtis 1989). Losses of choughs from parts of their range have usually been preceded by loss of the immature component of the population when traditional feeding areas cease to be available.

Some species require different foods in different seasons according to physiological and other needs. Many long-distance migrants need to lay down fat and protein reserves prior to migration. Thus the feeding grounds of migratory birds in periods before and during migration can be especially important, as can protection from disturbance so that birds can feed and put on weight.

The effect of differing dietary and habitat needs is that, for effective conservation, sites or site-networks must ensure the conservation of all essential habitats, even if some may be used by birds for only a short period each year. In many cases site-safeguard needs to be complemented by 'wider countryside' measures. The site accounts in this book indicate that a number of important 'staging posts' require protection in order to meet our international obligations.

Some birds have complex mating systems and require areas for social display. In these display areas, many males compete for the attention of unmated females. So-called leks are traditional and, although used for only a short period each year, can be crucial for successful breeding by social species such as capercaillie, black grouse and ruff (Johnsgard 1983). Leks in one area can be used also by birds (such as ruff) still on migration to nesting areas further north. These leks are therefore of importance not only to locally nesting birds, but also to the wider population (Van Rhijn 1983).

Some sites may be used during the night but only a little during the day. Indeed, ducks sometimes have night-time feeding areas which are distinct geographically and ecologically from their daytime localities (Tamisier 1979, 1985). Because data on usage of sites are more easily collected during the daytime, the importance of nocturnal sites may not be fully apparent (Jorde and Owen 1988). Examples, such as roosts of geese, can be assessed by counts of birds arriving at or leaving these areas. However, other situations may be less obvious.

When considering site boundaries, it is necessary to be aware not only of how many birds are present, but also of how, why and when they use an area. In this way ecologically sensible site boundaries can be drawn, and, where necessary, combinations of sites or sub-sites can be identified. In some situations, it is necessary to provide protected sites for certain stages in the life cycle, and initiatives in the 'wider countryside' for other stages, for the same birds.

1.5 PROTECTION OF BIRDS IN THE 'WIDER COUNTRYSIDE'

While networks of protected 'sites' are vitally important in themselves, it is essential not to neglect positive conservation measures in the countryside surrounding such 'sites'. For some species, a high proportion of a population will occur within a 'site', for example, some species of colonially nesting seabirds, which disperse over wide areas outside the breeding season. Other species may be thinly-spread across very wide areas of suitable habitat. Foremost amongst these are raptor species such as golden eagle.

It is thus not always possible to conserve bird populations using a site-based approach alone, and this is recognised in the EC Birds Directive (Articles 2 and 3), which requires wider measures 'in accordance with the ecological needs of habitats inside and outside the protected zones'. Article 4.4 requires '. . . appropriate steps to avoid pollution or deterioration of habitats or any disturbances affecting the birds, in so far as these would be significant having regard to the objectives of this Article'.

These 'wider countryside' conservation measures, as they have become known, are an essential complement to site-based conservation. Such measures, for example, include changes to land-use policies which may adversely affect dispersed populations of vulnerable birds. For example, in the uplands there is a need to avoid the afforestation of the moorland habitats of importance to birds such as golden eagle, merlin and golden plover, which are all listed on Annex 1 to the EC Birds Directive. Hitherto the UK Government has not implemented firm measures to protect such species outside SSSIs/ASSIs, although Agriculture Departments and the Forestry Commission now have obligations to balance their main duties with conservation.

Clearly, protection of only the nest site of a bird such as a merlin will not be an adequate conservation measure. The wide area of countryside around the nest, in which the merlin hunts for food, needs to be protected from undesirable change. Only this will keep the merlins breeding at that site (Bibby 1986). The same applies to all nesting birds, although the size of the area necessary to ensure successful breeding varies enormously. For a few birds, such as golden eagles, the home range is so large that site-based conservation cannot hope to cater for more than a small proportion of the breeding population's requirements. Although site-safeguard may form a useful part of a conservation strategy for the species, particularly in core or high density areas, conservation of the golden eagle and similar species must concentrate on measures taken largely in the 'wider country-side'.

For a number of areas it is appropriate to integrate site-based and wider countryside measures. For example, the water bodies used by breeding black-throated divers or Slavonian grebes are best protected using site-based mechanisms. This should be linked to 'wider countryside' approaches in, for example, the loch catchment areas, where land-use changes could have an adverse impact on water quality. Another example involves wintering geese. Here it is often appropriate to apply site protection to roosts, but inappropriate to extend this to the agricultural land on which they feed. Wider countryside mechanisms, such as Environmentally Sensitive Area designation, would be better suited for the agricultural land. In this example the different protection mechanisms are functionally linked by the movements of the geese.

1.6 PROTECTION OF SEABIRDS IN MARINE AREAS

The 'Birds Directive' applies to the whole territory of Member States, including sea areas. However, a consequence of using SSSIs/ASSIs as a precursor to designation of SPAs in the UK is that it has not been possible to designate many of the required SPAs covering inshore or offshore areas important to birds, despite the Government's obligation to do so. This is because the relevant provisions of the Wildlife and Countryside Act do not generally extend below the mean low water mark in England and Wales, or low water springs in Scotland (the position in Northern Ireland is not clear). There is no appropriate domestic legislative mechanism to protect as SPAs those marine areas of international conservation importance for seabirds. The available Marine Nature Reserve powers are designed primarily to conserve the sub-littoral interest of areas. They involve a hugely cumbersome bureaucracy (only two have been designated since 1981) and are not an appropriate mechanism for SPAs. New primary legislation would appear to be necessary to redress the deficiency.

The current inability to protect marine areas of importance for seabirds as SPAs means in practice that only nesting colonies are safeguarded. Some of the problems that this entails in conservation management are demonstrated in near-shore areas used by seaducks. One of the greatest threats to them is oil pollution on their moulting and wintering grounds. An oil spill or other incident in these areas could effectively negate all the protection provided to these species during the breeding season.

A review of marine areas important for seabirds, under the terms of the 'Birds Directive', is currently being undertaken at the request of Government by the Joint Nature Conservation Committee.

1.7 CRITERIA FOR SELECTION OF IMPORTANT BIRD AREAS

All the sites in this inventory have been included on the basis that they are of significance in the context of the European Community (and some globally) for the bird populations they support. This has been judged with particular reference to the objectives of the EC Directive on the Conservation of Wild Birds, and the 'Ramsar' Convention on Wetlands of International Importance. This section explains how that information contributes to the decision to include a site in the inventory – why it is regarded as internationally important. Scientific guidelines for assessing this have been in existence for many years, and have been progressively refined. For the purposes of this book, they have been applied consistently throughout Great Britain; and with some necessary slight variations for Northern Ireland, the Channel Islands and Isle of Man. The sources of data used for this are described in Chapter 2.

Three principal strands of activity have given rise to the combination of criteria used in compiling the 'IBA list' –a process not just geared to this publication, but part of the statutory conservation bodies' ongoing responsibilities. These comprise:

(a) Agreed criteria adopted by the Contracting Parties to the Ramsar Convention;

(b) ICBP criteria, devised for the European IBA inventory (Grimmett and Jones 1989) and in the course of work done by an EC Working Group in association with the European Commission;

(c) Nature Conservancy Council criteria expounded in 'Protecting Internationally Important Bird Sites' (Stroud *et al* 1990); linked with guidelines for selecting Sites of Special Scientific Interest.

The Ramsar Convention criteria, for international importance of wetlands only, are set out in Appendix IV together with guidelines for their application which have been adopted by Contracting Parties to the Convention. A key element of this, as far as birds are concerned, is the widely accepted notion that any area regularly supporting 1% or more of a biogeographical population is regarded as significant. This also features in all the other systems of criteria mentioned. It is first necessary to explain the terms 'biogeographical population' and 'regularly supporting', before examining the operation of a 1% threshold.

A biogeographical population is normally defined as a more or less discrete group of birds, which lives in a particular area (or group of areas in the case of a migratory population), interbreed freely within the group and rarely breed or exchange individuals with other groups (Mayr 1970). Several goose species provide good examples of distinct biogeographical populations.

There are, for example, three populations of barnacle goose with hardly any exchange at any season between them. Barnacle geese breeding in east Greenland over-winter in western Scotland and Ireland; those from Svalbard winter on the Solway Firth; and those from western Siberia winter in western mainland Europe.

In other cases, particularly where slight physical differences have developed between populations, a species may be divided into one or more sub-species. Such is the case for white-fronted geese, two populations (and sub-species) of which over-winter in the British Isles. The Greenland white-fronted goose breeds in west Greenland and winters in the western and northern British Isles; whereas the European white-fronted goose breeds in Siberia and winters in Europe and southern England. In this case, the sub-species of Greenland white-front consists of a single population, while the sub-species of European white-front consists of five discrete populations. These winter in north-western, central and eastern Europe respectively. Three other sub-species occur in North America.

The reason for treating each biogeographical population separately for conservation planning is that these populations will encounter different conditions in the various parts of their range. Consequently, there may also be differences in productivity or mortality between populations. This may make the uniform application of certain conservation or other policies (for example, wildfowling regulations) inapplicable at the species level. Where the range of a species is continuous and there is no obvious separation between groups, the discrete groups as described above do not occur. Here the approach, as approved by intergovernmental meetings, has been to take the number of birds in north-west Europe as the relevant biogeographical population for British purposes (where such data are available). Two such species are wigeon and pochard. In subsequent studies, this has been found to be biologically sensible in view of the conditions to which the birds are exposed in comparison with other sectors of the population.

The Conference of Contracting Parties to the Ramsar Convention has also defined the term 'regularly' as used in the criteria. A wetland regularly supports a population of a given size if:

(a) the requisite number of birds is known to have occurred in at least three-quarters of the seasons for which adequate data are available, the total number of seasons being not less than three; or

(b) the mean of the seasonal maxima, taken over at least five years, amounts to the required level (means based on three or four years may be quoted in provisional assessments only).

Such requirements indicate the need for long-term monitoring of national populations and site-use by birds. (Indeed, such monitoring is a requirement under Article 10 of the EC Birds Directive).

However, in establishing long-term use of a site by birds, there needs to be a full awareness of the ecological needs of the populations protected at that site. Thus, in the case, for example, of cold weather movements, as described above, the average number of birds using a site over several years may not adequately reflect the importance of the site. Thus, as always, there is a need for interpretation of data by qualified nature conservation scientists.

There is no fundamental biological reason to take 1% of a population as the threshold level for establishing international importance of a site. However, this percentage has been found by long experience and evaluation to be useful in giving an appropriate degree of protection to populations, and in the definition of ecologically sensible sites. The criterion has, therefore, gained wide acceptance by the Contracting Parties of the Ramsar Convention, and by other nations also. The 1% level of national species totals has also been taken as the basis of the assessment of national importance in various countries, including Great Britain. (If the British wintering population of a waterfowl species is so small that 1% is less than 50 birds then, by convention, 50 birds is normally used as the qualifying level for national importance).

This proportional measure is self-adjusting to rarity, which is clearly a necessity for such a method of evaluation. Thus, the scarcer a population, the greater the proportion of sites occupied by it which should be protected. This increased proportion of sites will be generated using the 1% level. This measure for site protection works adequately only for those populations which tend to concentrate into relatively small areas.

This feature is also desirable because species which concentrate will, by definition, be dependent on a relatively small proportion of the total territory and therefore are especially vulnerable to changes on those specific areas. These species will tend to be those with specialised ecological requirements, which will usually be met only at a few traditional locations. Examples would include whooper swan, brent goose and avocet. For both the national and international assessments, the 1% level is fairly conservative. This can be illustrated by applying it to the human species. Human populations are an extreme example of a numerous species which forms dense concentrations, so the assessment is appropriate for use in this context. The British population is approximately 56,000,000 people; therefore 1% is about 560,000. On this basis the only cities in Britain which would qualify as 'nationally important' would be London, Birmingham, Sheffield, Manchester and Liverpool. Glasgow could be included if its adjacent towns, such as Paisley, were grouped with it. Clearly a policy of conservation for buildings (habitats for the human population) based on this criterion would be excessively conservative. If one used the definition of 'international importance', only London would qualify.

A potential problem with the use of the 1% criterion is that it depends on the availability of good estimates of total population size, whether for biogeographical populations or for national totals. For most parts of the world, detailed data on the status of bird populations do not exist or are extremely incomplete. In the UK however, the various population monitoring schemes such as the WWT/JNCC National Waterfowl Counts and the BTO/JNCC/RSPB Birds of Estuaries Enquiry provide a means of obtaining and updating such information. Likewise there is good information on breeding seabirds available from the JNCC/Seabird Group's Seabird Colony Register. The totals for eastern Atlantic wader populations have recently been updated using data from such schemes throughout Europe (Smit and Piersma 1989) (See Appendix V).

It is essential to note that the 1% level is not a level to which populations on any one site may be reduced while still fulfilling international obligations. This rather odd view has gained some currency in proposals for development. The view is clearly wrong. If sites holding greater than 1% of a population of birds were to be reduced to '1%', then the total population would decline. This would lead to progressive lowering of the 1% level until population extinction occurs. Such an approach is clearly untenable, and would lead to breaches of both the 'Birds' Directive and the Ramsar Convention.

When a population is increasing, it is possible to infer preference for particular sites from the choices birds make between sites. Thus, at small population sizes, birds are likely to use first those sites which most fully provide for their requirements. As numbers increase, birds are obliged to use increasingly less favoured sites. However, the proportion of birds on most preferred sites declines as the overall population increases. It is possible to refine the 1% criterion to include ranking of sites on their 'preferredness' by species, where such information exists in addition to information on the numbers using a site. Factors such as site quality and preferredness are important and, when known, require consideration in determining the selection of sites which will best sustain population productivity and range. This is a complex process and has not been attempted in compiling the present list of Important Bird Areas.

The question of selection criteria for SPAs has been considered by an ICBP Technical Working Group at the request of the Commission of the European Communities in 1988. This work also underpinned the criteria used in compiling the European IBA inventory (Grimmett and Jones 1989) (criteria given in Stroud *et al* 1990 Appendices 3 and 7). It was considered by ICBP that the following objectives would need to be met for the successful application of any criteria to meet the requirements of Article 4 of the Birds Directive:

    (a) Ensuring the survival and reproduction of Annex 1 species in their area of distribution.

    (b) Ensuring the survival of the breeding, moulting and wintering areas, and staging posts of regularly occurring migratory species not listed in Annex 1 and particularly the protection of wetlands of international importance.

    (c) Ensuring that the areas within the network form a coherent whole which meets the protection requirements of these species.

    (d) Ensuring that the areas selected were identified because of their (European) Community importance for the species concerned and excluded sites of lesser (national or regional) importance.

In keeping with the Directive, the emphasis has been placed on the end target, with the identification of individual sites being decided on the basis of their contribution to this target. The challenge can be re-stated as two questions:

    (a) What target level of overall protection is required to provide a basis for the maintenance, survival and reproduction of each species population throughout its area of distribution?

    (b) Which sites should be selected to provide for this level of protection for the whole suite of species insofar as site-safeguard mechanisms are appropriate?

Clearly, many sites are so obviously important as to select themselves, but these alone will not be enough to fulfil the requirements of the Directive (leaving aside the questions of situations where site safeguard mechanisms are not appropriate). The criteria referred to establish priorities for attention, rather than addressing the question of what proportion of a population should be accommodated within SPAs. The wording of the Directive however does provide some guidance on this.

Article 4.2 requires Member States to pay particular attention to the protection of wetlands, and particularly to wetlands of international importance. This is a clear cross-reference to the Ramsar Convention, but indicates also that some sites which do not meet the Ramsar criteria of international importance should, however, qualify for protection as SPA. This is as one would expect because the Directive relates to a different scale of issues and areas from the Convention. The Ramsar Convention is a worldwide measure, whereas the EC Directive is far more local, relating essentially to part of Western Europe. Furthermore, one would not expect to give less protection to species listed on Annex 1, and to other vulnerable migrants, than one would give to waterfowl.

The requirement to consider range and productivity clearly indicates that it may not be appropriate to apply numerical criteria uniformly across the whole Community. This is especially the case if such uniformity of application conflicts with the need to protect outlying populations or population segments, the conservation of which is important to maintain overall species ranges.

Indeed, the international area is composed of many national areas, and while a uniform framework is essential within which to work, uniform numerical criteria across the whole international area may not be desirable if due account is to be taken of the need to maintain range and productivity. Thus, wider criteria to guide conservation actions for some species may be desirable in some parts of the international area. Due allowance must be made for such needs.

The problem then becomes one of how to assess priorities for action or for site selection at a national level. Some birds may be more common in some countries than others. A result of this might be that national information or assessments alone might indicate different priorities, compared with those derived from an international perspective. Conversely, the international perspective might seem to conflict with national priorities, until the need to maintain populations and range is considered. The problem is one of scale, and is exemplified by the case of some wintering geese, which appear very 'common' in the limited areas where they occur, but are in fact extremely scarce in a national or international context.

Thus, the direction of national conservation action needs to be guided by an awareness of international trends in range, distribution, productivity and population numbers. An integration of all these factors has been undertaken by E Bezzel for the European Commission (1980). Further details of this are set out in Stroud *et al* 1990.

Other factors embraced by the criteria systems described, and which have been taken into account in compiling the present inventory (and which are also treated in more detail by Stroud *et al* 1990) include: the need to protect hydrological integrity of wetland sites; 'turnover' of migratory birds at a given site (ie throughput of very large numbers which are not reflected in count totals calculated at any one point in time); and contextual information about population trends, seasonal use by the same population of different ecosystems, and so on.

References

Alexandersson, H 1987 Ljungpiparens *Pluvialis apricaria* förekomst och täthet pa kalmossar i sydvästra Sverige. Betydelsen av mossamas storlek och inbördes avstand. (Distribution and density of Golden Plover *Pluvialis apricaria* on raised bogs in southwest Sweden. The importance of area and distances between bogs.) *Acta Regiae Societatis Scientiarum et Litterarum Gothoburgensis. Zoologica* 14: 9-19.

Baillie, S R 1984 *The movements of migratory birds in periods of severe weather*. Report from the Nature Conservancy Council to the Council of Europe.

Bainbridge, I P, Minns, D W, Housden, S D and Lance, A N 1987 *Forestry in the Flows of Caithness and Sutherland*. RSPB, Sandy.

Batten, L A, Bibby, C J, Clement, P, Elliott, G D and Porter, R F (eds.) 1990 *Red Data Birds in Britain*. T and A D Poyser, London.

Beintema, A J 1983 Wet meadows in temperate Europe, threatened by agriculture. In: *Shorebirds and large waterbirds conservation, EEC Symposium 1983*, eds. P R Evans, H Hafner and P L'Hermite, 26-33. Brussels, European Commission.

Bezzel, E 1980 *An assessment of the endangered status of Europe's breeding birds and the importance of their biotopes as a basis for protective measures*. Report (DOC.ENV/22/80) to European Commission.

Bibby, C J 1978 Conservation of the Dartford Warbler on English lowland heaths, a review. *Biol. Conserv.* 13: 229-307.

Bibby, C J 1986 Merlins in Wales, site occupancy and breeding in relation to vegetation. *Journal of Applied Ecology* 23: 1-12.

Bibby, C J and Tubbs, C R 1975 Status and conservation of the Dartford Warbler in England. *British Birds* 68: 177–195.

Bignal, E M, Bignal, S and Easterbee, N 1988 The recent status and distribution of the Chough *Pyrrhocorax pyrrhocorax* in Scotland. *Nature Conservancy Council, CSD Report,* No. 843.

Bignal, E M and Curtis, D J *(eds.)* 1989 *Choughs and land-use in Europe.* Proceedings of an International Workshop on the Conservation of the Chough, *Pyrrhocorax pyrrhocorax,* in the EC. 11–14 November 1988. Tarbert, Scottish Chough Study Group.

Cadbury, C J 1987a UK Estuaries under threat. *RSPB Conserv. Rev.* 1: 41–46.

Cadbury, C J 1987b Moorland birds – Britain's international responsibility. *RSPB Conserv. Rev.* 1: 59–64.

Campbell, L H 1989 The importance of breeding waders of croft and farmland in Shetland. *RSPB Conserv. Rev.* 3: 75–78.

Carp, E 1972 *Proceedings of the international conference on the conservation of wetlands and waterfowl. Ramsar, Iran, 30 January –3 February 1971.* IWRB, Slimbridge.

Davidson, N C and Pienkowski, M W, *(eds.)* 1987 The conservation of international flyway populations of waders. *Wader Study Group Bulletin* 49, Supplement.

Diefenbach, D R, Nichols, J D and Hines, J E 1988 Distribution patterns during winter and fidelity to wintering areas of American black ducks. *Canadian Journal of Zoology* 66: 1506–1513.

Doody, P and Barnett, B 1987. *The Wash and its Environment.* Nature Conservancy Council, Peterborough. (Research & survey in nature conservation No. 7).

Evans, M E 1982 Movements of Bewick's Swans *Cygnus columbianus bewickii* marked at Slimbridge, England from 1960 to 1979. *Ardea* 70: 59–75.

Fox, A D 1987 Observations on the waders of Eqalungmiut Nunaat, west Greenland. *Wader Study Group Bulletin* 49: 11–13.

Fuller, R J, Reed, T M, Webb, A, Williams, T D and Pienkowski, M W 1986. Populations of breeding waders *Charadrii* and their habitats on the crofting lands of the Outer Hebrides, Scotland. *Biol. Conserv.* 37: 333–361.

Fuller, R M 1987 The changing extent and conservation interest of lowland grasslands in England and Wales, a review of grassland surveys 1930–84. *Biol. Conserv.* 40: 281–300.

Gilpin, M E 1987 Spatial structure and population vulnerability. In: *Viable populations for conservation,* ed. M. Soulé. 125–139. Cambridge University Press Cambridge.

Goodman, D 1987 How do any species persist? Lessons for conservation biology. *Conservation Biology* 1: 59–62.

Goss-Custard, J D 1985 Foraging Behaviour of Wading Birds and the Carrying Capacity of Estuaries. In: *Behavioural Ecology. Consequences of Adaptive Behaviour.* eds. R M Sibly, and R H Smith. Blackwell, Oxford.

Goss-Custard, J D and Moser, M E 1988 Rates of change in the numbers of Dunlin, *Calidris alpina,* wintering in British estuaries in relation to the spread of *Spartina anglica. Journal of Applied Ecology* 25: 95–109.

Green, G H, Greenwood, J J D, and Lloyd, C S 1977 The influence of snow conditions on the date of breeding of wading birds in north-east Greenland. *Journal of Zoology, London* 183: 311–328.

Green, R E and Cadbury, C J 1987 Breeding waders of lowland wet grasslands. *RSPB Conserv. Rev.* 1: 10–13.

Grimmett, R F A and Jones, T A 1989. *Important Bird Areas in Europe.* ICBP, Cambridge.

Harris, L D 1988 The nature of cumulative impacts on biotic diversity of wetland vertebrates. *Environmental Management* 12: 675–693.

Hill, M I 1988 *Saltmarsh vegetation of the Wash. An assessment of change from 1971 to 1985.* Nature Conservancy Council, Peterborough. (Research & survey in nature conservation No. 13).

Hudson, P J 1985 Population parameters for the Atlantic Alcidae. In: *The Atlantic Alcidae. The evolution, distribution and biology of the auks inhabiting the Atlantic Ocean and adjacent water areas,* eds. D N Nettleship and T R Birkhead, 233-261. Academic Press, London.

IUCN 1986 *Migratory species in international instruments: an overview.* International Union for the Conservation of Nature, Gland, Switzerland.

Johnsgard, P A 1983 *The grouse of the world.* Croom Helm, London.

Jorde, D G and Owen, R B 1988 The need for nocturnal activity and energy budgets for waterfowl. In: *Waterfowl in winter,* ed. M.W. Weller, 169-180. University of Minnesota Press, Minneapolis.

Lande, R and Barrowclough, G F 1987 Effective population size, genetic variation and their use in population management. In: *Viable populations for conservation,* ed. M. Soulé, 87-123. Cambridge University Press, Cambridge.

Laursen, K 1980 Fudle i Danske landbrugsomrader, med analyse af nogle landskabsele-menters indflydelse pa fuglenes fordeling. (Bird censuses in Danish farmland, with an analysis of bird distributions in relation to some landscape elements). *Dansk Ornithologisk Forenings Tidsskrift* 74: 11-26.

Lloyd, C, Tasker, M L and Partridge, K 1991 *The Status of Seabirds in Britain and Ireland.* T and A D Poyser, London.

Macarthur, R H and Wilson, E O 1967 *The theory of island biogeography.* Princeton University Press. (Monographs in Population Biology No. 1).

Madsen, J 1984 Status of the Svalbard population of light-bellied Brent Geese *Branta bernicla hrota* wintering in Denmark 1980-1983. *Norsk Polarinstitut Skrifter* 181: 119-124.

Madsen, J 1987 Status and Management of Goose Populations in Europe, with special reference to populations resting and breeding in Denmark. *Danish Review of Game Biology* 12: 1-76.

Madsen, J, Bregnballe, T and Mehlum, F 1989 Study of the breeding ecology and behaviour of the Svalbard population of Light-bellied Brent Goose *branta bernicla hrota.* *Polar Research* 7: 1-21.

Maltby, E 1986 *Waterlogged wealth. Why waste the world's wetlands?* Earthscan, London.

Marcot, B G and Holthausen, R 1987 Analyzing population viability of the Spotted Owl in the Pacific Northwest. *Transactions of the North American Wildlife and Natural Resources Conference* 52: 333-347.

Mayr, E 1970 *Populations, species and evolution.* Harvard University Press, Cambridge, Mass.

Meltofte, H 1985 Populations and breeding schedules of waders, *Charadrii,* in high arctic Greenland. *Meddleleser om Gronland, Bioscience* 16: 1-43.

Moore, N W 1962 The heaths of Dorset and their conservation. *Journal of Ecology* 50: 369-391.

Nature Conservancy Council 1984 *Nature conservation in Great Britain.* Nature Conservancy Council, Peterborough.

Norriss, D W and Wilson, H J 1988 Disturbance and flock size changes in Greenland White-fronted Geese wintering in Ireland. *Wildfowl* 39: 63-70.

O'Brien, M G and Smith, K M Changes in the status of waders breeding on wet lowland grassland between 1982 and 1989. *Bird Study,* in press.

O'Connor, R J and Shrubb, M 1986 *Farming and birds.* Cambridge University Press, Cambridge.

Owen, M 1980 *Wild geese of the world. Their life history and ecology.* Batsford, London.

Owen, M, Atkinson-Willes, G L and Salmon, D G 1986 *Wildfowl in Great Britain.* 2nd ed. Cambridge University Press, Cambridge.

Patterson, I J 1982 *The Shelduck: a study in behavioural ecology.* Cambridge University Press, Cambridge.

Pienkowski, M W and Evans, P R 1984 Migratory behaviour of shorebirds in the western Palearctic. In: *Shorebirds, migration and foraging behaviour,* eds. J Burger and B K Olla, pp 73–123. Plenum Press, New York.

Pienkowski, M W and Evans, P R 1985 The role of migration in the population dynamics of birds. In: *Behavioural ecology. Ecological consequences of adaptive behaviour,* eds. R M Sibly and R H Smith, pp 331–352. Symposium of British Ecological Society. Blackwell Scientific Publications, Oxford.

Pienkowski, M W and Pienkowski, A 1983 WSG project on the movement of wader populations in western Europe, eighth progress report. *Wader Study Group Bulletin* 38: 13–22.

Pirot, J-Y, Laursen, K, Madsen, J and Monval, J-Y 1989 Population estimates of swans, geese, ducks and Eurasian Coot *Fulica atra* in the Western Palearctic and Sahelian Africa. In: *Flyways and reserve networks. IWRB, Proceedings of the third meeting of the conference of the contracting parties, Regina, Canada,* 14–23. Canadian Wildlife Service/IWRB.

Prater, A J 1981 *Estuary birds of Britain and Ireland.* T and A D Poyser, Calton.

Prokosch, P 1984 Population, Jahresrhythmus und traditionelle Nahrungsplatzbindungen der Dunkelbäuchigen Ringelgans (*Branta b. bernicla,* L. 1758) im Nordfriesischen Wattenmeer. Ökologie der Vögel *(Ecology of Birds)* 6: 1–99.

Prokosch, P 1988 Das Schleswig-Holsteinische Wattenmeer als Fruhjars-Auftenhaltsgebiet Arktischer Watvogelpopulationen am Beispiel von Kiebitzregenpfeifer (*Pluvialis squatarola,* L. 1958). Knutt (*Calidris canutus,* L. 1758) und Pfuhlschenpfe (*Limosa lapponica,* L. 1758). *Corax* 12: 273–422

Ramsar Convention Bureau 1988. *Convention on Wetlands of International Importance Especially as Waterfowl Habitat. Proceedings of the third meeting of the Conference of Contracting Parties. Regina, Saskatchewan, Canada; 27 May to 5 June 1987.* Ramsar Convention Bureau, Switzerland.

Ruttledge, R F and Ogilvie, M A 1979 The past and current status of the Greenland White-fronted Goose in Ireland and Britain. *Irish Birds* 1: 293–363.

Salwasser, H, Mealey, S P and Johnson, K 1983 Wildlife population viability, a question of risk. *Transactions of the North American Wildlife and Natural Resources Conference* 49: 421–439.

Smart, M 1987 International Conventions. *Wader Study Group Bulletin 49, Supplement/ IWRB Special Publication* 7: 114–117.

Smit, C J and Piersma, T 1989 Numbers, midwinter distribution and migration of wader populations using the east Atlantic Flyway. In: *Flyways and reserve networks. IWRB, Proceedings of the third meeting of the conference of the contracting parties, Regina, Canada,* 24–63. Canadian Wildlife Service/IWRB.

Smith, K W 1983 The status and distribution of waders breeding on wet lowland grasslands in England and Wales. *Bird Study* 30: 177–192.

Soulé, M E 1987 *Viable populations for conservation.* Cambridge University Press, Cambridge.

Soulé, M E and Simberloff, D 1986 What do genetics and ecology tell us about the design of nature reserves? *Biol. Conserv.* 35: 19–40.

Stroud, D A (ed.) 1989 *Birds on Coll and Tiree: status, habitats and conservation.* Nature Conservancy Council/Scottish Ornithologists' Club, Edinburgh.

Stroud, D A, Reed, T M, Pienkowski, M W and Lindsay, R A 1987 *Birds, bogs and forestry: the peatlands of Caithness and Sutherland.* Nature Conservancy Council, Peterborough.

Stroud, D A, Mudge, G P and Pienkowski, M W 1990 *Protecting Internationally Important Bird Sites.* Nature Conservancy Council, Peterborough.

Tamisier, A 1979 The functional units of wintering ducks, a spatial integration of their comfort and feeding requirements. *Verhandlungen der Ornithologischen Gesellschaft in Bayern* 23: 229–238.

Tamisier, A 1985 Some considerations on the social requirements of ducks in winter. *Wildfowl* 36: 104–108.

Temple, S A and Cary, J R 1988 Modeling dynamics of habitat-interior bird populations in fragmented landscapes. *Conservation Biology* 2: 340–347.

Thompson, D B A, Stroud, D A, and Pienkowski, M W 1988 Afforestation and upland birds, consequences for population ecology. In: *Ecological change in the uplands,* eds. M B Usher and D B A Thompson, pp 237–259. Blackwell Scientific Publications, Oxford. (British Ecological Society Special Publication 7).

Townshend, D J 1982 The Lazarus syndrome in Grey Plovers. *Wader Study Group Bulletin* 34: 11–12.

Tubbs, C 1985 *The decline and present status of the English lowland heaths and their vertebrates.* Nature Conservancy Council, Peterborough. (Focus on nature conservation No. 11).

Van Rhijn, J G 1983 On the maintenance and origin of alternative strategies in the Ruff *Philomachus pugnax. Ibis* 125: 482–498.

Watson, A 1963 Bird numbers on tundra in Baffin Island. *Arctic* 16: 101–108.

Webb, N R 1990 Changes on the heathlands of Dorset, England, between 1978–1987. *Biol. Conserv.* 51: 273–286.

Williams, G and Bowers, J K 1987 Land drainage and birds in England and Wales. *RSPB Conserv. Rev.* 1: 25–30.

Williams, G and Hall, M 1987 The loss of coastal grazing marshes in south and east England, with special reference to east Essex, England. *Biol. Conserv.* 39, 243–253.

2. Guide to the Inventory

2.1 INTRODUCTION

This chapter provides an aid to the interpretation of the site accounts which form the bulk of the remainder of the book. A glossary of abbreviations used is given separately on pages xi–xii. After sections explaining the layout of the maps and list of sites, further sections follow the sequence of headings in the site accounts, each of which conforms to a consistent format.

Access

The overwhelming majority of areas described in this book are privately owned. Inclusion in the inventory must not be taken to imply anything concerning rights of access. In all cases the presumption must be that there is *no* right of public access unless local circumstances or public rights of way (often featured on Ordnance Survey maps) indicate otherwise: no information on this is given in this book.

More detailed information

Should you require further information about any of the sites mentioned in this book in order to assist you with your work, you are encouraged to contact your local office of the RSPB, the Countryside Council for Wales, English Nature, DoE (Northern Ireland) or Scottish Natural Heritage. A list of offices for all these organisations appears in Appendix VI.

Confidential information

Certain very rare or sensitive birds have not been mentioned in the site accounts in this book. This is done to minimise risks from illegal egg collectors, or from disturbance by birdwatchers. Where decisions on land use affecting any of the sites mentioned in this book are to be taken, the reader is encouraged to contact the bodies mentioned above in order to obtain a more complete picture.

Boundaries

Certain sites in this book do not have a finalised boundary and are represented in symbol form on the maps. As survey and field work progresses boundaries will be agreed, and it is hoped that in due course a revised edition of this book can be published containing this new information. *In the interim decision-makers are encouraged to consult with the statutory nature conservation agencies and RSPB* should a proposal appear likely to affect in any way a site in this book. In view of the Government's obligations under the EC 'Birds' Directive decision–makers are urged to adopt a precautionary approach.

2.2 OVERVIEW OF COVERAGE

The geographical area covered by this book includes the whole of the United Kingdom of Great Britain (England, Scotland and Wales) and Northern Ireland. In addition, the Isle of Man and the Channel Islands are also covered. Though biogeographically and politically linked to the UK, Channel Islands and the Isle of Man are not parts of it. The important differences relevant to this inventory are explained in separate introductory sections to those territories on pages 464 and 476 respectively.

Ornithological interest is not uniformly distributed throughout these countries and territories, and the total of 256 sites included in the inventory divides between them as follows:

England:	74 sites (including 1 cross–border site shared with Scotland; 2 shared with Wales are included in the Wales section).
Scotland:	132 sites (1 cross–border site shared with England is included in the England section).
Wales:	15 sites (including 2 cross–border sites shared with England).
Northern Ireland:	17 sites
Isle of Man:	5 sites
Channel Islands:	13 sites

2.3 MAPS

It is not the intention of this publication to give individual site boundary maps for each site described. The process of determining definitive boundaries for the proposed designation of international sites is undertaken by the Joint Nature Conservation Committee in consultation with the country nature conservation agencies.

A set of location maps appears on pages 45–71, with a key map to these on page 47. Most of the location maps are drawn to a scale of 1:1,255,000, covering the UK and island groups in 24 segments. Some of these segments overlap: where this is the case, all sites in each segment are shown, so that a few will appear on more than one page.

Each map shows the coastline and counties (England, Wales and Northern Ireland) or regions (Scotland). Within each county or region one or two principal towns or cities are shown (these are not necessarily the administrative centre in every case, but often will be).

Important Bird Areas are shown in one of two different ways. Where a site boundary has (through research and consultation) been generally agreed, the location and boundary of the site is approximately shown on the map. This in turn is done in one of two ways: the area concerned is either shown in black or by cross-shading. The latter applies generally only to extensive coastal/estuarine sites, and enables the line of the coast itself to remain distinguishable. Where landward areas are included in one of these coastal/estuarine sites, these are shown in black as with other landward sites. Large bodies of inland freshwater are also shown in black.

The other way in which sites have been represented is by an open circle symbol. This applies to sites where, although sufficient interest unquestionably exists to justify selection as an IBA (see pages 16-21), a precise boundary has not yet been defined because more research and/or consultation is required to finalise details. Such work progresses continuously and in due course agreed boundaries for all IBAs will be confirmed. In a very few cases a symbol has been used where a request was made to preserve a degree of anonymity for a site whose boundary would otherwise pick out an individual land-ownership, or might lead to disturbance of vulnerable species or habitat.

Sites shown by symbols are represented by circles of three different sizes. These equate to three size-classes, as follows:

$$\bigcirc \quad = \quad 1 - \quad 999 \text{ ha}$$
$$\large\bigcirc \quad = \quad 1,000 - 9,999 \text{ ha}$$
$$\Large\bigcirc \quad = \quad \qquad 10,000+ \text{ ha}$$

(Where a site's boundary has been indicated on a map, its approximate area is usually stated in that site's entry in the body of the text).

The numbers of sites falling in the different categories described above are as follows:

Approximate boundary shown:	149 sites (58%)
Symbol used:	107 sites (42%)
– comprising: 'small':	42 sites
'medium':	43 sites
'large':	22 sites

Against each site on the maps is given that site's unique code reference: commonly a three- or four-digit number usually followed by the suffix 'A'. This enables cross-reference to the list of sites and to the site accounts in the body of the text. These codes are also used as working references from day-to-day for other purposes by JNCC and the country agencies. The meaning of the numbers is explained on page 30.

2.4   THE LIST OF SITES INCLUDED

A list of sites included in the inventory (the 'IBA list') is given on pages 39-44. Approved site names and unique identifier codes provide internal and external consistency for cross-referencing as explained above. The sequence in which the sites have been listed corresponds to the sequence in which their respective descriptive accounts appear in the body of the book, and follows conventions adopted for listing them in previous years.

The IBA list has evolved progressively over many years, as legal requirements are clarified, scientific knowledge improves, and natural or man-induced changes occur in bird populations and habitats (see 1.2 above). This is only to be expected and will continue as these processes go on after the publication of this volume. At various times in the past the list has been published, either with a limited circulation in technical reports or more widely in the public domain. Such publications include reports by the Nature Conservancy Council (NCC) (Stroud *et al* 1990), Joint Nature Conservation Committee (JNCC), International Council for Bird Preservation (ICBP), International Waterfowl and Wetlands Research Bureau (IWRB), the Important Bird Areas in Europe book (Grimmett and Jones 1989), and successive written answers by UK Government Ministers in Hansard (the Parliamentary record; most recently on 17/18 July 1991). Changes of the type described above have led to a number of differences between each manifestation of the list. The present volume represents a consolidation of all these, acting as a 'snapshot in time', correct as at early 1992. Clearly, it is hoped that future changes will be few, but it must be acknowledged that some will occur. The significance of this publication is in the unprecedented full agreement between the publishing bodies, statutory and voluntary, over the complete list.

2.5 THE SITE ACCOUNTS: STANDARD INTRODUCTORY INFORMATION

Each site account begins on a separate page. At the head of the page is the name by which the Important Bird Area is known. This should in most cases be the same as the name of the relevant international site designation when made, unless part of the designation was made some time ago and has been overtaken by necessary modifications to the definition of the site. Other designations or local names may apply to the same area of land: some indication (for example, of sub-components) may be given in the 'site descriptions' part of the text.

This is then followed by the 'SPA/Ram' code reference, which equates to the unique identifier described on page 29. This is normally a three- or four-digit figure, followed by the letter 'A'. The numbers relate to the different country conservation agency regions, thus all sites between 101-199 are in NW Scotland Region; sites with 601-699 are in NE England, etc. Gaps in the numbering sequence in this book are normally due to the allocation of this number to a site which is no longer on the 'A' list of designated and proposed SPAs or Ramsar sites. An 'IBA Europe' number is also given where applicable, being the reference number used in Grimmett and Jones (1989). (It has not been possible simply to follow the 'IBA Europe' system in the present publication, so this second number provides an easy cross-reference between the two books).

The next two entries simply give the county (or region in Scotland) and district in which the site is situated. If it covers more than one county or district, they are listed in alphabetical order. 'Sheadings' are given for the Isle of Man sites. This is followed by the catalogue number(s) of the Ordnance Survey 1:50,000 map(s) on which the site can be found, and a grid reference (both under the heading 'OS sheet(s)'). The grid reference refers to an approximate centre-point of the site, with the degree of precision (6-figure, 4-figure etc) reflecting either the size of the site or the precision with which its extent has so far been confirmed. For linear sites (for example, sea-cliffs) two reference points are given, representing (where defined) the outer limits of the site. A cross-reference to the map page in this book is also given. A figure for the plan surface area of the site in hectares is given next. Where the boundary of the site has yet to be firmly set we have indicated one of three size-classes : 1-999ha; 1,000-9,999ha; 10,000+ha. These correspond to the map representations.

The entry headed 'NNR' will signify 'yes' if the site or part of it bears the statutory designation of National Nature Reserve (under the National Parks and Access to the Countryside Act 1949). The other principal national statutory designation which is relevant is that of Site of Special Scientific Interest or SSSI (Area of Special Scientific Interest or ASSI in Northern Ireland), under the Wildlife and Countryside Acts 1981-85 or the Nature Conservation and Amenity Lands Order 1985 respectively. Since it is UK Government policy that international (Ramsar site/Special Protection Area) designations will only be made on land which carries SSSI or ASSI status under domestic law, all sites in this book either have or should have such status: thus no heading for this is given in the text accounts.

The next entries (SPA/Ram designated/candidate) record Y (yes), or N (no) in each case. This indicates whether the site has been listed by the statutory authorities as a candidate for one or both of these designations, or has formally been designated. If only part of the site has been designated this is shown as Y for both 'designated' and 'candidate'. For a small number of sites we have also indicated here that 'wider countryside' measures are required in land adjacent to the Important Bird Areas in order to maintain the specific bird interest. Such an approach is indeed relevant to a much larger number of IBAs (see Section 1.5) but we have restricted the statement to those where such a link is considered to be of crucial importance at this stage. An example is an area listed for breeding divers or grebes. In such a case, SSSI/SPA designation would be an appropriate form of protection for the 'core area', ie the water-body and associated wetland habitats. However, the special bird interest is dependent upon maintenance of the integrity of the catchment. A consultation/buffer zone, using 'wider countryside' mechanisms, is required outside the 'core area' to guard against adverse land-use changes.

The final part of the standard introductory information for each site account comprises a short one- or two-sentence summary of the type of site involved, and the key ornithological interest which gives rise to its inclusion in the inventory. By occurring in the same position in every account, this should provide a convenient quick reference on the nature of the site's interest.

2.6   THE SITE DESCRIPTIONS: PHYSICAL DESCRIPTION OF HABITATS, ETC

The body of each account begins with a section headed 'site description'. This covers the physiography and habitat composition of the site, including any special faunal interest other than birds. Geographical sub-units are described where applicable. Where common names of plants are a better-known alternative to scientific names, common names are used. Full listings of both are given in Appendix II. Much of the detail for these sections has been contributed by regional staff of the former NCC. Information on non-bird aspects should not be regarded as complete or definitive.

2.7 BIRD INFORMATION: DATA-SOURCES USED

The bird data used in this book, both in selecting sites and compiling the individual site accounts come from a wide range of sources. National data sets we have used include :

- BTO/WWT/JNCC/RSPB Birds of Estuaries Enquiry and National Waterfowl Count scheme (reports of both published annually: note that site names described in these summary reports do not necessarily refer to exactly the same areas of land covered by the corresponding IBAs.
- JNCC/Seabird Group Seabird Colony Register (summarised in Lloyd *et al* 1991 – original data used for this inventory).
- Rare Birds Breeding Panel information.
- BTO/WSG Winter Shorebird Counts (Moser *et al* 1986).
- Widespread specific habitat survey programmes of JNCC/RSPB and others, for example, Moorland Bird Surveys, Breeding Waders of Wet Grassland Surveys.
- Species-specific monitoring or survey programmes involving RSPB or NCC, for example, corncrake, terns, bittern. Often uses latest unpublished data.

Further substantial input comes from unpublished NCC/RSPB data, personal knowledge and local experts. This information derives from an extensive consultation and data searching exercise carried out during the preparation of this book, involving approximately 100 consultees. Any particular relevant published references used as sources for individual sites are listed in the 'further reading' section at the end of each site account.

2.8 BIRD INFORMATION: GUIDE TO INTERPRETING THE SITE ACCOUNTS

At the beginning of the section headed 'Birds' in each site account is given a convenient one- or two-sentence summary of the significance of the site. This usually lists those species that occur on the site in nationally or internationally important numbers. A more detailed breakdown of this then follows. It must be stressed that this has been restricted so as to concentrate on the **species by virtue of which the site merits inclusion in the inventory**, according to the criteria in section 1.7 above.

Some bird information is of a sensitive or confidential nature, either because it concerns species which, if their whereabouts became known, might be subject to adverse attention: or because the gathering and use of the data has been constrained by agreements with landowners over access, etc. In the course of compiling this book, a policy on these matters was agreed between the publishing organisations, and guidelines issued to contributors and compilers. Several different devices have been employed in drafting the site accounts so as to respect important sensitivities of this kind. The simplest measure has been to exclude from the text any information about the presence of rare species which is not essential to the identification of the site as internationally important in the terms of the EC Directive or the Ramsar Convention. This applies to most of the species over which confidentiality anxieties were raised.

In a few cases where the species giving rise to the site's inclusion are themselves sensitive, they have not been mentioned by name but referred to only indirectly by reference to an assemblage or community of species. Decision-making authorities needing more details should approach the relevant statutory conservation body. In some cases site *definition* has been arranged so as to preserve the confidentiality of some aspect; either by showing the location on the map as a symbol rather than a delineated boundary (see 2.3 above); or by combining several areas of land into a single composite 'site' with one name and code reference.

Bird species are referred to in the text by their common names, with a full list of scientific names given in Appendix I. Details of important species occurring at the site are given in a sequence which generally follows the convention of covering those present in internationally important numbers first, followed by those occurring in nationally important numbers (both in bold type), followed by any others of special interest. Within each of these three categories, species are dealt with in conventional taxonomic order (Voous 1977).

Numbers of birds quoted have been rounded in a common sense way for consistency, readability, and to avoid giving an unwarranted impression of levels of accuracy. Percentages have normally been rounded to the nearest integer. In some cases, where it is appropriate, a range between an upper and lower figure is given, either when averages fluctuate within the range over time, or where numbers are not known sufficiently accurately to justify the use of a single figure.

The requirements as to regularity of use of a site by birds, which qualify it for inclusion, have been described in 1.7 above. Average numbers and regularity thresholds for those species that are counted on a regular basis tend conventionally to be based on a five–year period: that convention has been followed here. It is not possible to show how every such figure traces to a particular data source, because each has been based on the most up-to-date five years' worth of data available: clearly this will vary from species to species and from site to site. The assumption therefore should be that figures are derived from averages of the most recent five consecutive years' data. In some instances, of course, counts or surveys will not have been made this regularly. In some cases, although published data are available, unpublished data from the same census/survey programme for the latest season or year may have been used as well: so averages may not necessarily match averages so far published elsewhere at the time of going to print.

What have loosely been referred to as 'averages' above represent, in the case of wildfowl and waders, 'five year peak means' (as is the convention). The Birds of Estuaries Enquiry and National Waterfowl Count schemes produce totals for each of the winter months September–March for wildfowl, and November–March for waders. For a given species at a given site, the highest monthly total (the 'peak count') is the figure which, one for each year, is summed over the five most recent consecutive years to generate the peak mean.

The units used for numbers of breeding birds vary according to the breeding biology and corresponding census techniques for the species concerned. Unless otherwise stated the unit is 'the number of pairs of birds present'. For some cliff-nesting seabirds (for example, fulmar, kittiwake), it may instead be 'apparently occupied nests/sites'. For auk species, which do not build a nest, the census unit generally used is the number of individuals; and this has also been used in some cases for storm petrel and capercaillie. Numbers of territorial calling or singing birds is the measure generally used for bittern, nightjar, corncrake and firecrest. Marsh and hen harriers, which are polygamous, may be represented by 'nests' or 'breeding females'; and golden eagles by 'home ranges'. 'Lekking males' has been used in the case of ruff. Exceptions to all of these may be found among the site accounts given: where possible a standard convention has been followed, but data sources vary in the approach taken. No attempt has been made by the authors to 'convert' for example pairs to individuals for spurious increased comparability, since this is not always justified. A more detailed treatment of the units used for seabirds can be found in Lloyd *et al* 1991.

Following the peak mean or other absolute bird figures is usually given one or more percentage figures. These are usually rounded to the nearest integer. They describe the proportion of the relevant geographical population which the numbers at the site concerned represent. For sites in England, Wales and Scotland bird numbers are related firstly to the total British populations. The geographical scope of wider international comparisons vary between species groups and between breeding and wintering populations. These are determined primarily by biological context, but also by the constraints of data availability from other countries. Those used in this book are defined as follows:

British	=England, Scotland and Wales combined.
EC	=European Community: the 12 Member States combined, ie UK, Eire, France, Luxembourg, Belgium, Netherlands, Denmark, Germany, Italy, Spain, Portugal and Greece combined. Although not formally a part of the EC, Isle of Man and Channel Isles totals are included in this as well. In the case of 'Germany', although the Member State known as the Federal Republic now includes what was formerly East Germany, the bird totals upon which figures in this book are based derive only from what was formerly West Germany.
NW European	=North-west Europe, including the UK, Isle of Man, Channel Isles, Eire, Iceland, Faroes, Norway, Sweden, Finland, Denmark, Luxembourg, Belgium, Netherlands, 'west Germany' (see above), northern and western France, and north-west Spain.
Western European	=as NW Europe plus Italy, Switzerland, Portugal, south-east France and the remainder of Spain.
EAF	=East Atlantic Flyway: as defined for waders by Smit and Piersma 1989.
World/Total	=The total known range of the species/subspecies.

The total figures for each species in the relevant biogeographical areas are given in Appendix V. See also Stroud *et al* 1990.

Some accounts include reference to other 'notable' species whose numbers at the site do not exceed the 1% significance thresholds. These tend to arise where total numbers are large although the proportion of the geographical totals is not, and/or where the proportion is less than 1% but more than 0.4%. Location is relevant to this: for example, a colony of 1000 guillemots would be 'notable' in southern England or Wales but not in Scotland.

In a few more cases, numbers and percentages have been given notwithstanding the fact that the conventional national or international significance thresholds have not been met, but where it nevertheless appears helpful to quantify the interest. This would be the case, for example, with wintering ruff or greenshank, where '1%' of a given population would be a small number of birds, exceeded significantly at the site concerned, but not reaching the 50-bird minimum more conventionally used as the importance threshold in such cases (see page 18).

Some differences from all the foregoing explanations apply to the sections covering IBAs in Northern Ireland, the Channel Islands and the Isle of Man. For details of any such differences applying to the Channel Islands or Isle of Man, the reader is referred to the separate introductory sections relating to those areas (see pages 465 and 477). As far as Northern Ireland is concerned, the main point to note is that the 'national' population totals against which percentages have been calculated are GB totals, not UK totals, that is they do not actually include the birds making up the percentage concerned. Lack of complete survey data and inconsistencies in its method of collection between Northern Ireland and GB has made it impossible to calculate true 'UK totals'. Percentages are thus expressed as for example '1% of British'. While unfortunate, in most cases this makes little practical difference to the percentages which would be arrived at by a 'UK total' method of calculation.

The further consequence of this is that the description 'nationally important' where applied in the context of a Northern Ireland site, actually means that the bird interest concerned *would be* sufficient to rank as nationally important in a GB context *if that site were* in GB. If anything, this will be a conservative underestimate of the importance of that site in the alternative biogeographical context of 'all-Ireland' (for which no attempt at calculating values has been made in this publication). International significance measures are, of course, unaffected. Further work is in progress jointly for Northern Ireland and the Republic of Ireland to develop appropriate measures.

2.9   CONSERVATION ISSUES

This qualitative section of the site accounts gives a summary of some of the most important land-use and other issues affecting the future conservation of the site. Clearly this is a case of the information being a single 'snapshot in time' of a dynamic situation. Some of the comments made may therefore quickly become out of date: but the intention generally has been to concentrate on long-term issues. Most habitat-types exhibit some generic land-use problems, and brief reference to important examples is made before going on to site-specific issues. Much of the information has come from regional staff of all organisations with first-hand knowledge: the editing process has imposed some consistency of language, but has made no undue efforts to standardise the length of the entries under this heading. The section is not simply a catalogue of 'threats', since comments on beneficial management have been made in some cases. In all cases if a definitive picture is required, this should be sought from the publishing organisations.

2.10   FURTHER READING

The final section of each site account is not a comprehensive listing of all references relevant to that site, nor does it repeat references which relate to the national picture or otherwise cover a large suite of sites (these can be found at the end of Chapters 1 and 2). The aim is to list a selection of readily available publications particularly relevant to the site concerned. Unpublished sources of data are generally not given.

2.11   UPDATING

The dynamic nature of some of the information in this book has already been referred to. The editors would welcome new data or other comments on the sites in this book, or indeed suggestions for new sites qualifying as IBAs. While every attempt has been made to ensure accuracy, the editors take full responsibility for any errors which may have slipped through.

References

(Those not cited above relate to Appendix V)

Batten, L A, Bibby, C J, Clement, P, Elliott, G D and Porter, R F 1990 *Red Data Birds in Britain*. T and A D Poyser, London.

Gensbol, B 1984 *Collins guide to the birds of prey*. Collins, London.

Grimmett, R F A and Jones, T A *Important Bird Areas in Europe*. ICBP, Cambridge.

Lack, P 1986 *The atlas of wintering birds in Britain and Ireland*. T and A D Poyser, Calton.

Lloyd, C, Tasker, M L and Partridge, K 1991 *The Status of Seabirds in Britain and Ireland*. T and A D Poyser, London.

Moser, M E 1987 A revision of population estimates for waders (*Charadrii*) wintering on the coastline of Britain. *Biol. Conserv.* 39: 153-164.

Moser, M E, Broad, R A, Dennis, R H and Madders, M 1986 The distribution and abundance of some coastal birds on the West and North-west Coasts of Scotland in Winter. *Scottish Birds* 14: 61-67.

Nature Conservancy Council 1989 *Guidelines for selection of biological SSSIs*. Nature Conservancy Council, Peterborough.

Owen, M, Atkinson-Willes, G L and Salmon, D G 1986 *Wildfowl in Great Britain*. 2nd ed. Cambridge University Press, Cambridge.

Piersma, T 1986 Breeding Waders in Europe. A review of population size estimates and a bibliography of information sources. *Wader Study Group Bulletin* 48: Supplement.

Pirot, J-Y, Laursen, K, Madsen, J and Monval, J-Y 1989 Population estimates of swans, geese, ducks and Eurasian Coot *Fulica atra* in the Western Palearctic and Sahelian Africa. In: *Flyways and Reserve Networks*. IWRB. *Proceedings of the third meeting of the*

Conference of the Contracting Parties, Regina, Canada, 14–23. Canadian Wildlife Service/ IWRB.

Prater, A J 1981 *Estuary birds of Britain and Ireland.* T and A D Poyser, Calton.

Smit, C J and Piersma, T 1989 Numbers, midwinter distribution and migration of wader populations using the east Atlantic Flyway. In: *Flyways and reserve networks.* IWRB, *Proceedings of the third meeting of the Conference of the Contracting Parties, Regina, Canada,* 24–63. Canadian Wildlife Service/IWRB.

Stroud, D A, Mudge, G P and Pienkowski, M W 1990 *Protecting Internationally Important Bird Sites.* Nature Conservancy Council, Peterborough.

Voous, K H 1977 *List of Recent Holarctic Bird Species.* Academic Press, London, for BOU. Reprinted from *Ibis,* 85pp.

LIST OF SITES INCLUDED

SCOTLAND

101A	North Rona and Sula Sgeir
102A	Flannan Isles
103A	St Kilda
104A	Shiant Isles
105A	West Sound of Harris
107A	Monach Islands
108A	South Uist Machair and Lochs
111A	West Sound of Barra
112A	Mingulay and Berneray
113A	Pentland Firth Islands
115	The Peatlands
117A	Caithness Lochs
118A	Caithness Cliffs
123A	Cape Wrath
124A	Handa
126A	Priest Island
134A	Rhum (Rum)
145A	Balranald
148A	Baleshare and Kirkibost
150A	Loch Scadavay
151A	Inverpolly, Loch Urigill and Nearby Lochs
153A	Loch Maree
155A	Loch Ruthven and Nearby Lochs
156A	Central Highland Hills and Glens
157A	Lewis Peatlands
157B	North Harris Mountains
159A	Assynt Lochs
160A	Loch Stack, Loch Nam Brac, and Nearby Lochs
161A	Loch Shin and Nearby Lochs
162A	Moray Basin, Firths and Bays
163A	Beinn Dearg
164A	Ben Wyvis
165A	Glengarry Lochs
166A	Loch Tarff and Nearby Lochs
167A	North Inverness Lochs
201A	Hermaness and Saxa Vord, Unst
202A	Ramna Stacks and Gruney
203A	Fetlar
204A	North Roe and Tingon, Mainland Shetland
205A	Papa Stour
206A	Foula
208A	Noss
209A	Fair Isle
210A	West Westray
211A	Papa Westray (North Hill and Holm)

212A	Marwick Head
213A	Lochs of Harray and Stenness
214A	Hoy
215A	Copinsay
218A	Sule Skerry and Sule Stack
220A	Loch Spynie
221A	Loch of Strathbeg
222A	Ythan Estuary, Sands of Forvie, and Meikle Loch
223A	River Spey-Insh Marshes
224A	Cairngorms
226A	Loch of Skene
227A	Fowlsheugh
228A	Lochnagar
230A	Drumochter Hills
231A	West Mainland Moors
231B	North Mainland Coast
232A	South Westray Coast
233A	East Sanday
235A	Crussa Field and The Heogs
236A	Mousa
237A	Rousay (Part)
241A	North Ronaldsay Coast
242A	South-Eastern Stronsay
243A	Eday
247A	Troup, Pennan and Lion Heads
248A	St Cyrus
249B	Buchan Ness to Collieston Coast
251A	Sumburgh Head
253A	Monadhliath
254A	Alvie
255A	Ben Alder
256A	Abernethy Forest
258A	Kinveachy
261A	Creag Meagaidh
265A	Lochs of Spiggie and Brow
267A	Mill Dam, Shapinsay
268A	Rosehearty to Fraserburgh Coast
269A	Orphir and Stenness Hills
270A	Keelylang
271A	Loch of Isbister
272A	Blackpark and Gutcher
274A	Loch Oire
275A	Loch Vaa
277A	Glen Tanar
279A	Muir of Dinnet
280A	Moorland Areas, Central Shetland
283A	West Burrafirth
284A	Hill of Colvadale and Sobul
285A	An Socach –Carn A Gheoidh
302A	Loch Lomond

303A	Tiree and Coll
304A	Treshnish Isles
305A	Islay: Loch Gruinart
305B	Islay: Bridgend Flats
305C	Islay: Laggan
305D	Islay: Eilean Na Muice Duibh (Duich Moss)
305G	Islay: Rinns
305H	Islay: The Oa
306A	Inner Clyde Estuary
307A	Rhunahaorine Point
308A	Machrihanish and Tangy Loch
309A	Ailsa Craig
311A	Loch Ken and Dee Marshes
312A	Lochinch and Torrs Warren
316A	Wigtown Bay
317A	North Colonsay and Western Cliffs
318A	Sanda
319A	Castle Loch, Dumfries
401A	Caenlochan
403A	Montrose Basin
405A	Loch of Kinnordy
406A	Loch of Lintrathen
407A	Tay-Isla Valley
411A	Loch Leven
412A	Firth of Tay
413A	Cameron Reservoir
414A	Eden Estuary, Tentsmuir Point and Abertay Sands
417A	Forth Islands
419A	Flanders Moss and Lake of Menteith
423A	Gladhouse Reservoir
424A	Fala Flow
425A	Westwater
427A	St Abbs Head to Fast Castle
428A	Greenlaw Moor and Hule Moss
429A	Hoselaw Loch
440A	South Tayside Goose Roosts
441A	Firth of Forth

ENGLAND

501A	Upper Solway Flats and Marshes
503A	Duddon Estuary
508A	Morecambe Bay
509A	Leighton Moss
510A	Ribble and Alt Estuaries
511A	Martin Mere
513A	Mersey Estuary
515A	Bowland Fells
517A	Thorne and Hatfield Moors

520A	Shap Fells
523A	North of England Montane Sites
601A	Lindisfarne
602A	Farne Islands
603A	Coquet Island
604A	Holburn Lake and Moss
606A	Teesmouth and Cleveland Coast
609A	Derwent Ings
610A	Flamborough Head and Bempton Cliffs
611A	Humber Flats, Marshes and Coast
613A	Northumberland Coast
616A	North Yorkshire Moors
617A	Hornsea Mere
621A	Yorkshire Dale Moorlands
627A	North Pennine Moors
702A	Peak District Moors
705A	Walmore Common
802A	The Wash
803A	Nene Washes
804A	Ouse Washes
805A	Rutland Water
903A	North Norfolk Coast
910A	Minsmere –Walberswick
911A	Orfordness –Havergate
912A	Stour and Orwell Estuary
913A	Hamford Water
914A	Abberton Reservoir
917A	Benfleet and Southend Marshes
920A	Breckland Heaths
924A	Mid-Essex Coast
925A	Norfolk Broads
926A	Deben Estuary
927A	Great Yarmouth North Denes
1003A	Somerset Levels and Moors
1004A	Chew Valley Lake
1005A	Taw and Torridge Estuary
1006A	Isles of Scilly Coastal Habitats
1008A	Exe Estuary
1009A	Chesil Beach and The Fleet
1010A	Dorset Heathlands
1011A	Poole Harbour
1012A	East Devon Heaths
1014A	Tamar Complex
1014B	Bodmin Moor
1101A	Chichester and Langstone Harbours
1103A	The New Forest
1105A	Portsmouth Harbour
1106A	Southampton Water and Solent Marshes
1109A	Avon Valley
1110A	Porton Down

1111A   Windsor Forest and Great Park
1112A   Woolmer Forest
1201A   The Swale
1202A   Thames Estuary and Marshes
1203A   Medway Estuary and Marshes
1204A   Pagham Harbour
1207A   Thanet Coast
1208A   Pevensey Levels
1209A   Dungeness to Pett Levels
1211A   Lea Valley
1212A   Stodmarsh
1213A   Thursley, Hankley and Frensham Commons
1214A   Chobham to Yateley Commons
1216A   Amberley
1217A   South-West London Reservoirs and Gravel Pits

WALES

1301A   Dee Estuary
1303A   Traeth Lafan (Lavan Sands), Conway Bay
1306A   Ynys Feurig, Cemlyn Bay and The Skerries
1310A   Glannau Ynys Gybi (Holy Island Coast)
1311A   Berwyn
1312A   Glannau Aberdaron and Ynys Enlli (Aberdaron Coast and Bardsey Island)
1401A   Cors Fochno and Dyfi
1404A   Grassholm
1405A   Skokholm and Skomer
1406A   Pembrokeshire Cliffs
1409A   Carmarthen Bay
1411A   Elenydd –Mallaen
1501A   Burry Inlet
1502A   Severn Estuary
1503A   Swansea Bay –Blackpill

NORTHERN IRELAND

2001A   Rathlin Island
2002A   Sheep Island
2003A   Lough Foyle
2004A   Larne Lough and Swan Island
2005A   Pettigoe Plateau
2006A   Lower Lough Erne
2007A   Upper Lough Erne
2008A   Lower Lough Macnean
2009A   Lough Neagh and Lough Beg
2010A   Belfast Lough
2011A   Strangford Lough and Islands
2012A   Annaghroe, River Blackwater

2013A   Gun's Island including Sandy Island
2014A   Dundrum Inner Bay
2015A   Killough Harbour and Coney Island Bay
2016A   Carlingford Lough including Green Island
2017A   Outer Ards Peninsula

CHANNEL ISLANDS

001   Les Etacs (The Garden Rocks)
002   Ortac
003   Alderney Heathland
004   Guernsey Shoreline
005   Guernsey Heathland
006   Les Landes
007   Jardin D'Olivet
008   Noirmont
009   Portelet Common
010   Ouaisne
011   La Lande du Ouest (La Moye)
012   La Mare au Seigneur (St Ouen's Pond)
013   Jersey Shoreline

ISLE OF MAN

001   Isle of Man Sea Cliffs
002   Calf of Man
003   The Ayres
004   Ballaugh Curraghs
005   The Isle of Man Hills

SITE MAPS

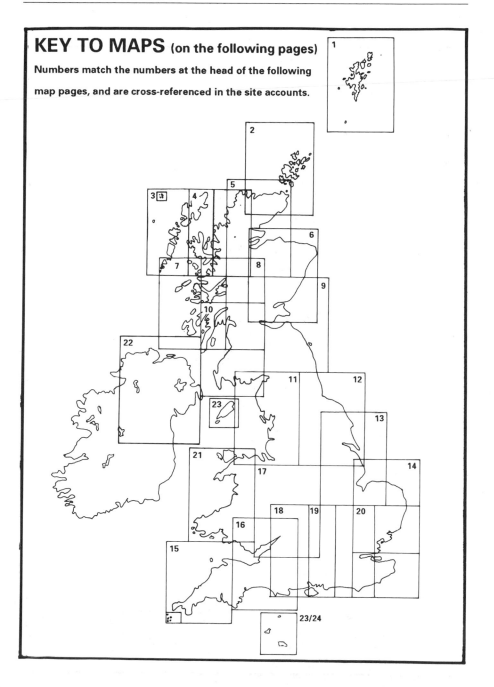

KEY TO MAPS (on the following pages)

Numbers match the numbers at the head of the following

map pages, and are cross-referenced in the site accounts.

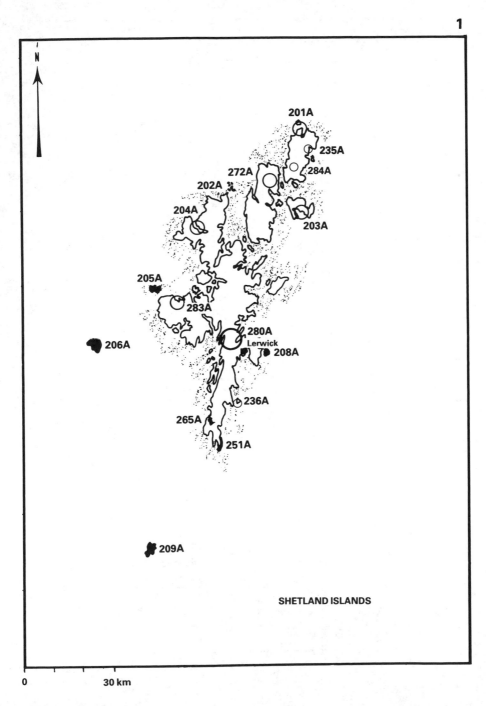

1

N

201A

235A

272A

284A

202A

204A

203A

205A

283A

280A

206A

Lerwick

208A

236A

265A

251A

209A

SHETLAND ISLANDS

0   30 km

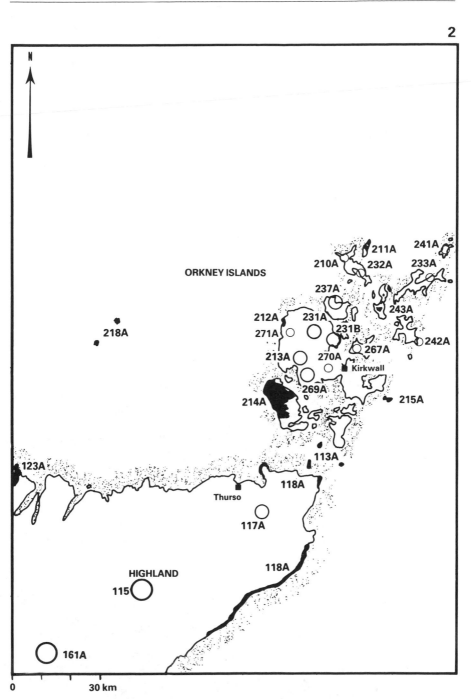

3

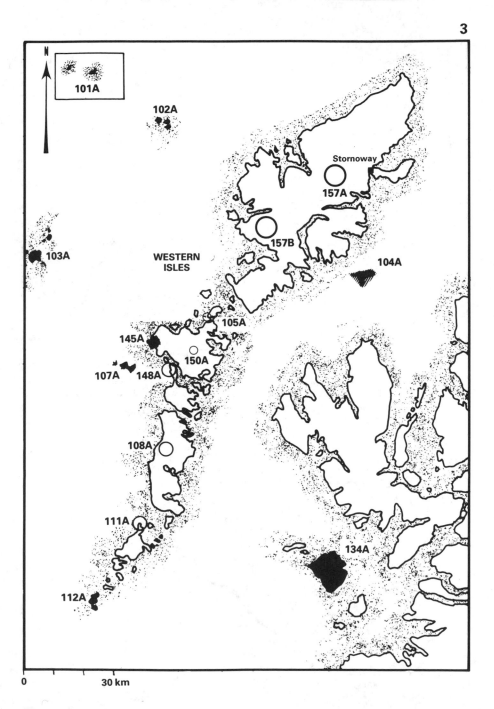

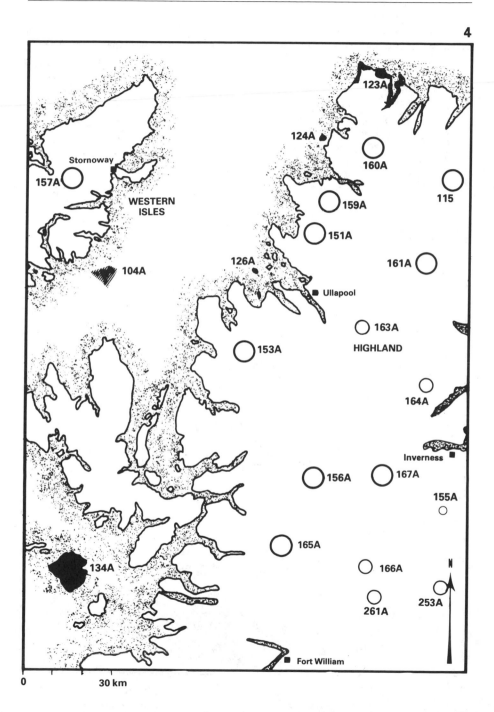

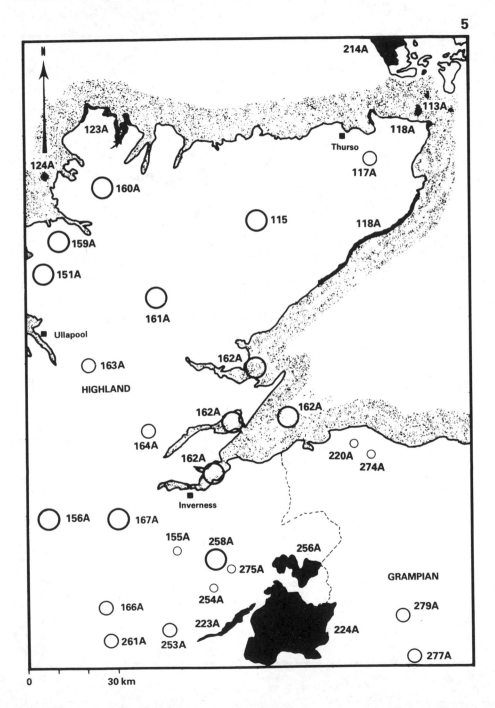

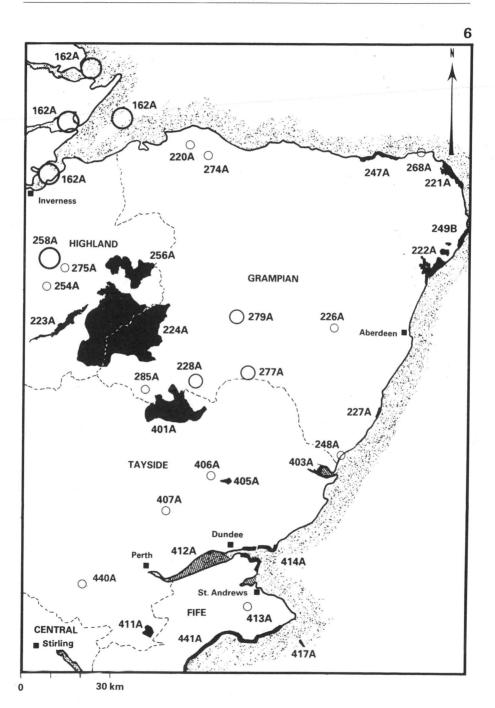

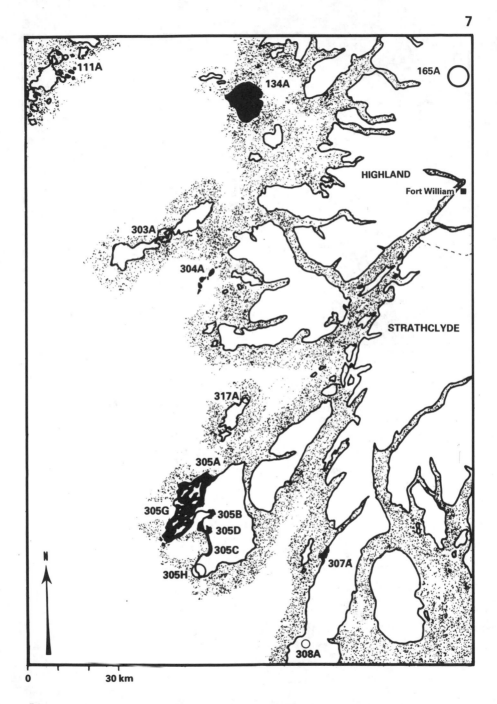

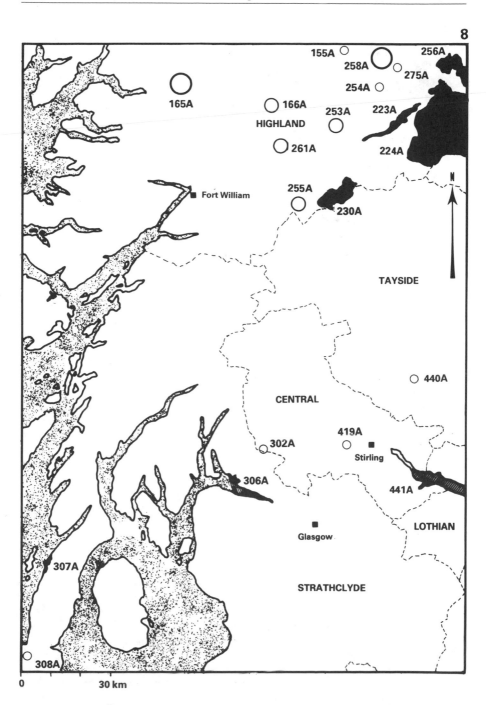

8

155A
258A
256A
275A
254A
165A
166A
253A
223A
HIGHLAND
261A
224A
N
255A
Fort William
230A
TAYSIDE
440A
CENTRAL
419A
302A
Stirling
306A
441A
LOTHIAN
Glasgow
307A
STRATHCLYDE
308A

0   30 km

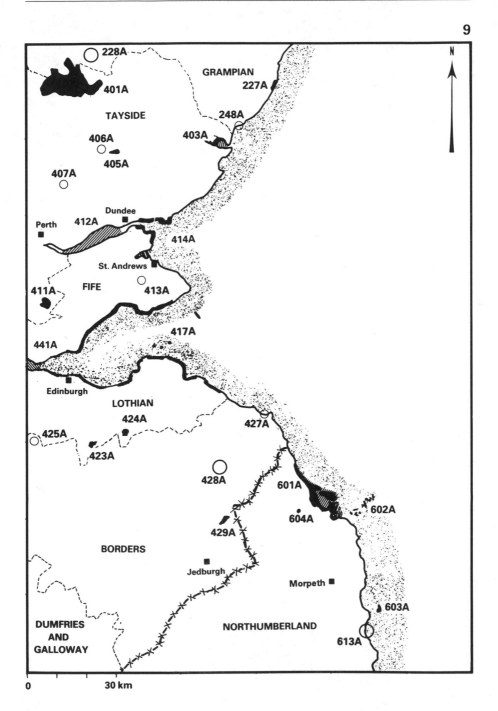

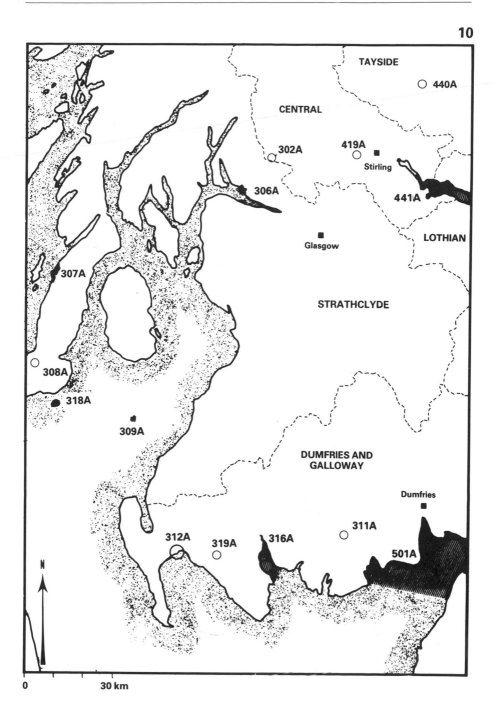

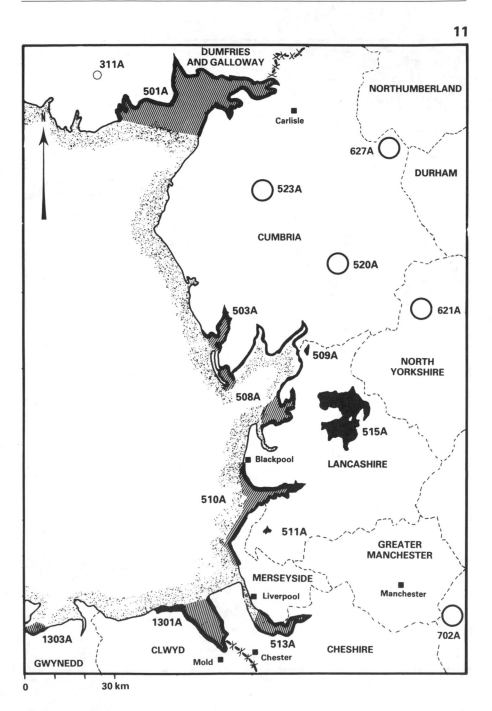

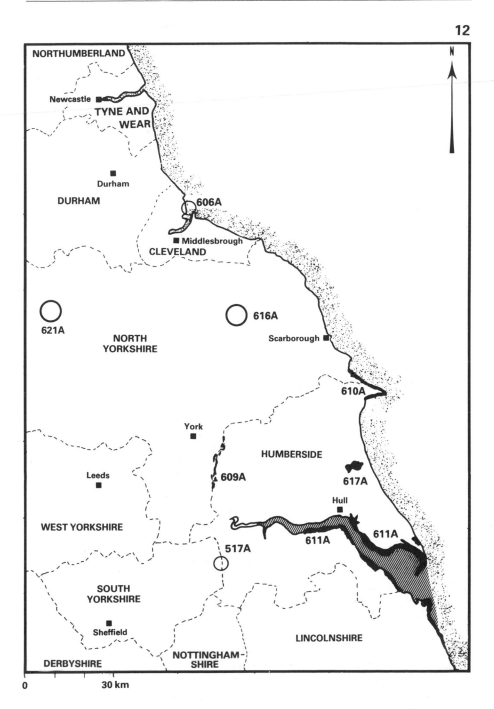

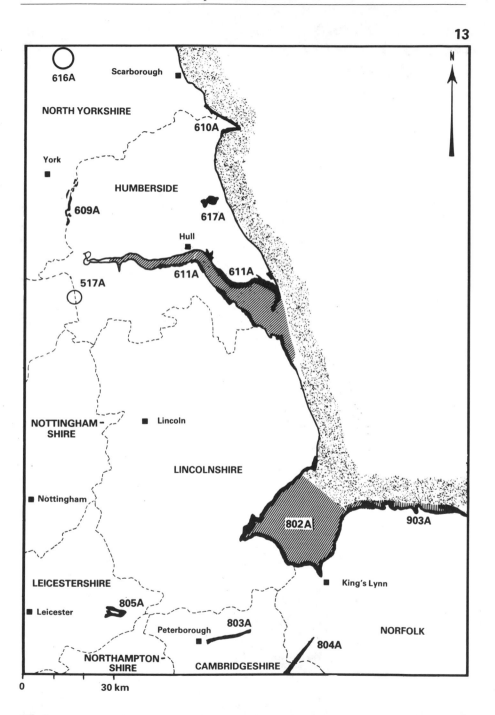

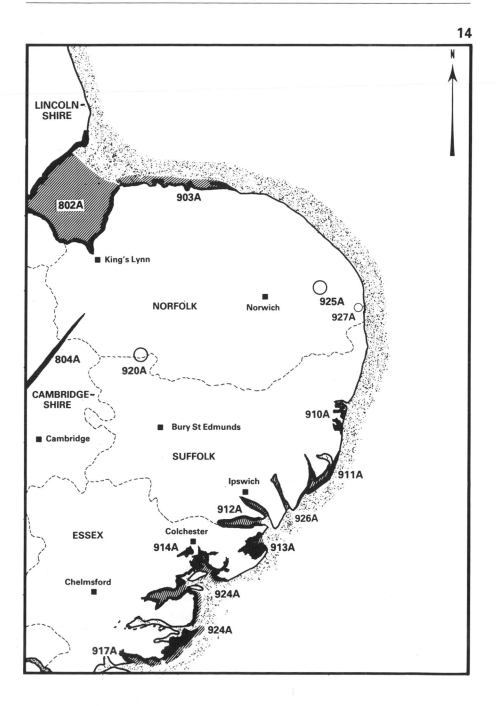

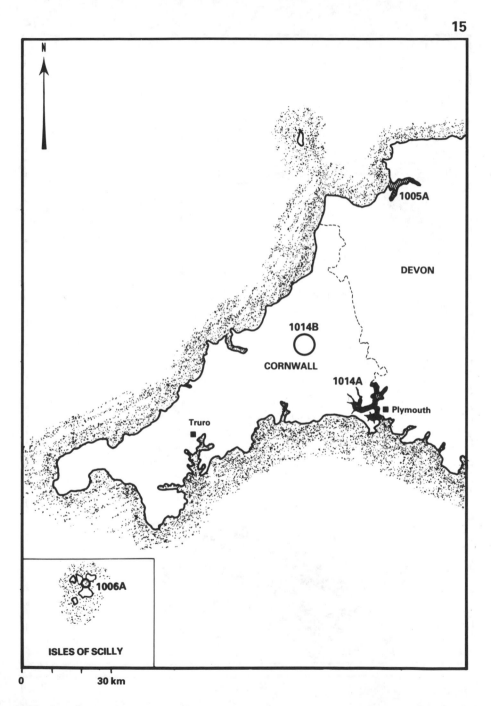

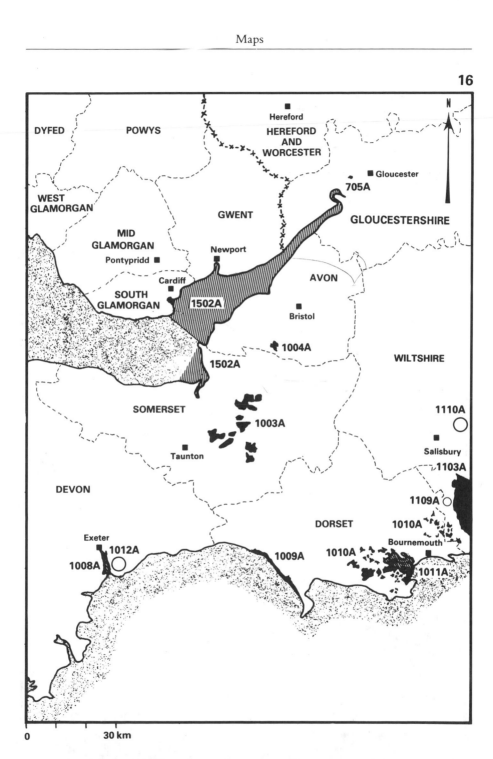

17

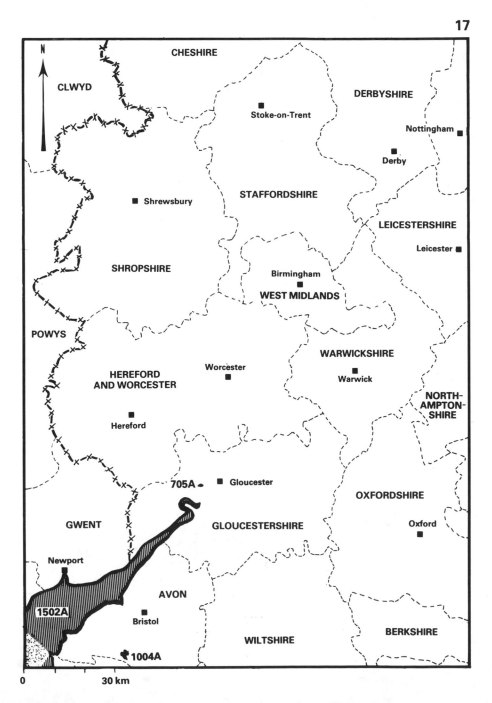

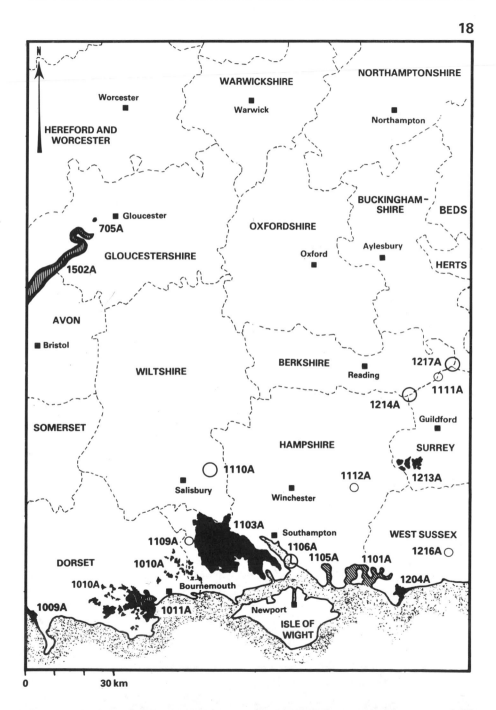

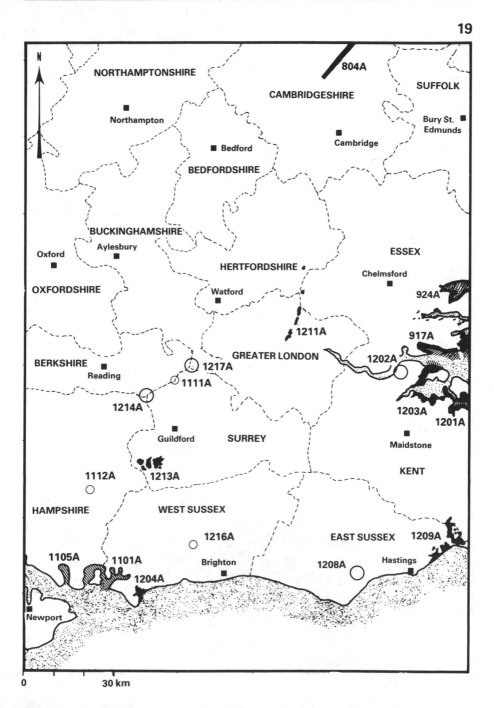

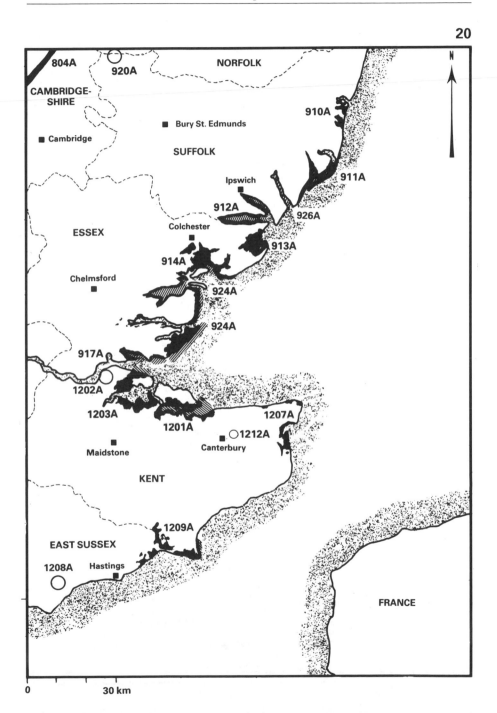

N

804A

920A

NORFOLK

CAMBRIDGE-
SHIRE

■ Bury St. Edmunds

■ Cambridge

910A

SUFFOLK

Ipswich ■

911A

912A

926A

ESSEX

Colchester ■

913A

914A

Chelmsford ■

924A

924A

917A

1202A

1203A

1207A

1201A

■○**1212A**

Canterbury

■
Maidstone

KENT

1209A

EAST SUSSEX

1208A Hastings
■

FRANCE

0   30 km

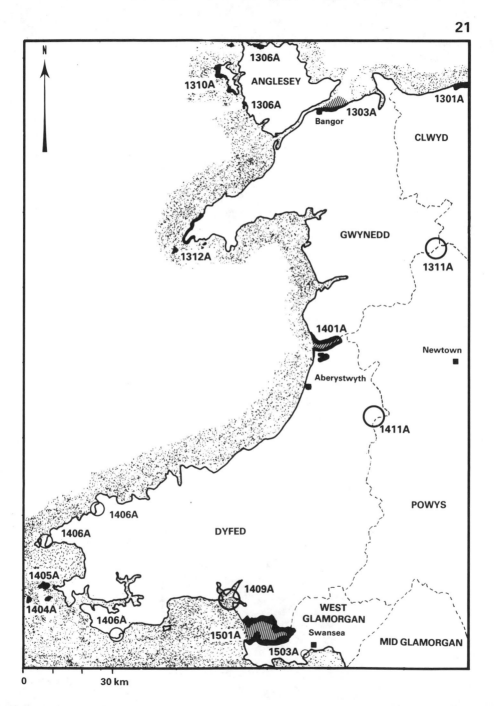

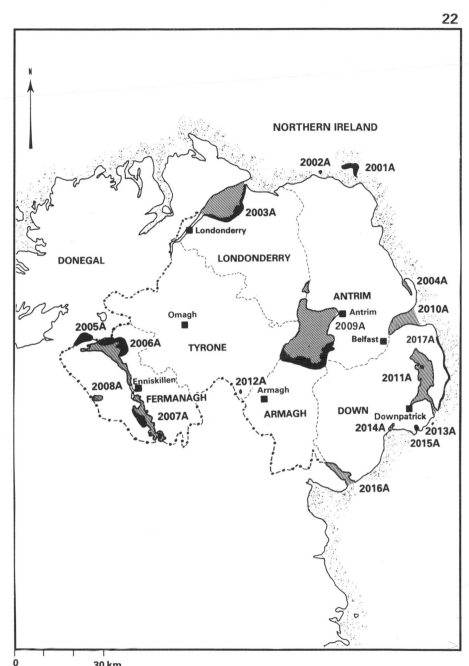

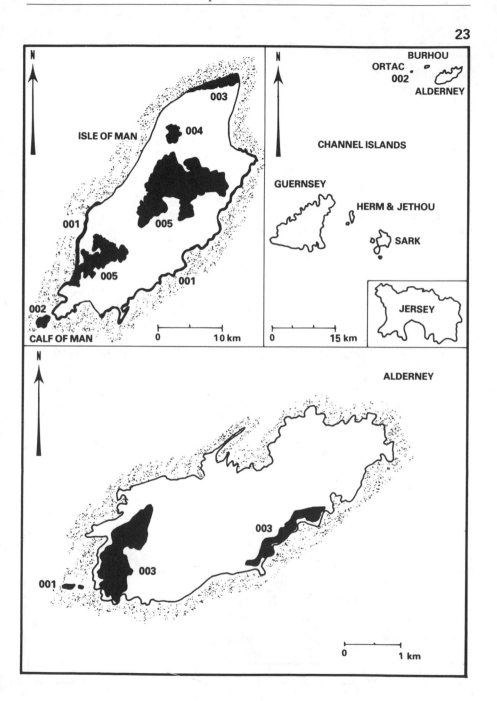

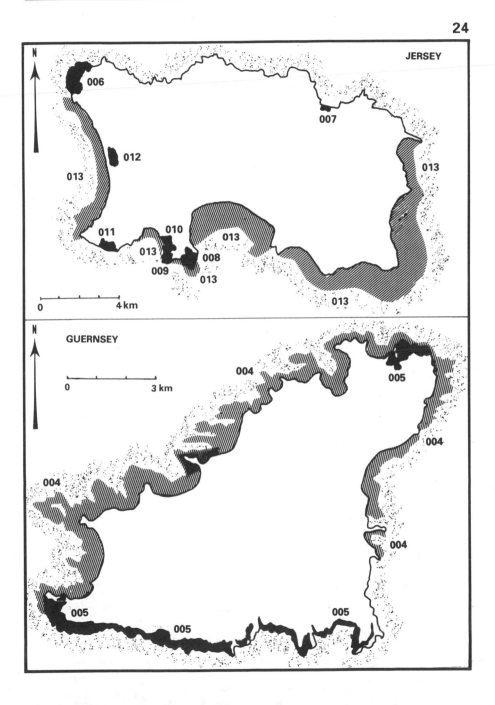

SITE ACCOUNTS: SCOTLAND

North Rona and Sula Sgeir

SPA/Ram Code	IBA Europe number
101A	001

County/Region	District(s)	OS sheet(s)	Grid Reference(s)	Map 3
Western Isles	N/A	8	HW 810324	
			HW 620305	

Area (ha)	NNR	SPA		Ramsar	
130	Yes	Designated	N	Designated	N
		Candidate	Y	Candidate	N

An offshore island site of major importance for breeding seabirds, with eight species occurring at nationally/internationally important levels.

Site description

These two islands, with a number of outlying rocky islets, lie about 65 km north of the island of Lewis. Sula Sgeir is about 15 km to the west of the far larger North Rona. They provide strategic nesting localities for seabirds which feed in waters off the north coast of Scotland. The predominant rock is hornblende gneiss. North Rona is well covered by peat or soil, vegetated by submaritime grassland, much modified locally by sea spray. As well as the seabirds, a nationally important population of grey seals breeds on the island. Permanent human occupation ceased in the mid 19th century. Sula Sgeir is subject to severe erosive pressure from sea spray and seabirds, and has little soil or vegetation.

Birds

The principal interest is for breeding seabirds with internationally important numbers of gannet and guillemot, and nationally important numbers of fulmar, storm petrel, Leach's petrel, great black-backed gull, kittiwake and razorbill.

In a detailed survey in 1986 the following breeding numbers were recorded : **fulmar** 11,600 pairs (2% of British population), **storm petrel** (colony size not known but thought to be large), **Leach's petrel** (colony size not known; the North Rona colony is considered to be the second largest in the UK after St Kilda; small numbers occur on Sula Sgeir), **gannet** 9100 pairs (4% of Western European, 6% of British), **great black-backed gull** 740 pairs (4% of British), **kittiwake** 5040 pairs (1% of British), **guillemot** 43,200 individuals (1% of Western European, 4% of British) and **razorbill** 2030 individuals (1% of British). Also notable are shag (150 pairs), great skua (14 pairs), puffin (5250 pairs) and black guillemot (156 individuals North Rona). Arctic tern has bred in the past.

Relatively few visits have been made by ornithologists outside the breeding season, mainly to North Rona, but in general low bird numbers occur in autumn and winter. Some geese occur on North Rona on autumn passage, including up to 200 barnacle geese.

Conservation issues

Seabirds are sensitive to changes in the quality of the marine environment, especially to changes in fish stocks and to oil pollution. Ground-nesting seabirds on offshore islands are vulnerable to the introduction of predatory mammals.

This site is vulnerable to pressure from increased numbers of visitors, including naturalists, divers and yachtsmen. Oil pollution (exploration licences have been granted for seas to the north-west) and industrial fisheries also pose a threat.

Further reading

Benn, S, Murray, S and Tasker, M L 1989 *The birds of North Rona and Sula Sgeir.* Nature Conservancy Council, Peterborough.

Storm petrel

Flannan Isles

SPA/Ram Code	IBA Europe number
102A	002

County/Region	District(s)	OS sheet(s)	Grid Reference(s)	Map 3
Western Isles	N/A	13	NA 692467	
			NA 726468	
			NA 726455	

Area (ha)	NNR	SPA		Ramsar	
81	No	Designated	N	Designated	N
		Candidate	Y	Candidate	N

A group of small offshore islands, of major importance for their breeding seabird colonies.

Site description
The Flannans are a group of six rocky islands, with outlying skerries, about 30 km west of Lewis. They provide a strategic nesting locality for seabirds, which feed in waters off the Western Isles. The vegetation is predominantly maritime grassland.

Birds
The principal interest is for breeding seabirds with nationally important numbers of storm petrel, Leach's petrel, guillemot, razorbill and puffin.

The islands were last counted in 1988 as part of the Seabird Colony Register. Breeding populations include **guillemot** 22,000 individuals (2% of British), **razorbill** 3200 individuals (2% of British) and puffin 4400 pairs (1% of British). The islands also support important breeding colonies of **storm petrel** and **Leach's petrel**. Although the numbers of these nocturnal, burrow-nesting species are difficult to count, it is known that they are restricted to relatively few islands each of which is important in population terms.

Notable also are fulmar (4700 pairs), gannet (410 pairs) and kittiwake (2800 pairs).

Conservation issues
Seabirds are sensitive to changes in the quality of the marine environment, especially to changes in fish stocks and to oil pollution. Ground-nesting seabirds on offshore islands are vulnerable to the introduction of predatory mammals.

This site is potentially vulnerable to disturbance from visiting people. Oil exploration licences have been granted for seas to the north-west.

St Kilda

SPA/Ram Code	IBA Europe number
103A	003

County/Region	District(s)	OS sheet(s)	Grid Reference(s)	Map 3
Western Isles	N/A	18	NA 155050	
			NA 095995	

Area (ha)	NNR	SPA		Ramsar	
853	Yes	Designated	N	Designated	N
		Candidate	Y	Candidate	N

A group of remote offshore islands of outstanding importance for their breeding seabirds, with 8 species occurring at nationally/internationally important levels.

Site description

Situated about 70 km west of North Uist, the St Kilda group consists of Hirta, the largest island, the nearby Dun and Soay, and Boreray with its flanking pinnacles of Stac Lee and Stac an Armin, plus some smaller rocky islets. The islands are steep, with precipitous cliffs reaching 430 m on Hirta; both Soay and Boreray reach 380 m. These islands provide a strategic nesting locality for seabirds that feed in rich waters to the west of Scotland. Permanent human habitation on the islands is confined to an army base on Hirta; the last islanders moved out in 1930. Feral sheep, including the primitive Soay, have remained on the islands, and still occur on Hirta, Boreray and Soay.

The vegetation is strongly influenced by sea spray and the presence of seabirds and livestock. Inland on Hirta, species-poor acidic grassland and sub-maritime heaths occupy large areas. However, nearer the coast and on other islands, sub-maritime grassland, enriched by salt spray, guano and dung, predominates. The influence of spray is wide, so that plants such as sea spleenwort and the moss *Schistidium maritima*, which normally are restricted to the coast, here grow inland. The prevalent damp oceanic conditions are reflected in the peaty nature of most of the soils, and the widespread occurrence of oceanic plants including some, like the liverwort *Frullania germana*, which are scarce in Britain.

Birds

The total population of breeding seabirds exceeds 400,000 pairs, making this one of the largest concentrations in the North Atlantic, and the largest in Britain. It supports internationally important numbers of Leach's petrel, fulmar, gannet and puffin, and nationally important numbers of storm petrel, kittiwake, guillemot and razorbill.

St Kilda was last surveyed comprehensively in 1987 for the Seabird Colony Register. Breeding populations include **fulmar** 63,000 pairs (1% of the Western European and 12% of the British breeding populations), **storm petrel** (a large colony), **Leach's petrel** (the largest colony in the East Atlantic), **gannet** 50,050 pairs (22% of Western European, 32% of British), **kittiwake** 7800 pairs (2% of British), **guillemot** 22,700 individuals (2% of British), **razorbill** 3800 individuals (3% of British) and **puffin** 155,000 pairs (17% of the Western European population of the *grabae* race, 35% of British). Notable also are Manx shearwater (over 1000 pairs) and great skua (55 pairs).

There is an endemic sub-species of wren *Troglodytes troglodytes hirtensis*. This, and the distinctive form of the wood mouse *Apodemus sylvaticus*, emphasise the remoteness of St Kilda.

Conservation issues

Seabirds are sensitive to changes in the quality of the marine environment, especially to changes in fish stocks and to oil pollution. Ground-nesting seabirds on offshore islands are vulnerable to the introduction of predatory mammals.

The seabirds that breed on St Kilda are vulnerable to disturbance from military activities and visitors.

Further reading

Harris, M P and Murray, S 1978 *Birds of St Kilda*. ITE, Cambridge.
Tasker, M C, Moore, P R, and Schofield, R A 1988 The Seabirds of St Kilda, 1987. *Scottish Birds* 15: 21-29.

Puffin

Shiant Isles

SPA/Ram Code	IBA Europe number
104A	004

County/Region	District(s)	OS sheet(s)	Grid Reference	Maps 3, 4
Western Isles	N/A	14	NG 418978	

Area (ha)	NNR	SPA	Ramsar
202	No	Designated N Candidate Y	Designated N Candidate N

A group of rocky offshore islands supporting nationally/internationally important breeding populations of five species of seabirds, and also used by wintering and passage Greenland barnacle geese.

Site description
The Shiants are a group of two large and two small islands, with their skerries, lying about 6 km east of Lewis in the Minch. Garbh Eilean, the largest island, rises to about 160 m above sea level, and like the other islands is composed mainly of a basaltic sill. There are various types of coast, including sheer cliffs and boulder screes, both of which provide suitable nesting localities for seabirds. Both larger islands are vegetated, with maritime grassland and heath, some of which is similar to that on St Kilda.

Birds
The principal interest is for breeding seabirds, with internationally important numbers of shag, razorbill and puffin, and nationally important numbers of fulmar and guillemot. Internationally important numbers of wintering/passage Greenland barnacle goose also occur.

Recent estimates of current seabird breeding population sizes from the Seabird Colony Register include **fulmar** 6800 pairs (1% of British), **shag** 1800 pairs (1% of Western Europe, 5% of British), **guillemot** 18,400 individuals (2% of British), **razorbill** 10,900 individuals (1% of Western Europe, 8% of British) and **puffin** 77,000 pairs (9% of the Western European population of the *grabae* subspecies, 17% of British). Notable also are great skua (6 pairs), kittiwake (1850 pairs) and black guillemot (31 individuals).

The site is of international importance for wintering and passage **barnacle geese** of the Greenland population. The mean number recorded during the last five spring aerial surveys was 490 birds (Fox and Ogilvie 1988), representing 1.5% of the world population and 2% of the number wintering in Britain.

Conservation issues
Seabirds are sensitive to changes in the quality of the marine environment, especially to changes in fish stocks and to oil pollution. Ground-nesting seabirds on offshore islands are vulnerable to the introduction of predatory mammals. The islands support a population of black rats *Rattus rattus*.

Further reading

Fox, A D, Ogilvie, M A, Easterbee, N and Bignal, E M 1990 East Greenland Barnacle Geese in Scotland, Spring 1988. *Scottish Birds* 16: 1-10.

Fox, A D and Ogilvie, M A 1988 *Aerial survey of barnacle geese in Scotland 1988.* NCC CSD commissioned research report No. 876.

West Sound of Harris

SPA/Ram Code	IBA Europe number
105A	005

County/Region	District(s)	OS sheet(s)	Grid Reference(s)	Map 3
Western Isles	N/A	18	NF 873763	

Area (ha)	NNR	SPA		Ramsar	
1-999	No	Designated	N	Designated	N
		Candidate	Y	Candidate	Y

Areas of machair grassland on northern North Uist and islands in the Sound of Harris, of international importance for wintering barnacle geese and breeding waders.

Site description
The dunes and machair of Clachan and Newton are particularly well developed, including dissected high machair plateaux, and low-lying slack-type marshy areas containing a gradation of calcareous to acidic vegetation. The machair vegetation varies with transitions into acidic communities. There are also tidal strands and a substantial area of mature salt marsh.

Pabbay is a fairly large, uninhabited island. The northern part consists of rocky hills rising to almost 200 m, while in the south there are dunes and machair on more level ground. A full range of machair types is present, including unusual conical dunes. A marked contrast exists between dry dunes dominated by marram, and base-rich slacks often dominated by black bog-rush, with interesting bryophyte communities. On lower slopes, there is extensive intermediate acid grassland dominated by fescues, but locally grading into more species-rich communities with frog orchid and adder's-tongue in more base-rich areas. Higher up, there is more acidic grassland and *Calluna* heath.

Other islands are low lying with predominantly maritime grassland or heathland vegetation.

Birds
This area is of international importance for wintering/passage Greenland barnacle geese and breeding dunlin, and national importance for breeding ringed plover and wintering purple sandpiper.

Some of the machair grasslands are grazed in winter by large numbers of **barnacle geese**. The mean number recorded during the last five spring aerial surveys was 1090 birds (Fox and Ogilvie 1988), representing 3% of the world population and 4% of the number wintering in Britain. The area supports in excess of 300 breeding **dunlin** (3% of the total and British population of the temperate *schinzii* race) and 270 pairs of **ringed plover** (2% of NW and Central European population, 3% of British). In winter the rocky shores support about 200 **purple sandpiper** (1% of British).

Conservation issues
Appropriate management of the machair grassland is important for the maintenance of the wintering goose population.

Further reading

Fox, A D, Ogilvie, M A, Easterbee, N and Bignal E M 1990 East Greenland Barnacle Geese in Scotland, Spring 1988. *Scottish Birds* 16: 1–10.

Monach Islands

SPA/Ram Code	IBA Europe number
107A	007

County/Region	District(s)	OS sheet(s)	Grid Reference(s)	Map 3
Western Isles	N/A	22	NF 626623	
			NF 661630	

Area (ha)	NNR	SPA		Ramsar	
577	Yes	Designated	N	Designated	N
		Candidate	Y	Candidate	N

Low-lying islands with much machair, attracting barnacle geese in winter, and breeding waders and seabirds in summer.

Site description

The Monach Islands lie about 10 km off the west coast of North Uist. They are now uninhabited, apart from lobster fishermen in the summer, but are still grazed by sheep and rabbits. The chain of five islands is based on Lewisian rock with extensive dune systems of calcareous sand deposited on them. It is regarded as the best uncultivated machair nationally. Vegetation types present include dunes, maritime grasslands, machair, fens, marshes and shallow brackish lochs, while the coastal environment has both sandy and rocky shores with varied marine communities. Terrestrial flora is rich, with over 200 species recorded.

Birds

The Monach Islands are of international importance for wintering/passage Greenland barnacle geese, and national importance for three species of breeding seabirds – common tern, little tern and black guillemot.

The mean number of **barnacle geese** of the Greenland population recorded during the last five spring aerial surveys was 760 birds (Fox and Ogilvie 1988), representing 2% of the world population and 3% of the number wintering in Britain.

Recent estimates of seabird breeding population sizes from the Seabird Colony Register include **common tern** 194 pairs (2% of British), **little tern** 26 pairs (1% of British) and **black guillemot** 850 birds (2% of British). Notable also are fulmar (600 pairs), cormorant (c 75 pairs on Stockay), shag (175 pairs on Stockay), eider (148 pairs), oystercatcher (73 pairs), ringed plover (30 pairs), Sandwich tern (72 pairs) and arctic tern (122 pairs).

Conservation issues

Seabirds are sensitive to changes in the quality of the marine environment, especially to changes in fish stocks and to oil pollution. Ground-nesting seabirds on offshore islands are vulnerable to the introduction of predatory mammals.

Sympathetic grassland management is important for maintenance of the wintering goose population.

Further reading

Fox, A D, Ogilvie, M A, Easterbee, N and Bignal E M 1990 East Greenland Barnacle Geese in Scotland, Spring 1988. *Scottish Birds* 16: 1-10.

Hepburn, I R, Schofield, P and Schofield, R A 1977 The Birds of the Monach Islands, Outer Hebrides. *Bird Study* 24: 25-43.

South Uist Machair and Lochs

SPA/Ram Code	IBA Europe numbers
108A	010, 011, 012, 013

County/Region	District(s)	OS sheet(s)	Grid Reference(s)	Map 3
Western Isles	N/A	22, 31	NF 782378	
			(Loch Druidibeg)	

Area (ha)	NNR	SPA		SPA		Ramsar	
1000-9999	Part	Designated	Y	Wider		Designated	Y
		Candidate	Y	Countryside		Candidate	Y
				Measures			
				Candidate			

Wet and dry machair with scattered lochs, supporting a rich assemblage of breeding and wintering birds.

Site description

The coastal strip of this site is typical machair. Long sandy beaches separated by rocky headlands back on to a low dune line which grades into dry and then wet machair, before the acidic peaty blackland is reached. The calcareous soils of the machair support a rich flora, with the diversity boosted by traditional rotational cultivation and varied grazing pressure from sheep and cattle. At the inner margin of the machair, there are marshes and lochs often with rich vegetation, including several nationally scarce plants.

Loch Bee is the largest, shallow, brackish-water loch in the Western Isles, and is surrounded by machair, rocky grassland and acid moorland. It is connected to the sea by channels in the north-west and the south-east, and consequently the salinity varies from almost fresh to fairly saline; this variation is reflected in the plant and animal life in the loch.

Around the west side of Loch Bee is a typical machair sequence, from the sandy Atlantic beach eastwards through dunes, dry and wet machair, to the blackland and moorland around the east of Loch Bee. Traditional strip cultivation and grazing, together with areas which have remained fallow for years, have allowed diverse plant and animal communities to develop. The dune slack communities are especially rich, variously dominated by sedges, rushes and herbs, and with species of interest including baltic rush, adder's-tongue, lesser clubmoss and early marsh-orchid. Some areas are more saline, where sea club-rush and saltmarsh flat-sedge are found. An unusual feature of this machair is that patches of heath are present.

Loch Druidibeg and smaller lochs to the east are mostly surrounded by blanket bog, and a range of flora and fauna, different again from that of the blackland, is found in the nutrient-poor conditions. Many islands in Loch Druidibeg are wooded, with wind-pruned willows, rowan, birch and juniper above a ground flora of bluebell, primrose and royal fern among others.

The shallow, nutrient-rich water of Loch Hallan has allowed the development of a large reedbed of common reed and grey club-rush, with much cowbane, a species which is rare this far north. The reeds grade into species-rich marsh in which the nationally rare holygrass and other notable species occur. The open water of Loch Hallan and other machair lochs, especially Loch na Liana Moire near Frobost, has a diverse flora, including at least ten species of *Potamogeton*, of which the flat-stalked, slender-leaved and long-stalked pondweeds are scarce nationally. Loch na Liana Moire is also notable for its fauna, with an unusually high diversity of water beetles.

The Howmore estuary and Loch Roag are tidally influenced, and contain plants and animals which range from those typical of saline conditions, through brackish to freshwater species. In places along the Abhainn Roag grow scrub willow and rowan.

The area includes an extensive intertidal stretch between Benbecula and South Uist.

SSSI/SPA designation is appropriate for the core areas of bird interest within this extensive tract of land, while 'wider countryside' conservation measures are appropriate in other parts.

Birds
The following represent minimal estimates of the numbers of breeding and wintering birds in the area as a whole. South Uist is one of the remaining strongholds for breeding **corncrake** with a total of 95 calling birds recorded during 1988 (2% of the Western European population, 16% of British). Breeding waders include **oystercatcher** (490 pairs, 1% of British), **ringed plover** (490 pairs, 4% of the NW and Central European population, 6% of British) and **dunlin** (190+ pairs, 2% of the total and British population of the temperate *schinzii* race). Greylag geese of the native North Scottish population (about 40 pairs) breed on islands and around lochs, especially at Loch Druidibeg. In 1990 35+ pairs of **little terns** (1% of British) nested on South Uist. Notable also are large numbers of breeding lapwing, snipe and redshank. Arctic terns also breed.

Wintering waders include **ringed plover** (2010 birds, 4% of the EAF population, 9% of British), **sanderling** (1710 birds, 1% of EAF, 13% of British), **purple sandpiper** (780 birds, 2% of EAF, 5% of British), **bar-tailed godwit** (1090 birds, 1% of EAF, 2% of British) and **turnstone** (1550 birds, 2% of EAF, 3% of British).

Wintering wildfowl include **mute swan** (200 birds, 1% of British, with up to 400 birds recorded at moult – Thom 1986) and Greenland white-fronted geese (55, Nov. 1989).

Conservation issues
The wildlife interest of this site is vulnerable to changes in drainage depth and agricultural change.

Further reading
Boyd, J M and Boyd, I L 1990 *The Hebrides*. Collins, New Naturalist, London.

Fuller, R J, Reed, T M, Webb, A, Williams, T D and Pienkowski, M W 1986 Populations of breeding waders Charadrii and their habitats on the crofting lands of the Outer Hebrides, Scotland. *Biol. Conserv.* 37: 333-361.

This is a composite site created by replacing four original Important Bird Areas from the European book: Bagh nam Faoilean to Ardivachar, Iochdair and Geirinish Machair and Loch Bee, Na Meadhoinean Iar (including Loch Druidibeg), Machair Lochs (including Lochs Hallan and Kilpheder), South Uist.

Hudson, A, Stowe, T T J and Aspinall, S J 1990 Status and distribution of corncrakes in Britain in 1988. *British Birds* 83: 173–187

Corncrake

West Sound of Barra

SPA/Ram Code	IBA Europe number
111A	014

County/Region	District(s)	OS sheet(s)	Grid Reference(s)	Maps 3, 7
Western Isles	N/A	31	NF 700061	

Area (ha)	NNR	SPA		Ramsar	
1000-9999	No	Designated	N	Designated	N
		Candidate	Y	Candidate	Y

These islands support important wintering populations of Greenland barnacle geese and wading birds.

Site description
The isthmus at Eoligarry, in the north of Barra, has machair which is grazed by cattle. Little cultivation takes place because of the fragility of the habitat. At this exposed site, there are numerous blow-outs, and the machair extends up the southern slope of Beinn Eoligarry. The machair includes slacks and flushes and is botanically varied, with an especially high density of primroses and many moss species. Traigh Mhor, to the east, is a vast expanse of sand flats, with a profusion of inter-tidal cockle shell banks.

Other islands are low lying with predominantly maritime grassland and heathland vegetation.

Birds
This area is of international importance for wintering/passage Greenland barnacle geese and national importance for wintering ringed plover, sanderling, purple sandpiper and turnstone.

The mean number of **barnacle geese** recorded during the last five spring aerial surveys was 370 birds (Fox and Ogilvie 1988), representing 1% of the world and 2% of the British populations. In winter the rocky and sandy shores support 330 **ringed plover** (1% of British), 580 **sanderling** (4% of British), 330 **purple sandpiper** (2% of British), and 610 **turnstone** (1% of British).

Conservation issues
Appropriate management of the machair grassland is important for the maintenance of the wintering goose population.

Further reading
Fox, A D, Ogilvie, M A, Easterbee, N and Bignal E M 1990 East Greenland Barnacle Geese in Scotland, Spring 1988. *Scottish Birds* 16: 1-10.

Mingulay and Berneray

SPA/Ram Code	IBA Europe number
112A	015

County/Region	District(s)	OS sheet(s)	Grid Reference(s)	Map 3
Western Isles	N/A	31	NL 560830 (Mingulay)	
			NL 560800 (Berneray)	

Area (ha)	NNR	SPA		Ramsar	
819	No	Designated	N	Designated	N
		Candidate	Y	Candidate	N

Two adjacent islands of major importance for breeding seabirds, with six species occurring at nationally/internationally important levels.

Site description

Mingulay and Berneray lie at the southern end of the Outer Hebridean chain. Mingulay, the more northerly, is the larger, rising to 275 m with sheer cliffs of Lewisian gneiss up to 210 m; Berneray rises to about 190 m. There are a number of adjacent stacks. The vegetation is mainly maritime and paramaritime grassland, with an area of machair and some heath. These islands, with their extensive cliff ledges, provide strategic nesting localities for seabirds which feed in the waters of the southern Minch.

Birds

The principal interest is for breeding seabirds with internationally important numbers of razorbill, and nationally important numbers of fulmar, shag, great black-backed gull, kittiwake and guillemot.

Recent estimates of current breeding population sizes from the Seabird Colony Register include : **fulmar** 10,500 pairs (2% of British), **shag** 720 pairs (2% of British), **kittiwake** 8600 pairs (2% of British), **greater black-backed gull** 170 pairs (1% of British), **guillemot** 30,900 individuals (3% of British) and **razorbill** 16,900 individuals (2% of Western European population, 12% of British). Notable also is puffin (4000+ individuals).

Conservation issues

Seabirds are sensitive to changes in the quality of the marine environment, especially to changes in fish stocks and to oil pollution. Ground-nesting seabirds on offshore islands are vulnerable to the introduction of predatory mammals.

Pentland Firth Islands

SPA/Ram Code	IBA Europe number
113A	064

County/Region	District(s)	OS sheet(s)	Grid Reference(s)	Maps 2, 5
Highland	Caithness	7, 12	ND 350780 (Stroma)	
Orkney	N/A			

Area (ha)	NNR	SPA		Ramsar	
150+	No	Designated	N	Designated	N
		Candidate	Y	Candidate	N

Two islands and a group of rocky islets in the Pentland Firth which together support large numbers of breeding seabirds, including nationally/internationally important populations of five species.

Site description
The islands contain a variety of habitats including cliffs, rocky shores, maritime heath, moorland, rough grassland, marsh and open freshwater. They provide strategic nesting localities for terns and other seabirds, which feed in the rich waters of the Pentland Firth.

Birds
The islands of Stroma, Swona and Pentland Skerries support internationally important numbers of Sandwich tern and arctic tern, and nationally important numbers of great black-backed gull and guillemot (probably storm petrel also)

The locations of the tern colonies and numbers of birds fluctuate from year to year. Numbers of **arctic terns** have been as high as 7100 pairs (9% of British, 2% of Western and Central European), but a more recent census found 3600 pairs (4% British, 1% of Western and Central European). Likewise, numbers of **Sandwich terns** have been as high as 650 pairs (4% of British, 1% Western European), but more recently 300 pairs (2% of British). **Great black-backed gulls** number 260 pairs (1% of British), while the **guillemot** colony on Stroma numbers 13,700 birds (1% of British). Storm petrels are present but uncensused. Notable also are breeding fulmar (1870 pairs), shag (115 pairs), common gull (200 pairs), kittiwake (2600 pairs), common tern (65 pairs), razorbill (350 individuals), black guillemot (240 individuals) and puffin (430 individuals). Other breeding species include peregrine, oystercatcher and curlew.

Tern numbers have declined in line with national changes, although numbers of arctic terns here have held up much better than elsewhere in Orkney and in Shetland. Breeding colonies of terns are typically volatile. They are important Annex 1 species for which Britain has a special responsibility. Our network of SPAs for terns must cater for this volatility. The colonies on the Pentland Firth islands have increased in importance in recent years in the light of massive declines in tern numbers elsewhere.

Conservation issues
Seabirds are sensitive to changes in the quality of the marine environment, especially to changes in fish stocks and to oil pollution. Ground-nesting seabirds on offshore islands are vulnerable to the introduction of predatory mammals. Colonies of breeding terns in

northern Scotland are currently under considerable pressure from food shortages, which have resulted in several consecutive years of very poor breeding success.

Parts of this site have been threatened by agricultural intensification.

The Peatlands

SPA/Ram Code	IBA Europe number
115	021

County/Region	District(s)	OS sheet(s)	Grid Reference(s)	Maps 2, 4, 5
Highland	Caithness, Sutherland	9,10,11,15,16,17	NC 84	

Area (ha)	NNR	SPA		SPA	Ramsar	
10,000+	Yes	Designated	N	Wider	Designated	N
		Candidate	Y	Countryside Measures Candidate	Candidate	Y

The Peatlands of Caithness and Sutherland (the Flow Country) are of outstanding national/international importance for breeding divers, ducks, waders and raptors.

Site description

The Peatlands of Caithness and Sutherland form the largest and most intact area of blanket bog in Scotland. Blanket bog is a rare peatland type in world terms, with Britain having 13% of the total of this type of habitat. The Peatlands composite site represents the extreme northern Atlantic part of the range in variation. Together with associated open waters and moorland it supports breeding populations of nationally rare birds.

Blanket bog develops where a persistently wet, cool climate allows the growth of *Sphagnum*-dominated vegetation over extensive areas of sloping ground, as well as in hollows and on flat terrain, to form a mantle covering all but steep rocky slopes and open waters. One of the distinguishing characteristics of these bogs is the presence of intricate patterns of pools on level and gently sloping ground. A typical pattern has a cluster of larger rounded pools on flat or slightly rounded summits, spurs or terraces.

The landscape mainly comprises a series of parallel straths with a north–south orientation. Between the straths are higher plateaux (100-200 m) with numerous glacial features such as knolls and lochs. Higher hills and mountains occur towards the western part of this area. Isolated peat lochans (*dubh lochain*), larger lochs with stony shores, rivers, burns and rocky ridges with drier heath vegetation add further variety to the terrain.

In common with most blanket mires throughout Britain, the vegetation is dominated by dwarf shrubs, sedges and *Sphagnum* mosses. Amongst the dwarf shrubs, heather and cross-leaved heath are common and widespread, whereas bell heather decreases towards the drier east. Bog-myrtle and purple moor grass are increasingly common towards the west. Deersedge is widespread and abundant, with cotton grass locally abundant. The most widespread and abundant *Sphagnum* species are *Sphagnum papillosum*, *S. tenellum* and *S. capillifolium*, and *Sphagnum* mosses form the greatest part of the peat deposit. Rarer *Sphagnum* species and those of restricted distribution tend to be confined to undamaged mires or less common mire types. The flora of the pools and depressions typically comprises *Sphagnum cuspidatum* and *S. auriculatum*, while bogbean grows in deeper pools. Abundant lichens tend to occur on the drier mire types.

The patterns of vegetation associated with physical features and their spatial relationships form wildlife habitats supporting characteristic communities of vertebrate and invertebrate fauna. Of particular interest and importance are the birds, the structural mosaic within the peatlands providing a habitat which satisfies the breeding and feeding requirements of waders, waterfowl and raptors. Many of these are typically northern species found here at the southern limit of their range.

SSSI/SPA designation is appropriate for the core areas of bird interest within this extensive tract of land, while 'wider countryside' conservation measures are appropriate in other parts.

Birds
The Peatlands hold internationally important numbers of breeding red-throated diver, black-throated diver, golden eagle, peregrine and dunlin and nationally important numbers of breeding wigeon, common scoter, hen harrier, merlin, golden plover, greenshank, arctic skua and short-eared owl.

Most birds breed at low densities in the peatlands, but the extent of the habitat means that substantial proportions of the populations of many species are present. They include **red-throated diver** (150 pairs, 11% of the British and EC population), **black-throated diver** (30 pairs, 20% of British and EC), greylag goose (c. 300 pairs), **wigeon** (80 pairs, 20% of British), **common scoter** (30+ pairs, 30% of British and EC population), **hen harrier** (30 pairs, 5% of British), **golden eagle** (30 pairs, 2% of NW European population of the nominate race, 7% of British), **merlin** (30 pairs, 5% of British), **peregrine** (35 pairs, 2% of NW European, 4% of British), **golden plover** (3980 pairs, 17% of British), **dunlin** (3830 pairs, 35% of the total population of temperate *schinzii* dunlin, 42% of British), **greenshank** (630 pairs, 41% of British), **arctic skua** (60+ pairs, 2% of British) and **short-eared owl** (50 pairs, 5% of British).

Conservation issues
The integrity of the Flow Country as an ecological unit has been damaged by afforestation. Additional threats include peat extraction, agricultural extensification, drainage, some muirburn (that is when irresponsibly carried out) and damage by red deer.

Further reading
Lindsay, R A, Chairman, D J, Everingham, F, O'Reilly, R M, Palmer, M A, Rowell, T A and Stroud, D A 1988 *The Flow Country: the peatlands of Caithness and Sutherland.* Nature Conservancy Council, Peterborough.
RSPB 1985 *Forestry in the flow country – the threat to birds.* RSPB, Sandy.
Stroud, D A, Reed, T M, Pienkowski, M W and Lindsay, R A 1987 *Birds, Bogs and Forestry: the peatlands of Caithness and Sutherland.* Nature Conservancy Council, Peterborough.

Caithness Lochs

SPA/Ram Code	IBA Europe number
117A	020

County/Region	District(s)	OS sheet(s)	Grid Reference(s)	Maps 2, 5
Highland	Caithness	12	ND 255684	

Area (ha)	NNR	SPA		SPA	Ramsar	
1000-9999	No	Designated	N	Wider	Designated	N
		Candidate	Y	Countryside	Candidate	Y
				Measures		
				Candidate		

A series of mainly shallow, mesotrophic and eutrophic lochs and mires which attract wintering swans, geese and ducks.

Site description

The components of the site are spread over a wide area of north-east Caithness, roughly in the triangle formed by Wick, Duncansby Head and Thurso. They include Loch Heilen, Broubster Leans, Loch of Winless, Loch of Wester, Moss of Killimster, Loch of Mey, Loch Watten, Loch Scarmclate and Loch of Toftingall. These lochs and their associated wetlands provide roosting as well as feeding areas for wintering wildfowl. Most of the lochs are eutrophic or mesotrophic in character. Broubster Leans is a complex area of mire which has developed along the abandoned channels of the River Forss. The lochs display a diverse aquatic flora, including scarce and locally rare species. Loch Watten is nationally important as an open water habitat with a diverse floral and faunal interest.

SSSI/SPA designation is appropriate for the key water bodies and associated wetland habitats, while 'wider countryside' conservation measures are appropriate for the remainder of the catchment area that is relevant to the bird interest.

Birds

The principal interest is for wintering wildfowl, including internationally important numbers of Greenland white-fronted goose and nationally important numbers of whooper swan.

Over the five-winter period 1985/86 to 1989/90 the average peak count for **Greenland white-fronted goose** was 315 birds (1% of the world population and 3% of the number wintering in Britain) and for **whooper swan** was 157 birds (3% of British). Notable also are wintering mute swan, greylag goose, wigeon, teal, mallard, pochard, tufted duck, and goldeneye.

Although numbers of wintering Greenland white-fronted geese have declined from a peak of 730 in the 1970s, the Caithness site remains especially important in view of its status as an outlier of the two main wintering areas (Islay and Wexford, Eire). The geese and swans forage over farmland throughout lowland Caithness, but rely on these undisturbed water bodies as safe roost sites.

Conservation issues

The wildfowl interest on these lochs is vulnerable to a range of factors including: afforestation within the catchments leading to acid run–off and sedimentation; drainage; agricultural intensification with the associated nitrate run–off; increased recreational use; and the development of fish farming and commercial eel fishing.

Further reading

Greenland White-fronted Goose Study 1990 *Greenland white-fronted geese in Britain 1987/88-1989/90*. GWFGS Research Report No. 7, Aberystwyth.

Laybourne, S and Fox, A D 1988 *Greenland White-fronted Geese in Caithness*. Report to Nature Conservancy Council.

Laybourne, S and Fox, A D 1988 Greenland White-fronted Geese in Caithness. *Scottish Birds* 15: 30–35.

Talbot, T 1989 *Wintering wildfowl and waders in Caithness 1987-88 and 1988-89. A study of selected sites*. Report to Nature Conservancy Council.

Caithness Cliffs

SPA/Ram Code	IBA Europe number
118A	019

County/Region	District(s)	OS sheet(s)	Grid Reference(s)	Maps 2, 5
Highland	Caithness	11, 12, 17	Coastline sections from ND 207713 to ND 057174	

Area (ha)	NNR	SPA		Ramsar	
652	No	Designated	N	Designated	N
		Candidate	Y	Candidate	N

Stretches of mainland cliff supporting important numbers of nine species of seabirds.

Site description

Three sections of cliff-lined coast are included within the site: Dunnet Head, Duncansby Head to Skirza Head, and Wick to Helmsdale with a short break at Dunbeath. The cliffs of the north-facing coast (Duncansby and Dunnet Heads) are of old red sandstone, generally of 30–60 m in height, but rising to over 90 m in places at Dunnet Head. Cliff ledges, stacks and geos support varied vegetation and provide ideal nesting sites for seabirds. Broad cliff ledges support characteristic northern plants such as roseroot and Scots lovage, and aspen and willow scrub grow in sheltered spots. Patches of species-rich maritime heath with spring squill and Scottish primrose, a species with a limited northern distribution, are found on the cliff top. Inland, the maritime influence is quickly lost and acidic heathland takes over. Steep, rocky, east-facing cliffs, also of old red sandstone, rise to over 150 m near Berriedale, although they are lower than this along most of this coast, and are capped in varying thicknesses of base-rich till. Species-rich maritime grassland and heath dominated by red fescue occur on the cliff top, and scrub and tall-herb grassland on till slopes. Characteristic maritime species are found on ledges and crevices.

These cliffs overlook the Pentland and Moray Firths, which provide rich feeding areas for fish-eating seabirds.

Birds

The principal interest is for breeding seabirds with internationally important numbers of kittiwake, guillemot and razorbill, and nationally important numbers of fulmar, cormorant, shag, herring gull, great black-backed gull and black guillemot, as well as cliff-nesting peregrine.

Detailed surveys in recent years (Mudge 1977, 1986; Parsons 1986) have revealed the following numbers of breeding seabirds : **fulmar** 27,900 AOS (5% of the British population), **cormorant** 280 pairs (4% of British), **shag** 2090 pairs (6% of British), **herring gull** 12,900 pairs (9% of British), **great black-backed gull** 855 pairs (5% of British), **kittiwake** 46,650 pairs (2% of Western European, 9% of British), **guillemot** 130,200 individuals (4% of Western European, 12% of British), **razorbill** 16,150 individuals (1% of Western European, 11% of British) and **black guillemot** 1865 individuals (5% of British). **Peregrine** (12 pairs, 1% of British) breed on the cliffs.

Notable also are breeding great skua (7+ pairs), puffin (3500 individuals) and several pairs of ravens.

Conservation issues

Seabirds are sensitive to changes in the quality of the marine environment, especially to changes in fish stocks and to oil pollution.

Seabirds breeding at this site are at risk from potential oil pollution from nearby oil production platforms and from spills from passing tankers; from continued over-fishing; from recreational disturbance; and from dumping of rubbish into geos. A proposal to develop Berriedale Cliffs as a marine 'super' quarry has been suggested in the past.

Further reading

Mudge, G P 1986 Trends of population change at colonies of cliff-nesting seabirds in the Moray Firth. *Proc. Roy. Soc. Edin.* 91B:73–80.

Cape Wrath

SPA/Ram Code	IBA Europe number
123A	022

County/Region	District(s)	OS sheet(s)	Grid Reference(s)	Maps 4, 5
Highland	Sutherland	9	NC 260740	

Area (ha)	NNR	SPA		Ramsar	
1-999	No	Designated	N	Designated	N
		Candidate	Y	Candidate	N

Cliffs at the north-westernmost tip of the Scottish mainland supporting nationally important numbers of four species of seabirds.

Site description
This site consists of two stretches of Torridonian sandstone and Lewisian gneiss cliff (total length 15 km) around Cape Wrath headland. These cliffs provide suitable nest sites for large numbers of breeding seabirds. West of Cape Wrath, the cliffs are broken, with undercliffs vegetated by heather, heather/juniper heath (in exposed places), and ferns (in fissures). Two alpine species, moss campion and purple saxifrage, are found on base-rich eroded areas. East of the headland, cliffs rise to about 200 m and are far more precipitous. Least willow occurs at 135 m, one of the lowest stations in Britain for this species. At Clo Mor and Stac an Dunain vegetation is limited to cliff-ledge flora and bird greens. The maritime influence extends well back from the cliff top. At Cape Wrath itself, a high level dune system formed by lime-rich wind-blown sand supports bryophytes on the sides exposed to moist Atlantic winds. A woodrush/tall fern community is found on the more sheltered cliff faces.

Birds
The principal interest is for breeding seabirds with nationally important numbers of kittiwake, guillemot, razorbill and puffin.

Recent estimates of current breeding population sizes from the Seabird Colony Register include: **kittiwake** 9300 pairs (2% of the British population), **guillemot** 12,300 individuals (1% of British), **razorbill** 1600 individuals (1% of British) and **puffin** 5900 pairs (2% of British). Great skuas breed here at one of their few mainland sites, as do peregrines. Notable also is fulmar (2300 AOS).

Conservation issues
Seabirds are sensitive to changes in the quality of the marine environment, especially to changes in fish stocks and to oil pollution.

Part of this area is used as an MoD live firing/bombing range.

Handa

SPA/Ram Code	IBA Europe number
124A	023

County/Region	District(s)	OS sheet(s)	Grid Reference(s)	Maps 4, 5
Highland	Sutherland	9	NC 138480	

Area (ha)	NNR	SPA	Ramsar
363	No	Designated Y Candidate N/A	Designated N Candidate N

An island with high sea-cliffs and moors of major importance for breeding seabirds, with four species occurring at nationally or internationally important levels.

Site description

Handa is a Torridonian sandstone island with precipitous cliffs, a short way off the west Sutherland coast. It provides a strategic nesting locality for seabirds which feed in the rich waters of the northern Minch. Most of the island is vegetated with submaritime grasslands and heaths. Cliff-tops support a range of communities, including thrift/sea plantain 'meadow', species-rich and species-poor maritime heaths, some dominated by heather, others by crowberry. Herb-rich grassland dominated by Yorkshire-fog and bents is found in more sheltered areas. Some small lochs and marshes are also found on the island.

Birds

The principal interest is for breeding seabirds with internationally important numbers of guillemot and razorbill and nationally important numbers of kittiwake and great skua.

Recent estimates of current breeding population sizes from the Seabird Colony Register include : **great skua** 80+ pairs (1% of British), **kittiwake** 10,700 pairs (2% of the British population), **guillemot** 98,700 individuals (3% of Western Europe, 9% of British; the largest colony in Britain and Ireland) and **razorbill** 16,400 individuals (2% of Western Europe, 11% of British). Notable also are red-throated diver (2 pairs), fulmar (3500 AOS), shag (260 pairs), arctic skua (21+ pairs) and puffin (803 individuals).

Conservation issues

Seabirds are sensitive to changes in the quality of the marine environment, especially to changes in fish stocks and to oil pollution.

Priest Island

SPA/Ram Code	IBA Europe number
126A	026

County/Region	District(s)	OS sheet(s)	Grid Reference(s)	Map 4
Highland	Ross and Cromarty	15	NB 925022	

Area (ha)	NNR	SPA		Ramsar	
138	No	Designated	N	Designated	N
		Candidate	Y	Candidate	N

An offshore island supporting a large colony of storm petrels.

Site description
Priest Island is the outermost and most exposed of the Summer Isles, lying about 6 km off the coast west of Ullapool. The island rises to about 75 m and supports heath communities, numerous lochs and a small amount of woodland. Enrichment from salt spray and bird guano enables more species-rich maritime heath and cliff communities to exist around the coast.

Birds
Priest Island supports one of the largest **storm petrel** colonies in Britain, thought to contain around 10,000 pairs.

Other breeding seabird species include fulmar (350 AOS), shag (140 pairs) and black guillemot (40-50 pairs). Native greylag geese (2-4 pairs) and peregrine (1 pair) also breed.

In winter, barnacle geese are present – mean of 100 birds counted during last five aerial spring surveys. These birds use this island, amongst others, as a feeding and roosting area.

Conservation issues
Seabirds are sensitive to changes in the quality of the marine environment, especially to changes in fish stocks and to oil pollution. Ground-nesting seabirds on offshore islands are vulnerable to the introduction of predatory mammals.

Rhum (Rum)

SPA/Ram Code	IBA Europe number
134A	025

County/Region	District(s)	OS sheet(s)	Grid Reference(s)	Maps 3, 4, 7
Highland	Lochaber	32, 39	NM 370980	

Area (ha)	NNR	SPA	Ramsar
10,864	Yes	Designated Y	Designated N
		Candidate N/A	Candidate N

A large island supporting an internationally important breeding colony of Manx shearwaters and with many other features of national importance, both geological and biological.

Site description

Rhum's large size, its mountainous terrain, and the contrasting rock types of acid sandstone, calcareous basalt and Triassic limestone, and igneous rocks, contribute to the island's diversity of plants and animals. The igneous mountains, which rise to 812 m, are craggy, but dominated by montane and sub-montane grassland, dwarf shrub heath and mires. On the magnesium-rich ultra basic soils, there is fertile bent-fescue grassland associated with the shearwater colonies, and herb-rich heath. High level acid rocks support moss heath with such plants as stiff sedge and dwarf willow, the crags supporting a range of saxifrages and other alpine species. The moorlands are a mix of mat-grass swards, wet heath dominated by heather, deer-grass, purple moor-grass, and cotton-grass, and blanket mire rich in *Sphagnum* mosses. Several of these vegetation types contain uncommon plants, including the nationally rare arctic sandwort. Further variety is provided by the coastal habitats of stony beaches, intertidal mudflats and sand dunes, and inland lochs and burns.

Human activity in the past has greatly influenced Rhum; grazing and burning have given rise to an almost treeless landscape, although fragments of natural woodland remain in rocky places, and more recent plantations exist around Kinloch. The island is now important for ecological research into vegetation, invertebrates (the fauna is rich with rare and local forms), mammals, notably red deer, and birds.

Birds

Rhum is noted especially for its huge colony of **Manx shearwaters** which nest high on the mountains. Estimates of numbers vary from 62,000 to over 100,000 pairs (Furness 1990). Rhum is possibly the largest colony in the world. Birds of prey include golden eagle (2-4 pairs), merlin (3-4 pairs) and peregrine (2 pairs). The island has recently become prominent as the release site for the white-tailed eagle reintroduction programme (Love 1988).

Small numbers of other seabird species breed around the coastline. Inland, on the moors, golden plovers and red-throated divers breed on the lochs.

Conservation issues

Seabirds are sensitive to changes in the quality of the marine environment, especially to changes in fish stocks and to oil pollution. Ground-nesting seabirds on offshore islands are vulnerable to the introduction of predatory mammals.

The restoration of native woodland is an important ongoing project which has resulted in increasing populations of woodland birds such as willow warbler and sparrowhawk.

Further reading

Furness, R W 1990 *Numbers and population trends of Manx shearwaters on Rhum*. CSD Report No. 1168.

Love, J A *Checklist of the Birds of Rhum*.

Love, J A 1988 *The reintroduction of the white-tailed sea eagle to Scotland: 1975-1987*. Research and Survey in Nature Conservation No. 12. Nature Conservancy Council, Peterborough.

Manx shearwater

Balranald

	SPA/Ram Code	IBA Europe number
	145A	008

County/Region	District(s)	OS sheet(s)	Grid Reference(s)	Map 3
Western Isles	N/A	18	NF 712705	

Area (ha)	NNR	SPA		Ramsar	
838	No	Designated	N	Designated	N
		Candidate	Y	Candidate	Y

Coastal dunes, machair and marshes, important for their breeding and wintering waders, and breeding corncrakes.

Site description

Located on the west coast of North Uist, this area extends from rocky headlands and sandy beaches, through high dunes and machair, some of it cultivated, to marshes and rough pasture in the east. There is also saltmarsh on the edges of Loch Paible. The whole area is a fine example of the machair system in its widest sense, and includes a broad range of vegetation types, and many plant species. The nutrient-rich marsh at Loch nam Feithean is particularly notable for its diverse flora and fauna.

Birds

The site holds internationally important numbers of breeding **dunlin** (105 pairs, 1% of the total and British population of the temperate *schinzii* race) together with nationally important populations of breeding **corncrake** (14 calling birds, 2% of the British population) and **ringed plover** (120 pairs, 1% of NW and Central European population, 1% of British), and wintering **ringed plover** (370 birds, 2% of British) and **sanderling** (210 birds, 1.5% of British).

Notable also are breeding oystercatcher (220 pairs), lapwing (340 pairs), snipe (30 pairs) and redshank (130 pairs).

Conservation issues

The wildlife interest of this site is vulnerable to changes in drainage depth and agricultural change.

Further reading

Fuller, R J 1981 The breeding habitats of waders on North Uist Machair. *Scottish Birds* 11: 142-152.

Fuller, R J, Reed, T M, Webb, A, Williams, T D and Pienkowski, M W 1986 Populations of breeding waders *Charadrii* and their habitats on the crofting lands of the Outer Hebrides, Scotland. *Biol. Conserv.* 37: 333-361.

Hudson, A, Stowe, T T J and Aspinall, S J 1990 Status and distribution of corncrakes in Britain in 1988. *British Birds* 83: 173-187.

Baleshare and Kirkibost

SPA/Ram Code	IBA Europe number
148A	009

County/Region	District(s)	OS sheet(s)	Grid Reference(s)	Map 3
Western Isles	N/A	18, 22	NF 785623	

Area (ha)	NNR	SPA		Ramsar	
1000-9999	No	Designated	N	Designated	N
		Candidate	Y	Candidate	Y

Two machair islands, with large breeding wader populations and also important for wintering geese.

Site description
Baleshare and the smaller island of Kirkibost are notable for the extent of their sand dune systems. Dunes in the west grade into dry and wet machair before reaching, on Baleshare, rocky peatland in the east. Most areas are grazed by sheep and cattle, and the central flat machair of Baleshare is cultivated in the traditional manner. Additional variety is found in the salt and brackish marshes along the sheltered eastern shores, in dune slacks and in freshwater lochs with their associated fens and marshes.

Birds
These islands support internationally important breeding concentrations of **ringed plover** (330 pairs, 3% of NW and Central European population, 4% of British) and **dunlin** (120 pairs, 1% of the total population of temperate *schinzii* dunlin).

In winter, the islands attract many wildfowl, including internationally important numbers of **greylag goose** of the native North Scottish population (900 birds, 45% of the Western Isles population) and **barnacle goose** from the Greenland population (600 birds, 2% of the world population), as well as nationally important numbers of **sanderling** (140 birds, 1% of British).

Notable also are breeding oystercatcher (235 pairs), lapwing (230 pairs), snipe (40 pairs) and redshank (125 pairs).

Conservation issues
The wildlife interest of this site is vulnerable to drainage and agricultural intensification.

Further reading
Fuller, R J, Reed, T M, Webb, A, Williams, T D and Pienkowski, M W 1986 Populations of breeding waders *Charadrii* and their habitats on the crofting lands of the Outer Hebrides, Scotland. *Biol. Conserv.* 37: 333–361.

Boyd, J M and Boyd, I L 1990 *The Hebrides*. Collins, New Naturalist, London.

Loch Scadavay

SPA/Ram Code	IBA Europe number
150A	018

County/Region	District(s)	OS sheet(s)	Grid Reference(s)	Map 3
Western Isles	N/A	18	NF 856686	

Area (ha)	NNR	SPA		Ramsar	
1-999	No	Designated	N	Designated	N
		Candidate	Y	Candidate	N

A large oligotrophic loch, supporting important concentrations of breeding waterfowl.

Site description
Loch Scadavay, the largest freshwater body in North Uist, has an intricate shoreline and many islands. Its nutrient-poor waters support vegetation typical of these conditions, with species such as white water-lily, water lobelia and bogbean. Yellow water-lily and various pondweeds also are present. Islands in the loch are covered by tall heather and there is also some scrub.

Birds
A breeding site for **red-throated diver** (10-15 pairs, 1% of British and EC), **black-throated diver** (2 pairs, 1% of British and EC) and greylag geese of the native North Scottish population (10 pairs). Notable also are breeding merlin and arctic skua.

Conservation issues
Birds that rely on northern freshwater lochs are vulnerable to changes in water quality and the consequent impacts on food resources. Damage can be caused by the acidic run-off from conifer plantations in the catchment area and from fish farm developments.

Further reading
Boyd, J M and Boyd, I L 1990 *The Hebrides*. Collins, New Naturalist, London.

Inverpolly, Loch Urigill and Nearby Lochs

SPA/Ram Code	IBA Europe number
151A	024

County/Region	District(s)	OS sheet(s)	Grid Reference(s)	Maps 4, 5
Highland	Ross and Cromarty, Sutherland	15	NC 1027	

Area (ha)	NNR	SPA		SPA	Ramsar	
10,000+	Part	Designated N Candidate Y		Wider Countryside Measures Candidate	Designated N Candidate Y	

A collection of large, oligotrophic, freshwater lochs, important for breeding black-throated diver and other species.

Site description

Several large lochs and many lochans are found within the site. Most of the lochs are oligotrophic and contain a submerged flora and restricted fauna typical of nutrient-poor conditions.

The various catchments that include Inverpolly contain a wide range of habitats characteristic of the north-west Highlands, including upland heath, upland mire, upland broadleaved woodland, lochs, lochans, rivers and streams. Birch-dominated woodland is scattered throughout the catchments up to 275 m above sea-level, with ungrazed or lightly grazed ancient woodland being found on the Cam Loch islands. Rowan, alder, bird cherry and holly dominate these woods, with oak restricted to coastal scrub. On lower ground, plant communities comprise wet heath, blanket mire and valley mire, with acid and poor fen vegetation. A particularly good example of a small oceanic valley mire is found west of Loch Sionascaig. Limestone outcrops occur on Ben More Assynt and at Knockan Cliff and run-off from these results in the lochs in this area having a relatively high alkalinity.

SSSI/SPA designation is appropriate for the key water bodies and associated wetland habitats, while 'wider countryside' conservation measures are appropriate for the remainder of the catchment area that is relevant to the bird interest.

Birds

These lochs form part of the core breeding range of **black-throated divers** with 10 pairs regularly breeding (7% of the British and EC population).

Notable also in associated wetlands is breeding red-throated diver (10+ pairs). The loch catchment areas support **golden eagle** (5 home ranges, 1% of British), hen harrier (2 pairs), merlin (several pairs), peregrine (4 pairs) and **greenshank** (20+ pairs, 1% of British).

Conservation issues

Birds that rely on freshwater lochs are vulnerable to changes in water quality and the consequent impacts on food resources. Damage can be caused by the acidic run-off from conifer plantations in the catchment area and from fish farm developments. Breeding success of black-throated divers is closely linked with water levels.

Conifer afforestation exacerbates the acidification of surface water, and causes increased run-off due to ploughing and drainage, resulting in increased fluctuations of loch water levels. Acidification can have an adverse impact on the biological productivity of water bodies which in turn affects food supplies for nesting divers and other species. Fluctuating water levels often result in nest failure either through flooding or drying out. Large proportions of several important loch catchments in this area have already been afforested, and further afforestation is likely. There should be a presumption against new commercial forestry developments within these catchments.

Several trout hatcheries have been established, and recent proposals to site salmon smolt cages on black-throated diver breeding lochs would be potentially damaging.

Centuries of overgrazing and overburning have resulted in extensive areas of degraded habitat in the loch catchments. Continued high grazing pressure from sheep and red deer has drastically reduced deciduous woodland cover and is greatly limiting natural regeneration within remaining areas. These changes can be expected to have had an impact on the biological productivity of the associated waterbodies.

Commercial marble extraction is taking place near Ledmore, with further schemes proposed or granted outline planning permission. This poses a threat to black-throated diver interest through disturbance and by alterations to the water quality of breeding/feeding lochs through discharge from the developments.

A consultation/buffer zone in the catchment areas surrounding these lochs will be necessary to minimise the risk of unsympathetic land-use changes.

Further reading

Campbell, L H and Talbot, T R 1987 The breeding status of black-throated diver (*Gavia arctica*) in Scotland. *British Birds* 80: 1-8.

Loch Maree

	SPA/Ram Code 153A	IBA Europe number 027

County/Region	District(s)	OS sheet(s)	Grid Reference(s)	Map 4
Highland	Ross and Cromarty	19	NG 9172	

Area (ha)	NNR	SPA		SPA		Ramsar	
10,000+	Part	Designated	N	Wider		Designated	N
		Candidate	Y	Countryside Measures Candidate		Candidate	Y

A large, oligotrophic, freshwater loch, important for breeding black-throated diver and other species.

Site description

Loch Maree is a large, oligotrophic loch with many wooded islands. The adjacent catchments support a range of habitats including freshwater lochs, upland heath, upland mire, native pinewood, upland broadleaved woodland and montane screes and heaths on the highest ground.

Important stands of native pinewood remain within Beinn Eighe NNR, on Loch Maree Islands NNR and at Coulin. However, the predominant habitat types within the catchment areas are upland heath and mire, oligotrophic lochs, and montane screes and montane heaths.

SSSI/SPA designation is appropriate for the water body and associated wetland habitats, while 'wider countryside' conservation measures are appropriate for the remainder of the catchment area that is relevant to the bird interest.

Birds

These lochs form part of the core breeding range of **black-throated divers**, with at least 17 pairs regularly breeding (11% of the British and EC population).

Notable also in associated wetlands and elsewhere in the catchment area are breeding red-throated diver, **golden eagle**, merlin, peregrine and **greenshank**.

Conservation issues

Birds that rely on freshwater lochs are vulnerable to changes in water quality and the consequent impacts on food resources. Damage can be caused by the acidic run-off from conifer plantations in the catchment area and from fish farm developments. Breeding success of black-throated divers is closely linked with water levels.

Conifer afforestation exacerbates the acidification of surface water, and causes increased run-off due to ploughing and drainage, resulting in increased fluctuation of loch water levels. Acidification can have an adverse impact on the biological productivity of water bodies, which in turn affects food supplies for nesting divers and other species.

Fluctuating water levels often result in nest failure either through flooding or drying out. Some commercial afforestation has taken place within the catchment area. There should be a presumption against new commercial forestry developments within these catchments.

There have been recent proposals for fish farming on Loch Maree. Such development is in potential conflict with black-throated diver interest.

Centuries of overgrazing and overburning have resulted in extensive areas of degraded habitat in the loch catchments. Continued high grazing pressure from red deer has drastically reduced deciduous woodland cover and is greatly limiting natural regeneration within remaining areas, although NCC/SNH has successfully established fenced exclusion areas within the NNR. These changes can be expected to have had an impact on the biological productivity of the associated waterbodies.

A consultation/buffer zone in the catchment area surrounding Loch Maree will be necessary to minimise the risk of unsympathetic land-use changes.

Further reading
Campbell, L H and Talbot, T R 1987 The breeding status of black-throated diver (*Gavia arctica*) in Scotland. *British Birds* 80: 1-8.

Loch Ruthven and Nearby Lochs

SPA/Ram Code	IBA Europe number
155A	032

County/Region	District(s)	OS sheet(s)	Grid Reference(s)	Maps 4, 5, 8
Highland	Inverness	26	NH 620276	

Area (ha)	NNR	SPA		SPA	Ramsar	
1-999	No	Designated N Candidate Y		Wider Countryside Measures Candidate	Designated N Candidate N	

A group of mesotrophic, freshwater lochs and surrounding catchments, important for breeding Slavonian grebes and other bird species.

Site description

Lochs Ashie and Ruthven are medium-sized, mesotrophic lochs, with rocky margins, but with stands of bottle sedge around much of their perimeters. Locally more extensive marshy zones exist, such as at the west end of Loch Ruthven where there is a transition from open water, through swamp and fen, to sedge-rich acidic grassland. Loch Ruthven is largely surrounded by birchwood and the catchment areas support a range of other habitats such as upland heath and grassland, upland mire, swamp/fen/carr, wet lowland grassland, rivers and streams.

SSSI/SPA designation is appropriate for the key water bodies and associated wetland habitats, while 'wider countryside' conservation measures are appropriate for the remainder of the catchment area that is relevant to the bird interest.

Birds

These lochs form the core area of the breeding range of **Slavonian grebes** in Britain with 30 regular summering pairs (44% of the British and EC population). Loch Ashie is an important gathering site for Slavonian grebes in spring, before the birds disperse to other breeding lochs, and in the autumn when both adults and young gather there. During this autumn gathering the adults undergo their post-breeding moult and become flightless. It is likely that adults from a wide area on both sides of the Great Glen congregate on Loch Ashie: 30-60 birds are regularly present in these gatherings, and up to 80 birds have been recorded, making this by far the most important gathering loch in Scotland.

Notable also in associated wetlands are breeding red-throated diver (1+ pair), black-throated diver (1-2 pairs) and **goldeneye** (1-2 pairs, 1% of British). The catchment areas surrounding these lochs support hen harrier (2-3 pairs), merlin (2+ pairs) and peregrine (3-4 pairs).

Conservation issues

Birds that rely on freshwater lochs are vulnerable to changes in water quality and the consequent impacts on food resources. Damage can be caused by the acidic run-off from conifer plantations in the catchment area and from fish farm developments. Breeding success of Slavonian grebes is closely linked with water levels.

Conifer afforestation exacerbates the acidification of surface water, and causes increased run-off due to ploughing and drainage, resulting in increased fluctuation of loch water levels. Acidification can have an adverse impact on the biological productivity of water bodies, which in turn affects food supplies for nesting grebes and other species. Fluctuating water levels often result in nest failure either through flooding or drying out. Large proportions of several important loch catchments in this area have already been afforested, and further afforestation is likely. There should be a presumption against new commercial forestry developments within these catchments.

A consultation/buffer zone in the catchment areas surrounding these lochs will be necessary to minimise the risk of unsympathetic land-use changes.

Slavonian grebes are highly vulnerable to disturbance from recreational activities, particularly by birdwatchers and anglers. The use of motor boats is a potential problem. A further likely problem is the stocking of the lochs with rainbow trout, which compete directly for food with the grebes. In addition to pike, mammalian predators, such as otter, mink and fox, are known to predate both the adults and young of Slavonian grebes.

Establishment of an RSPB Reserve at Loch Ruthven has helped to manage and control visitor disturbance to the highly sensitive breeding grebes.

Central Highland Hills and Glens

	SPA/Ram Code	IBA Europe number
	156A	031

County/Region	District(s)	OS sheet(s)	Grid Reference(s)	Maps 4, 5
Highland	Inverness, Ross and Cromarty	20, 25, 26, 33, 34	NH 1630	

Area (ha)	NNR	SPA		SPA	Ramsar	
10,000+	No	Designated N Candidate Y		Wider Countryside Measures Candidate	Designated N Candidate N	

A large area of mountainous country with glens and extensive stands of native pinewood; important for raptors and other specialist montane and forest birds.

Site description

This area comprises a range of mountains from the Central mountains of Ross and Cromarty in the north and the Affric-Cannich mountains to the south. A series of glens running from east to west are present and include Glen Cannich, Glen Strathfarrar and Glen Affric. The two latter glens contain some of the largest and finest stands of native pinewood remaining in Scotland. Other important bird habitats in addition to the montane and native pinewoods are upland mire, upland heath, upland broadleaved woodland, oligotrophic and mesotrophic lochs and lochans, rivers, streams and wet lowland grassland.

The hills rise to almost 1200 m. Their lower slopes have a typical mixture of sub-montane heathland and blanket mire, with occasional species-rich zones of base-rich grassland, soligenous mires and flushes. On the higher hills, many different plant communities are present, including dwarf shrub heaths, lichen heaths and moss heaths, with the last well represented in herb-rich forms.

Native pinewood stands in Glen Affric and Glen Strathfarrar are intermediate between the east and west highland types, and include some of the largest stands remaining in Scotland. There are also extensive birch stands, and remnants of wych elm/hazel and alder/willow gorge woodland. Alder and sallow woodland occurs in wet hollows. Well developed transitions exist, through to wet and dry heath in glades, swamp to open water habitats, and to submontane heaths at the natural tree line. The epiphytic lichen communities of the Glen Affric and especially Glen Strathfarrar pinewoods are particularly rich.

The fauna includes a typical range of highland animals, including pine marten and red squirrel in the woodlands. The wetlands are notable for their dragonflies, which include nationally scarce species.

SSSI/SPA designation is appropriate for the core areas of bird interest within this extensive tract of land, while 'wider countryside' conservation measures are appropriate in other parts.

Birds

Within the wider boundaries of this site there are a total of 48 contiguous **golden eagle** home ranges. These represent 3% of the NW European population of the nominate race and 11% of the British breeding population. Of these home ranges, 40–45 are currently occupied by breeding pairs, while at least three are currently unoccupied. Also breeding are 10-25 pairs of **red-throated divers** (1% of the British and EC population), 10 pairs of **black-throated divers** (7% of the British and EC population), c. 25 pairs of **common scoter** (23% of the British and EC population), 10 pairs of **hen harriers** (2% of British), 25-35 pairs of **merlins** (5% of British), c. 20 pairs of **peregrines** (3% of British) and 30-50 pairs of **dotterel** (5% of British and EC). Notable also are breeding capercaillie, greenshank, redwing, crested tit, Scottish crossbill and snow bunting.

Conservation issues

Centuries of overgrazing and overburning have resulted in extensive areas of degraded habitats within the site. Additionally, the native pinewoods of this area, in common with the rest of the Scottish Highlands, have been reduced by felling and fire. Continued overgrazing by red deer and sheep severely restricts natural regeneration of native pine and broadleaved woodland and of moorland habitats. Maintenance and good management of remaining areas of native pinewood is a strong conservation priority.

Large scale blanket conifer afforestation is a potential threat to this area. It would have a detrimental effect on the populations of golden eagle, merlin, peregrine and other species by reducing hunting range and affecting prey abundance. Additionally, it can affect waterbirds, such as divers, through its detrimental effect on both water quality (through acid run-off and leaching of chemicals) and on water levels (through changes in hydrology associated with ploughing and drainage).

Birds that rely on freshwater lochs are vulnerable to changes in water quality and the consequent impacts on food resources. Breeding success of divers is closely linked with water levels. Fluctuating water levels on several lochs in the area are exacerbated by the presence of hydro–electric dams.

Lewis Peatlands

SPA/Ram Code	IBA Europe number
157A	016

County/Region	District(s)	OS sheet(s)	Grid Reference	Maps 3, 4
Western Isles	N/A	8, 13	NB 33	

Area (ha)	NNR	SPA		SPA	Ramsar	
10,000+	No	Designated	N	Wider	Designated	N
		Candidate	Y	Countryside	Candidate	Y
				Measures		
				Candidate		

A large area of blanket peatland interspersed with freshwater lochs, important for breeding waders, divers and raptors.

Site description
The peatlands cover the greater part of the island, and comprise an extensive area of deep blanket bog interspersed with freshwater lochs and complexes of bog pools. Grazed, poor quality grassland also occurs, with heather dominant on the coast. In the south, the blanket bog becomes increasingly broken up by rocky outcrops and larger lochs. The continuous and largely unfragmented extent of the peatland is a striking feature of the area, in comparison with the Flow country of Caithness and Sutherland, which has been damaged by conifer afforestation.

SSSI/SPA designation is appropriate for the core areas of bird interest within this extensive tract of land, while 'wider countryside' conservation measures are appropriate in other parts.

Birds
The blanket bogs support large numbers of breeding waders, divers and birds of prey.

Sample surveys of about 15% of the blanket bog area of Lewis in 1987 (Stroud *et al* 1988) confirmed the presence of important breeding concentrations of golden plover, dunlin and greenshank. The surveys located 210 **golden plover** (1%+ of British), 660 pairs of **dunlin** (6% of the total population of temperate *schinzii* dunlin, 7% of British) and 46 pairs of **greenshank** (3% of British). Other important breeding populations in the overall area include **red-throated diver** (23 pairs, 2% of British and EC), **black-throated diver** (up to 10 pairs, 7% of British and EC), **golden eagle** (15 pairs, 1% of NW European, 4% of British), and **merlin** (20 pairs, 3% of British). Whimbrel, arctic skua and great skua also breed. The populations of red-throated diver, black-throated diver and greenshank are especially important in an EC context.

Conservation issues
The major threat to the site is afforestation. A 'shelter belt' has begun to be planted to the east of the A857, despite NCC opposition. It is planned for this to extend for several miles across central north Lewis. This could affect significant numbers of key bird species. Potential threats include commercial peat extraction and drainage for agricultural intensification.

Further reading

Stroud, D A, Condie, M, Holloway, S J, Rothwell, A J, Shepherd, K B, Simons, J R, and Turner, J 1988 *A survey of moorland birds on the Isle of Lewis in 1987*. Nature Conservancy Council, CSD Report No. 776

North Harris Mountains

SPA/Ram Code	IBA Europe number
157B	017

County/Region	District(s)	OS sheet(s)	Grid Reference(s)	Map 3
Western Isles	N/A	13	NB 0611	

Area (ha)	NNR	SPA		Ramsar	
10,000+	Yes	Designated	N	Designated	N
		Candidate	Y	Candidate	N

An extensive area of montane grassland and moorland, supporting a high density of breeding golden eagles.

Site description
These rocky hills rise steeply from sea level to about 730 m. Most of the vegetation is typical of acidic peat uplands, founded on Lewisian gneiss and granite. There is a strongly oceanic character, which has resulted in an abundance of species-poor wet heath. Bryophytes typical of Atlantic coasts are well represented, including the strikingly large moss *Campylopus shawii* which has its world distribution restricted to western Scotland and Ireland and the Isle of Man. The hills are drained by fast flowing streams, and there are numerous oligotrophic and dystrophic lochs.

Birds
This site supports one of the densest populations of **golden eagle** in Britain with 10 pairs (2% of the British population). Other breeding species include black-throated diver, merlin and peregrine.

Conservation issues
Raptors that inhabit uplands and open moorland are vulnerable to blanket afforestation and to other changes in agricultural policy. Carrion forms a large part of the diet of eagles at this site.

Assynt Lochs

SPA/Ram Code	IBA Europe number
159A	024

County/Region	District(s)	OS sheet(s)	Grid Reference(s)	Maps 4, 5
Highland	Sutherland	15	NC 1027	

Area (ha)	NNR	SPA		SPA		Ramsar	
10,000+	Part (Inchna-damph NNR)	Designated	N	Wider Countryside Measures Candidate		Designated	N
		Candidate	Y			Candidate	Y

A collection of large, oligotrophic, freshwater lochs and surrounding moorland catchments, important for breeding black-throated diver and other species.

Site description

The 'knochan-lochan' terrain of the Assynt catchment contains a wide range of habitats characteristic of the north-west Highlands, including upland heath, upland mire, upland broadleaved woodland, lochs, lochans, rivers and streams. Loch Assynt is the largest of the scattered lochs. Most are oligotrophic and contain a submerged flora and restricted fauna typical of nutrient-poor conditions.

Woodland such as that on the Beannach Islands survives as a relict of north-western forest and is dominated by birch and rowan and supports a varied understorey. On lower ground, plant communities comprise wet heath, blanket mire and valley mire with acid and poor fen vegetation.

This combination of open moorland, woodland and freshwater habitats provide suitable feeding and breeding areas for a wide range of upland bird species.

SSSI/SPA designation is appropriate for the key water bodies and associated wetland habitats, while 'wider countryside' conservation measures are appropriate for the remainder of the catchment area that is relevant to the bird interest.

Birds

These lochs form part of the core breeding range of **black-throated divers** with 7 pairs regularly breeding (5% of the British and EC population).

Notable also in associated wetlands is breeding red-throated diver (10+ pairs). Also present in the loch catchment areas are golden eagle (4 home ranges), merlin (several pairs), peregrine (2 pairs) and **greenshank** (20+ pairs, 1% of British).

Conservation issues

Birds that rely on freshwater lochs are vulnerable to changes in water quality and the consequent impacts on food resources. Damage can be caused by the acidic run-off from conifer plantations in the catchment area and from fish farm developments. Breeding success of black-throated divers is closely linked with water levels.

Conifer afforestation exacerbates the acidification of surface water, and causes increased run-off due to ploughing and drainage, resulting in increased fluctuation of loch water levels. Acidification can have an adverse impact on the biological productivity of water bodies, which in turn affects food supplies for nesting divers and other species. Fluctuating water levels often result in nest failure either through flooding or drying out. There should be a presumption against new commercial forestry developments within these catchments.

Centuries of overgrazing and overburning have resulted in extensive areas of degraded habitat in the loch catchments. Continued high grazing pressure from sheep and red deer has drastically reduced deciduous woodland cover and is greatly limiting natural regeneration within remaining areas. These changes can be expected to have had an impact on the biological productivity of the associated waterbodies.

Commercial mining and quarrying pose a threat to breeding divers through disturbance and by discharges from the developments causing alterations to the water quality of lochs used for feeding and breeding.

A consultation/buffer zone in the catchment areas surrounding these lochs will be necessary to minimise the risk of unsympathetic land-use changes.

Further reading
Campbell, L H and Talbot, T R 1987 The breeding status of black-throated diver (*Gavia arctica*) in Scotland. *British Birds* 80: 1-8.

Black-throated diver

Loch Stack, Loch nam Brac and Nearby Lochs

SPA/Ram Code	IBA Europe number
160A	N/A

County/Region	District(s)	OS sheet(s)	Grid Reference(s)	Maps 4, 5
Highland	Sutherland	9	NC 3042	

Area (ha)	NNR	SPA		SPA		Ramsar	
10,000+	No	Designated	N	Wider		Designated	N
		Candidate	Y	Countryside		Candidate	N
				Measures			
				Candidate			

A collection of large, oligotrophic, freshwater lochs and surrounding moorland catchments, important for breeding black-throated diver and other species.

Site description

The wide range of habitats found in this series of catchments includes blanket bogs on flat or gently sloping gneiss terrain and valley bogs with patterned bogs and hummocks. Numerous open water bodies range from dubh lochans to quite large, shallow oligotrophic lochs, of which Loch Stack is the largest. These lochs contain a submerged flora and restricted fauna typical of nutrient-poor conditions.

SSSI/SPA designation is appropriate for the key water bodies and associated wetland habitats, while 'wider countryside' conservation measures are appropriate for the remainder of the catchment area that is relevant to the bird interest.

Birds

These lochs form part of the core breeding range of **black-throated divers** with 5 pairs regularly breeding (3% of the British and EC population).

Notable also in associated wetlands is breeding red-throated diver (2-4 pairs). The loch catchment areas support golden eagle (3-4 home ranges), merlin (3-4 pairs), peregrine (3 pairs) and greenshank (12 pairs).

Conservation issues

Birds that rely on freshwater lochs are vulnerable to changes in water quality and the consequent impacts on food resources. Damage can be caused by the acidic run-off from conifer plantations in the catchment area and from fish farm developments. Breeding success of black-throated divers is closely linked with water levels.

Conifer afforestation exacerbates the acidification of surface water, and causes increased run-off due to ploughing and drainage, resulting in increased fluctuation of loch water levels. Acidification can have an adverse impact on the biological productivity of water bodies, which in turn affects food supplies for nesting divers and other species. Fluctuating water levels often result in nest failure either through flooding or drying out. A proportion of some loch catchments in this area has already been afforested, and further afforestation is possible. There should be a presumption against new commercial forestry developments within these catchments.

Salmon smolt cages have been established on Loch nam Brac and further proposals would be in conflict with breeding black-throated diver interest.

Centuries of overgrazing and overburning have resulted in extensive areas of degraded habitat in the loch catchments. Continued high grazing pressure from sheep and red deer has drastically reduced deciduous woodland cover and is greatly limiting natural regeneration within remaining areas. These changes can be expected to have had an impact on the biological productivity of the associated waterbodies.

A consultation/buffer zone in the catchment areas surrounding these lochs will be necessary to minimise the risk of unsympathetic land-use changes.

Further reading
Campbell, L H and Talbot, T R 1987 The breeding status of black-throated diver (*Gavia arctica*) in Scotland. *British Birds* 80: 1-8.

Loch Shin and Nearby Lochs

SPA/Ram Code	IBA Europe number
161A	N/A

County/Region	District(s)	OS sheet(s)	Grid Reference(s)	Maps 2, 4, 5
Highland	Sutherland	15, 16	NC 480180	

Area (ha)	NNR	SPA		SPA		Ramsar	
10,000+	No	Designated	N	Wider		Designated	N
		Candidate	Y	Countryside		Candidate	N
				Measures			
				Candidate			

A collection of oligotrophic freshwater lochs, important for breeding black-throated divers and other species.

Site description
The site includes one very large, and several smaller, oligotrophic lochs. The catchment area consists largely of upland heath and upland mire, together with upland broadleaved woodland and montane heath and screes.

SSSI/SPA designation is appropriate for the key water bodies and associated wetland habitats, while 'wider countryside' conservation measures are appropriate for the remainder of the catchment area that is relevant to the bird interest.

Birds
These lochs form part of the core breeding range of **black-throated diver** with 5 pairs regularly breeding (3% of British and EC populations).

Also present is **red-throated diver** (16 pairs, 1% of British). The catchment areas support **hen harrier** (7 pairs, 1% of British), **merlin** (10+ pairs, 2% of British), **greenshank** (30+ pairs, 2% of British), golden eagle, peregrine and **redwing** (c. 20 pairs, 56% of British).

Conservation issues
A large proportion of the catchment of Loch Shin has been subjected to conifer afforestation. Lochs Beannach, Craggie, Dola and Tigh na Creige are now virtually surrounded by conifers. Large scale conifer afforestation can have adverse effects on breeding divers through increased run-off due to altered hydrology and changes in water quality due to acid run-off and leaching of chemicals and fertilisers. Changes in water quality can affect the nutrient status of the lochs and food supply for divers.

Loch Shin has a hydro-electric dam and therefore water levels are subject to unnaturally high fluctuations, which are exacerbated by increased run-off due to forestry-associated ploughing and drainage. Black-throated divers are vulnerable to nest failure from flooding or drying out due to fluctuating water levels.

Salmon smolt cages have been approved for Loch Shin and further proposals have been put forward. Fish farming can conflict with black-throated interest, particularly if cages are located near diver breeding sites.

Centuries of overgrazing and overburning have resulted in large areas of degraded habitat. Continued high grazing pressure from sheep and red deer has greatly reduced deciduous woodland cover and is greatly limiting natural regeneration in remaining areas.

A consultation/buffer zone in the catchment areas surrounding these lochs will be necessary to minimise the risk of further unsympathetic land-use changes.

Further reading
Campbell, L H and Talbot, T R 1987 The breeding status of black-throated diver (*Gavia arctica*) in Scotland. *British Birds* 80: 1–8.

Moray Basin, Firths and Bays

	SPA/Ram Code	IBA Europe number
	162A, formerly 128A, 129A, 131A, 132A, 133A and 234A	028, 029, 030, 033, 034 and 066

County/Region	District(s)	OS sheet(s)	Grid Reference(s)	Maps 5, 6
Highland	Inverness, Ross and Cromarty, Sutherland	17, 21, 26, 27, 28	NH 8060	
Grampian	Moray, Nairn			

Area (ha)	NNR	SPA		Ramsar	
10,000+	Yes (Nigg and Udale Bays; the Mound)	Designated Candidate	Y Y	Designated Candidate	Y Y

Moray Basin, Firths and Bays includes the following former IBAs: Loch Fleet and the Mound (127A), Dornoch Firth (128A), Loch Eye (129A), Cromarty Firth (131A), Beauly Firth (132A), Moray Firth: Munlochy Bay to Findhorn Bay (133A) and Moray Firth: Burghead and Spey Bays (234A).

An extensive area comprising a series of adjacent firths, bays and inshore waters forming an integral unit for internationally important populations of wintering and passage waterfowl.

Site description
The Moray Firth is a complex area of coastal and estuarine habitats, extending from Helmsdale in the north to Spey Bay in the south-east. It includes the Dornoch, Cromarty, Beauly and Inverness Firths, Loch Fleet, Findhorn Bay, Burghead Bay and Spey Bay, together with the intervening stretches of more open coast and the freshwater loch of Loch Eye.

Extensive intertidal flats are found at Loch Fleet, in the Dornoch, Cromarty, Beauly and Inverness Firths, at Whiteness Head, Culbin Sands and at Findhorn Bay and Munlochy Bay. The extent of these mud and sand flats is far greater than anywhere else in Highland Scotland, and their rich invertebrate fauna and beds of eelgrass, glasswort species and *Enteromorpha* algae all provide an important food source for large numbers of wintering and migrating waterfowl.

Extensive areas of saltmarsh are to be found at Loch Fleet, Dornoch Point, the Morrich More, in the Cromarty Firth at Nigg, Udale and Alness Bays and around Dingwall, in the Beauly Firth, in the Inverness Firth at Munlochy and Castle Stuart Bays, at Whiteness Head, Culbin Sands and at Findhorn Bay. These are used for feeding and roosting by waterfowl.

Extensive and complex systems of sand dunes and shingle ridges are to be found at Loch Fleet, Dornoch Point, the Morrich More, Whiteness Head, Culbin Sands, Burghead Bay and Spey Bay. The flora of these dynamic landforms is varied, including coastal heathland, species-rich dune grassland, wooded slacks and substantial areas of saltmarsh. The sandy substrate of the coastal waters of these sites holds mussel scalps and shellfish beds of importance to wintering and migrating waders and seaducks, while the dune and shingle systems provide suitable breeding habitat for terns and other bird species. Several areas, most notably the Morrich More, Whiteness Head, Culbin Sands and Spey Bay are of great land form importance in addition to their biological status.

Steep rocky shores predominate from Tarbat Ness to Rosemarkie, at the entrance to the Inverness Firth. Between Tarbat Ness and Balintore the coastline is fairly low in altitude, rising from Balintore southwards into a line of seacliffs up to 100 metres in height, broken at the Sutors of Cromarty by the narrow entrance to the Cromarty Firth. Crustaceans and molluscs provide food for wintering waders and seaduck, and the cliffs provide breeding habitat for a variety of seabirds, a pattern repeated between Burghead and Lossiemouth, where the cliffs are, however, much lower.

Loch Eye lies between the Dornoch and Cromarty Firths and is regarded as the best example of a eutrophic loch north of the Highland boundary fault. Its richness in nutrients attracts large numbers of wintering and migrating wildfowl, many of which move readily between here and the two adjacent firths. It has a highly diverse aquatic flora, including many uncommon species, with communities characteristic of both oligotrophic and eutrophic conditions.

Other habitat types to be found within the area include alderswamp at The Mound (Loch Fleet), reedbeds in the Cromarty Firth around Dingwall and in the Inverness Firth and at Munlochy Bay, coastal scrub and freshwater and brackish swamp, fen and carr.

The Moray Firth is also notable for its marine mammals, including bottle-nosed dolphins and porpoises, and for the immature stages of commercially important fish species which constitute a food resource for many species of waterbird. Common seals haul out and breed on sand banks in the Dornoch, Cromarty and Beauly Firths. Otters also occur.

Birds
This area supports internationally important numbers of wintering whooper swan, greylag goose, wigeon, red-breasted merganser, goosander, oystercatcher, ringed plover, purple sandpiper, bar-tailed godwit, curlew, redshank and turnstone, and nationally important numbers of wintering red-throated diver, black-throated diver, Slavonian grebe, cormorant, mute swan, shelduck, teal, mallard, pintail, tufted duck, scaup, eider, long-tailed duck, common scoter, velvet scoter, goldeneye, knot and dunlin.

Moray Basin, Firths and Bays is a wetland of international importance by virtue of regularly supporting over 20,000 waterfowl. In the five-winter period 1985/86 to 1989/90 the average peak counts were 550 **red-throated divers** (8% of British), 30 **black-throated divers** (2% of British), 35 **Slavonian grebes** (9% of British), 710 **cormorants** (4% of British), 325 **mute swans** (2% of British), 780 **whooper swans** (5% of the world total, 13% of the number wintering in Britain), 15,550 **Icelandic greylag geese** (15% of world total), 1320 **shelduck** (2% of British), 31,400 **wigeon** (4% of NW European, 13% of British), 4100 **teal** (4% of British), 5500 **mallard** (1% of British), 300 **pintail** (1% of British), 1070 **tufted duck** (2% of British), 375 **scaup** (9% of British), 2240 **eider** (5% of British), 8200+ **long-tailed duck** (41% of British), c. 1450

common scoter (c. 4% of British), c. 850 **velvet scoter** (c. 28% of British), 950 **goldeneye** (6% of British), 2000 **red-breasted merganser** (2% of NW European, 20% of British), 1400 **goosander** (1% of NW European, 25% of British), 11,500 **oyster-catcher** (1% of EAF, 4% of British), 530 **ringed plover** (1% of EAF, 2% of British), 2800 **knot** (1% of British), 500 **purple sandpiper** (1% of EAF, 3% of British), 9300 **dunlin** (2% of British), 3800 **bar-tailed godwit** (3% of EAF, 6% of British), 3900 **curlew** (1% of EAF, 4% of British), 5500 **redshank** (4% of EAF, 8% of British) and 940 **turnstone** (1% of EAF, 2% of British).

During the summer the area is of substantial importance as a feeding area for many pairs of ospreys. Nationally important numbers of **common tern** (min. 625 prs 1990, 5% of British) breed within the site. Large colonies of Sandwich terns were formerly present here, but breeding has been sporadic over the last 20 years. There are several heronries within the site, and a large colony of **cormorants** at the North Sutor of Cromarty with about 200 pairs in recent years (3% of British). Notable also are breeding fulmar, shag, shelduck, arctic tern, little tern and guillemot.

During late summer/autumn up to 1000 **Canada geese** (about 2% British) gather to moult on the Beauly Firth. Large flocks of eider (up to 2000) and common scoter (up to c. 1000) use Loch Fleet and the Outer Dornoch Firth as a moulting ground.

Conservation issues

Waterfowl that winter on estuaries are vulnerable to land-claim and other developments, such as the construction of barrages that would disturb or damage the existing ecology of these sites. Other human influences such as recreational disturbance, commercial exploitation of shellfish and worms, and oil and industrial pollution, are also potentially damaging to the conservation interest of estuaries.

The area is at risk from industrial development and land-claim of intertidal areas. At present the Cromarty Firth is most affected, particularly by oil-related developments at Nigg Bay. The Morrich More in the Dornoch Firth now has an oil pipeline construction plant in operation, Whiteness Head has been severely affected by the construction of an oil rig fabrication yard. Land-claim is currently in progress at Longman Bay in the Inverness Firth where refuse is being dumped.

Small oil tankers use the Cromarty and Inverness Firths, and there are oil depots at Nigg, Invergordon and Inverness. There is a history of oil pollution incidents in the Moray Firth, and a major spill would have very serious implications for the bird populations of the Moray Firth.

Modification currently under discussion to the sewage disposal system at Inverness will have an impact on bird usage of the Ness Mouth area.

Proposals for commercial shellfisheries in the Dornoch Firth, if successful, would compete directly with common and velvet scoters. Conflict between fish-farming proposals and predatory bird species has occurred. Both salmon cages and mussel ropes are present within the Firth with more currently proposed.

Uncontrolled wildfowling in sensitive areas could adversely affect bird populations; heavy wildfowling occurs in parts of the Moray Firth, with consequent disturbance to wildfowl.

Recreational disturbance to habitats and birds includes the use of horses and trail bikes, and the recent establishment of a hovercraft club may well lead to disturbance to important bird populations.

Further reading

Campbell, L H, Barrett, J and Barrett, C F 1986 Seaducks in the Moray Firth: a review of their current status and distribution. *Proc. Roy. Soc. Edin.* 91B: 105–112.

Mudge, G P and Allen, D S 1980 Wintering seaducks in the Moray and Dornoch Firths, Scotland. *Wildfowl* 31: 123–130.

Swann, R L and Mudge, G P 1989 Moray Basin wader populations. *Scottish Birds* 15: 97–105.

Beinn Dearg

SPA/Ram Code	IBA Europe number
163A	N/A

County/Region	District(s)	OS sheet(s)	Grid Reference(s)	Maps 4, 5
Highland	Ross and Cromarty, Sutherland	20	NH 2781	

Area (ha)	NNR	SPA		Ramsar	
1000-9999	No	Designated	N	Designated	N
		Candidate	Y	Candidate	N

A montane area with an important assemblage of upland breeding birds.

Site description
This large and diverse massif has been deeply dissected by glacial action, but has more broad, rounded summits above 900 m than most west Highland mountains. Diversity of landform and rock has led to the presence of a wide range of plant communities. Native woodland, blanket mire, open water, dwarf shrub heath and grassland, summit and snowbed heath, spring and mire, scree and cliff are all represented, each with their characteristic range of plants and animals.

Of particular interest are the communities of the extensive summits. Exposed spurs have prostrate heather and other dwarf shrubs. Above 750 m this passes into moss heath which is rich in cushion herbs, lichens and mosses. There is a complete range of NW Highland snowbed communities, as well as springs, fern beds and grassland.

Botanically, this is the third most diverse mountain system in Britain and the most outstanding in the northern Highlands.

Birds
This site is important for its assemblage of specialist montane bird species. In particular it holds over 1% of the British and EC breeding population of dotterel.

Conservation issues
The birds that use this site are vulnerable to human disturbance from increased public access, particularly from hill-walkers, to the high tops, and to habitat degradation through high livestock levels.

Further reading
Nethersole-Thompson, D 1973 *The dotterel*. Collins, London.

Ben Wyvis

SPA/Ram Code	IBA Europe number
164A	N/A

County/Region	District(s)	OS sheet(s)	Grid Reference(s)	Maps 4, 5
Highland	Ross and Cromarty	20	NH 4769	

Area (ha)	NNR	SPA		Ramsar	
1000-9999	Yes	Designated	N	Designated	N
		Candidate	Y	Candidate	N

A montane area with an important assemblage of upland breeding birds.

Site description
Ben Wyvis is the only major mountain massif in the eastern Highlands north of the Great Glen. Its size, altitude and location give it a unique ecological character midway between the continental Cairngorm massif to the south-east and the oceanic mountains of the western Highlands.

The massif contains a variety of habitats including summit heath, lochans, high level springs and flushes and bryophyte-rich snowbed areas. Montane and submontane dwarf-shrub heath are also well represented. A substantial upland birchwood occurs on the south side of Loch Glass. The southern slopes of the mountain support blanket bog, which is rich in dwarf birch and alpine bearberry. This is one of the best examples of this type of peatland, which is rapidly decreasing throughout its range in Scotland.

Birds
This site is important for its assemblage of specialist montane bird species. In particular it holds over 1% of the British and EC breeding population of dotterel.

Conservation issues
The birds that use this site are vulnerable to human disturbance from increased public access, particularly from hill-walkers, to the high tops, and to habitat degradation through high livestock levels.

Further reading
Nethersole-Thompson, D 1973 *The dotterel*. Collins, London.

Glengarry Lochs

SPA/Ram Code	IBA Europe number
165A	N/A

County/Region	District(s)	OS sheet(s)	Grid Reference(s)	Maps 4, 7, 8
Highland	Inverness, Lochaber, Skye and Lochalsh	33, 34	NH 1203	

Area (ha)	NNR	SPA		SPA		Ramsar	
10,000+	No	Designated Candidate	N Y	Wider Countryside Measures Candidate		Designated Candidate	N N

A number of oligotrophic lochs, important for breeding black-throated diver, common scoter and other bird species.

Site description
Glengarry lochs comprise a number of oligotrophic lochs and lochans, with fringing aquatic vegetation. The catchment areas support a range of other habitats such as upland heath, upland mire, upland broadleaved woodland, montane, rivers and streams. Large areas of commercial forestry plantation are also present.

SSSI/SPA designation is appropriate for the key water bodies and associated wetland habitats, while 'wider countryside' conservation measures are appropriate for the remainder of the catchment area that is relevant to the bird interest.

Birds
The Glengarry lochs support a high concentration of **black-throated divers** (6-7 pairs, 4% of British and EC population) and **common scoter** (19-24 pairs, 19-24% of British and EC population).

Notable also in associated wetlands is breeding red-throated diver (8-10 pairs). The catchment areas support breeding hen harrier (3 pairs), golden eagle (4 pairs), **merlin** (c. 10 pairs, 2% of British), peregrine (2+ pairs), dotterel (5-6 pairs), golden plover, greenshank, short-eared owl and redwing.

Conservation issues
Birds that rely on freshwater lochs are vulnerable to changes in water quality and the consequent impacts on food resources. Damage can be caused by the acidic run-off from conifer plantations in the catchment area and from fish farm developments. Salmon smolt cages have been established on some lochs.

Conifer afforestation exacerbates the acidification of surface water, and causes increased run-off due to ploughing and drainage, resulting in increased fluctuation of loch water levels. Acidification can have an adverse impact on the biological productivity of water bodies, which in turn affects food supplies for nesting grebes and other species. Fluctuating water levels often result in nest failure either through flooding or drying out.

Natural water level fluctuations are exacerbated by environmental degradation and by changes in hydrology associated with commercial forestry. Large proportions of several important loch catchments in this area have already been afforested, and further afforestation is likely. There should be a presumption against new commercial forestry developments within these catchments.

The presence of hydro-electric dams on some lochs has resulted in unnaturally high fluctuations in water levels, which can result in the flooding of black-throated diver nests, and renders common scoter nest sites vulnerable to disturbance and predation.

A consultation/buffer zone in the catchment areas surrounding these lochs will be necessary to minimise the risk of unsympathetic land-use changes.

Further reading
NCC/RSPB 1990 *Red Data Birds in Britain*. T and A D Poyser, London.
Nethersole-Thompson, D and M 1979 *Greenshanks*. T and A D Poyser, Berkhamsted.
Sharrock, J T R 1976 *The Atlas of Breeding Birds in Britain and Ireland*. BTO, Tring.

Loch Tarff and Nearby Lochs

SPA/Ram Code 166A	IBA Europe number N/A

County/Region	District(s)	OS sheet(s)	Grid Reference(s)	Maps 4, 5, 8
Highland	Inverness	34	NH 4209	

Area (ha)	NNR	SPA		SPA	Ramsar	
1000-9999	No	Designated	N	Wider	Designated	N
		Candidate	Y	Countryside	Candidate	N
				Measures		
				Candidate		

A number of mesotrophic lochs and lochans and surrounding catchments, important for breeding Slavonian grebes and other bird species.

Site description

Loch Tarff and nearby lochs comprise a number of mesotrophic lochs and lochans, with wooded islands and locally extensive sedge beds. The catchment areas support a range of other habitats such as upland heath and grassland, upland mire, upland broadleaved woodland, swamp/fen/carr and streams.

SSSI/SPA designation is appropriate for the key water bodies and associated wetland habitats, while 'wider countryside' conservation measures are appropriate for the remainder of the catchment area that is relevant to the bird interest.

Birds

These lochs support a high concentration of breeding **Slavonian grebes** with over 5 summering pairs (c. 7% of the UK and EC population).

Notable also in associated wetlands are breeding **black–throated diver** (2 pairs, 1% of British and EC population) and goldeneye (regularly summering birds).

Conservation issues

Birds that rely on freshwater lochs are vulnerable to changes in water quality and the consequent impacts on food resources. Damage can be caused by the acidic run-off from conifer plantations in the catchment area and by fish farm developments.

A large proportion of the catchment area within this site has been afforested. Conifer afforestation exacerbates the acidification of surface water, causes increased run-off due to ploughing and drainage and destroys breeding habitat for moorland bird species. Acidification can have an adverse impact on the biological productivity of water bodies, which in turn affects food supplies for nesting grebes and other species. Further afforestation is likely. There should be a presumption against new commercial forestry developments within these catchments.

A consultation/buffer zone in the catchment areas surrounding these lochs will be necessary to minimise the risk of unsympathetic land-use changes.

Slavonian grebes and black-throated divers are vulnerable to inadvertent disturbance by tourists, anglers and birdwatchers and to the illegal attentions of egg collectors and nest photographers. The presence of mink and other predators, and the stocking of the lochs with rainbow trout are also considered likely to affect breeding success.

Breeding success of black-throated divers and Slavonian grebes is closely linked with water levels. Fluctuating water levels often result in nest failure through flooding or drying out. Natural water level fluctuations are exacerbated by environmental degradation and by the hydrological changes caused by commercial forestry. Because Loch Tarff is the reservoir for Fort Augustus, man-made changes in water level are a frequent occurrence and are considered to be a serious factor in reducing breeding success at this site.

Further reading
Crooke C H, Harvey M I, Dennis R H and Summers, R W (in prep). Population size and breeding success of Slavonian grebes (*Podiceps auritus*) in Scotland.

Slavonian grebe

North Inverness Lochs

SPA/Ram Code	IBA Europe number
167A	N/A

County/Region	District(s)	OS sheet(s)	Grid Reference(s)	Maps 4, 5
Highland	Inverness	26	NH460350	

Area (ha)	NNR	SPA		SPA		Ramsar	
10,000+	No	Designated	N	Wider		Designated	N
		Candidate	Y	Countryside		Candidate	N
				Measures			
				Candidate			

A group of mesotrophic, freshwater lochs, lochans and surrounding catchments, important for breeding Slavonian grebes and other bird species.

Site description

North of the Great Glen are a number of mesotrophic lochs and lochans, with locally extensive sedgebeds. The catchment areas support a range of other habitats such as upland heath and grassland, upland mire, upland broadleaved woodland, swamp/fen/ carr, wet lowland grassland, rivers and streams.

SSSI/SPA designation is appropriate for the key water bodies and associated wetland habitats, while 'wider countryside' conservation measures are appropriate for the remainder of the catchment area that is relevant to the bird interest.

Birds

These lochs comprise a very important area for breeding **Slavonian grebes**, supporting a total of 20-21 pairs (30% of the British and EC population).

Notable also in associated wetlands are breeding red-throated diver (4-6 pairs), black–throated diver (1 pair) and **goldeneye** (1-2 pairs, 1% of British). The catchment areas surrounding these lochs support **hen harrier** (c. 8 pairs, 1% of British), golden eagle (1+ pair), **merlin** (7+ pairs, 1% of British), peregrine (4 pairs), golden plover (good numbers breeding in suitable habitat), greenshank (6+ pairs), short-eared owl, fieldfare (one pair has bred successfully) and **redwing** (at least 6 pairs present most years, 17% of British). There is a high diversity of other breeding species.

Conservation issues

Birds that rely on freshwater lochs are vulnerable to changes in water quality and the consequent impacts on food resources. Damage can be caused by the acidic run-off from conifer plantations in the catchment area and by fish farm developments.

Conifer afforestation exacerbates the acidification of surface water, causes increased run-off due to ploughing and drainage and destroys breeding habitat for moorland bird species. Acidification can have an adverse impact on the biological productivity of water bodies, which in turn affects food supplies for nesting grebes and other species. Large proportions of one important loch catchment in this area have already been afforested, and further afforestation is likely. There should be a presumption against new commercial forestry developments within these catchments.

A consultation/buffer zone in the catchment areas surrounding these lochs will be necessary to minimise the risk of unsympathetic land-use changes.

Breeding success of Slavonian grebes is closely linked with water levels. Fluctuating water levels often result in nest failure through flooding or drying out. Natural water level fluctuations are exacerbated by environmental degradation and by changes in hydrology associated with commercial forestry.

Slavonian grebes are vulnerable to inadvertent and deliberate disturbance by tourists, anglers and birdwatchers and to the illegal attentions of egg collectors. The presence of mammalian predators, including mink, and the stocking of the lochs with rainbow trout are also considered likely to affect the breeding species.

Further reading
Crooke C H, Harvey M I, Dennis R H and Summers, R W (in prep). Population size and breeding success of Slavonian grebes (*Podiceps auritus*) in Scotland.
RSPB/NCC 1990 *Red Data Birds in Britain*. T and A D Poyser, London.

Hermaness and Saxa Vord, Unst

SPA/Ram Code	IBA Europe number
201A	035

County/Region	District(s)	OS sheet(s)	Grid Reference(s)	Map 1
Shetland	N/A	1	HP 6016 (Hermaness)	

Area (ha)	NNR	SPA		Ramsar	
1000-9999	Part	Designated	N	Designated	N
		Candidate	Y	Candidate	Y

Sea cliffs and moorland with large colonies of breeding seabirds.

Site description
Located at the northernmost tip of Britain, the vegetation of Hermaness is mainly *Calluna/Eriophorum* blanket bog, with acidic grassland dominated by mat-grass; there are also small oligotrophic lochans and burns. More species-rich, closely grazed, maritime grasslands line the cliff top. The cliffs of Hermaness, Saxa Vord, and the off-lying stacks (including Muckle Flugga) are mostly 100–200 m high. Entomologically, Hermaness is noted for the presence of dark forms of certain widespread moths.

Birds
The area supports internationally important numbers of breeding gannet, shag and great skua and nationally important numbers of breeding fulmar, guillemot and puffin.

Counts from the Seabird Colony Register in the late 1980s include 25,200 pairs of **fulmars** (5% of British), 9900 pairs of **gannets** (4.5% of Western European, 6% of British population), 1245 pairs of **shags** (1% of Western European, 3% of British), 900 pairs of **great skuas** (7% of Western European, 11% of British), 21,000 individual **guillemots** (2% of British) and c. 28,000 pairs of **puffins** (4% of British).

Notable also are breeding red-throated diver, golden plover, arctic skua, kittiwake, razorbill, black guillemot and twite.

Conservation issues
Seabirds are sensitive to changes in the quality of the marine environment, especially to changes in fish stocks and to oil pollution. Kittiwakes and puffins in particular have suffered from the crash in sandeel stocks in the 1980s. Birds that use the moorland areas are also vulnerable to reseeding and changes in grazing pressure.

Ramna Stacks and Gruney

SPA/Ram Code	IBA Europe number
202A	039

County/Region	District(s)	OS sheet(s)	Grid Reference(s)	Map 1
Shetland	N/A	1	HU 380970	

Area (ha)	NNR	SPA		Ramsar	
11	No	Designated	N	Designated	N
		Candidate	Y	Candidate	N

A group of small rocky islands with breeding seabirds.

Site description

Ramna Stacks have little or no vegetation. The vegetation on Gruney consists of seabird enriched maritime grassland.

Grey seals pup on Gruney.

Birds

Ramna Stacks is one of only seven known breeding stations of **Leach's petrel** in Britain and the EC. The stacks support up to 25 pairs.

Notable also are breeding fulmar, great black-backed gull, kittiwake, guillemot, razorbill and puffin.

Conservation issues

Seabirds are sensitive to changes in the quality of the marine environment, especially to changes in fish stocks and to oil pollution. Ground-nesting seabirds on offshore islands are vulnerable to the introduction of predatory mammals. The close proximity of this site to the Sullom Voe oil terminal makes the risk of oil pollution very strong.

Fetlar

SPA/Ram Code	IBA Europe number
203A	037

County/Region	District(s)	OS sheet(s)	Grid Reference(s)	Map 1
Shetland	N/A	1, 2	HU 6293	

Area (ha)	NNR	SPA		Ramsar	
1000-9999	No	Designated	N	Designated	N
		Candidate	Y	Candidate	N

Heathlands, marshes, cliffs and rocky shores occupy much of the island of Fetlar and are important for breeding seabirds and waders.

Site description

Fetlar's bird interest centres on the northern part of the island and the south-western peninsula of Lamb Hoga. Fetlar is fairly low-lying, reaching only 160 m. Most of the north of the island is vegetated by heathland and grasslands which are relatively species-rich due to the influence of underlying serpentine base-rich rocks. A variety of both acid and base tolerant plant species are present. In wetter areas, small lochs and sedge rich mires are found. In general, these are dominated by bottle sedge, but are floristically diverse with species such as bogbean, marsh cinquefoil and ragged-robin, and locally scarce species including greater tussock-sedge.

Further variety exists on serpentine rocky outcrops at Stakkaberg, where plants include stone bramble and dwarf willow. Around the coasts, there are floristically rich maritime grasslands and heathlands.

Lamb Hoga has heather moorland with areas of blanket mire dominated by cottongrass. Even here, however, more diverse grassland and heathland communities are present along the cliff tops.

Beaches in the north of Fetlar form one of the largest grey seal pupping colonies in Shetland, and offshore skerries are important breeding and haul out areas for common seals.

Birds

The area supports internationally important numbers of breeding great skua, and nationally important numbers of breeding red-throated diver, fulmar, Manx shearwater, dunlin, whimbrel, red-necked phalarope, arctic skua and black guillemot.

Seabirds breeding on the cliffs and the broken rocky screes include **fulmar** (13,100 pairs 2.5% of British), the largest Manx shearwater colony in Shetland (a minimum of 30-40 pairs), storm petrel and **black guillemot** (1190 individuals, 3% of British) The breeding moorland and upland mire communities include **red-throated diver** (16 pairs, 1% of British and EC), **dunlin** (90 pairs, 1% of British), **whimbrel** (70 pairs, 15% of British and EC), **red-necked phalarope** (12-13 pairs, 70% of British), **arctic skua** (143 pairs, 4% of British) and **great skua** (220 pairs, 2% of Western European, 3% of British). Snowy owls, which bred during 1967-75, are resident.

Notable also are breeding shag, kittiwake, puffin, ringed plover, golden plover and arctic tern.

Conservation issues

Seabirds are sensitive to changes in the quality of the marine environment, especially to changes in fish stocks and to oil pollution. Ground-nesting seabirds on offshore islands are vulnerable to the introduction of predatory mammals.

Birds that use the site are vulnerable to agricultural changes, especially reseeding and changes in grazing pressure. Kittiwakes, arctic terns and puffins have proved extremely vulnerable to the crash in sandeel stocks of the 1980s. Active management of some of the mires has been and will continue to be necessary for the continued survival of red–necked phalarope at this, its British stronghold. The creation of open water areas surrounded by suitable fen communities is also crucial for this species.

Further reading

Berry, R J and Johnson, J L 1980 *The natural history of Shetland*. Collins, New Naturalist, London.

Grant, M 1989 *The breeding ecology of Whimbrel* (Numenius phaeopus) *in Shetland; with particular reference to the effects of agricultural improvement of heathland nesting habitats*. Phd thesis. University of Durham.

North Roe and Tingon, Mainland Shetland

SPA/Ram Code	IBA Europe number
204A	040

County/Region	District(s)	OS sheet(s)	Grid Reference(s)	Map 1
Shetland	N/A	1, 3	HU 3285	

Area (ha)	NNR	SPA		Ramsar	
1000-9999	No	Designated	N	Designated	N
		Candidate	Y	Candidate	Y

Areas of blanket bog supporting an important assemblage of breeding birds.

Site description

The flatter parts of Tingon and North Roe have many pools and acidic lochans set within an open landscape of blanket bog and maritime heath. The invertebrate fauna, like the flora, includes numerous arctic-alpine species.

The area is of particular note as holding some of the highest quality blanket bog in Shetland, which is floristically rich and uneroded. Small islands in the lochs and inaccessible crags hold some tree and shrub cover, of importance in a Shetland context. Species present include downy birch, rowan, sallow and prostrate juniper.

Birds

The area supports nationally important numbers of breeding red-throated diver, merlin, whimbrel, arctic skua and great skua.

A comprehensive breeding season survey in 1986 recorded 67 pairs of **red-throated divers** (5% of British and EC population), 7 pairs of **merlins** (1% of British), 23 pairs of **whimbrels** (5% of British and EC), 107 pairs of **arctic skuas** (3% of British) and 125 pairs of **great skuas** (2% of British). Notable also are breeding golden plover and dunlin.

Conservation issues

Birds that use the site are vulnerable to agricultural changes, especially reseeding and changes in grazing pressure.

Papa Stour

SPA/Ram Code	IBA Europe number
205A	041

County/Region	District(s)	OS sheet(s)	Grid Reference(s)	Map 1
Shetland	N/A	3	HU 165610	

Area (ha)	NNR	SPA		Ramsar	
593	No	Designated	N	Designated	N
		Candidate	Y	Candidate	N

An island with heathland and cliffs supporting an important assemblage of breeding birds, including large seabird colonies.

Site description
The site occupies the northern and western parts of Papa Stour, which consists of rocky hillsides, rising to about 90 m, and a number of lochs. There are also a few offshore skerries. The principal vegetation is a lichen rich heath, which has developed on substrates scalped of peat and turf in the past. Exposure and the maritime influence is evident throughout the area. Heather is dominant, and other frequent species are the moss *Racomitrium lanuginosum*, sea plantain, mountain everlasting and spring squill.

Birds
The breeding moorland community includes nationally important numbers of **ringed plover** (100 pairs, 1% of British) and **arctic skua** (90 pairs, 3% of British).

Notable also is the large assemblage of breeding seabirds, including large numbers of fulmar, shag, great skua, kittiwake, arctic tern, guillemot, razorbill and black guillemot.

Conservation issues
Birds that use the site are vulnerable to agricultural changes, especially reseeding and changes in grazing pressure. Seabirds are sensitive to changes in the quality of the marine environment, especially to changes in fish stocks and to oil pollution.

Foula

SPA/Ram Code	IBA Europe number
206A	042

County/Region	District(s)	OS sheet(s)	Grid Reference(s)	Map 1
Shetland	N/A	4	HT 960390	

Area (ha)	NNR	SPA		Ramsar	
1327	No	Designated	N	Designated	N
		Candidate	Y	Candidate	Y

A large island, with very large populations of cliff and moorland nesting seabirds.

Site description

Foula is an island of steep slopes, reaching about 420 m, and with western cliffs of up to 370 m. It is partly composed of old red sandstone, and the vegetation predominantly reflects its acidic nature. The cool oceanic climate has enabled extensive peat formation, and much of the island is covered by mires, largely dominated by hare's-tail cottongrass and crowberry. On higher ground, there is a submaritime community dominated by great wood-rush. The presence of stiff sedge, bog bilberry and dwarf willow in these areas indicates the montane conditions. Spray influenced vegetation on the cliff tops is composed largely of sea and buck's-horn plantains and thrift. The area of bird interest also includes inbye and crofting land.

Birds

The area supports internationally important numbers of breeding great skua, guillemot and puffin, and nationally important numbers of breeding fulmar, shag, arctic skua and razorbill.

Eighteen breeding species of seabird occur on Foula. Counts carried out between 1987 and 1990 have recorded 46,800 pairs of **fulmars** (9% of British), small colonies of Manx shearwaters, storm petrels, and Leach's petrels (the largest colony in Shetland), 2400 pairs of **shags** (7% of British), 120 pairs of **arctic skuas** (3% of British), 2340 pairs of **great skuas** (17% of Western European, 30% of British; the largest colony in the world), 37,500 individual **guillemots** (1% of Western European, 4% of British), 6200 individual **razorbills** (4% of British) and 48,000 pairs of **puffins** (6% of the world population of the *grabae* race, 14% of British).

Notable also are breeding red-throated diver, gannet, kittiwake, arctic tern and black guillemot.

Conservation issues

Birds that use the site are vulnerable to agricultural changes, especially reseeding and changes in grazing pressure. Seabirds are sensitive to changes in the quality of the marine environment, especially to changes in fish stocks and to oil pollution. Ground-nesting seabirds on offshore islands are vulnerable to the introduction of predatory mammals. The presence of cats and hedgehogs on Foula poses a threat to the breeding seabird populations. Kittiwakes, arctic terns and puffins have proved extremely vulnerable to the crash in sandeel stocks of the 1980s.

Further reading

Ewins, P J, Ellis, P M, Bird, D B and Prior, A 1988 The distribution and status of Arctic and Great Skuas in Shetland 1985-86. *Scottish Birds* 15: 9-20.

Furness, R W 1983 Foula, Shetland. Vol.4. *The Birds of Foula*. Brathay Hall Trust, Ambleside.

Furness, R W 1981 Seabird populations on Foula. *Scottish Birds* 11: 237-253.

Noss

SPA/Ram Code	IBA Europe number
208A	043

County/Region	District(s)	OS sheet(s)	Grid Reference(s)	Map 1
Shetland	N/A	4	HU 545444	

Area (ha)	NNR	SPA		Ramsar	
313	Yes	Designated	N	Designated	N
		Candidate	Y	Candidate	N

High cliffs supporting one of the largest seabird colonies in Britain.

Site description

Noss is an island located off the east coast of Bressay, which in turn lies off the east coast of mainland Shetland. It slopes up from the west, reaching 180 m in the spectacular old red sandstone cliffs in the east. The variable erosion of horizontal beds of red, yellow and grey sandstone have created ideal conditions for many seabirds.

The steeper eastern part of the island is maritime and *Calluna/Eriophorum* heath, whilst the lower land to the west is semi-improved grassland.

Birds

The area supports internationally important numbers of breeding gannet, guillemot and great skua, and nationally important numbers of breeding fulmar and kittiwake.

Counts carried out in the late 1980s as part of the Seabird Colony Register include 6350 pairs of **fulmars** (1% of British), 7200 pairs of **gannets** (3% of Western European, 5% of British), 400 pairs of **great skuas** (3% of Western European, 5% of British), 9400 pairs of **kittiwakes** (2% of British) and 37,700 individual **guillemots** (1% of Western European, 4% of British).

Notable also are breeding shag, arctic skua, arctic tern, razorbill, black guillemot and puffin.

Conservation issues

Seabirds are sensitive to changes in the quality of the marine environment, especially to changes in fish stocks and to oil pollution. Ground-nesting seabirds on offshore islands are vulnerable to the introduction of predatory mammals. Kittiwakes, arctic terns and puffins have proved extremely vulnerable to the crash in sandeel stocks of the 1980s. Small numbers of great skuas have been culled under licence. Introduced rabbits and cats are subject to control measures.

Further reading

Tulloch, R and Scott, W 1973 *Noss Nature Reserve*. Shetland Times, Lerwick.
Willcox, N A, Richardson, M G and Dore, C P 1986 Breeding seabirds of Noss, Shetland. *Scottish Birds*, 14, 25–32.

Fair Isle

SPA/Ram Code	IBA Europe number
209A	046

County/Region	District(s)	OS sheet(s)	Grid Reference(s)	Map 1
Shetland	N/A	4	HY 213720	

Area (ha)	NNR	SPA		Ramsar	
592	No	Designated	N	Designates	N
		Candidate	Y	Candidate	N

An island with large colonies of breeding seabirds, also famous as a migration study point.

Site description
Fair Isle is an old red sandstone island, situated half way between the Shetland mainland and Orkney. The vegetation of the northern parts of the island consists mainly of heather moorland, with spray-influenced maritime grassland around the coasts. The moorland is notable for the abundance of prostrate juniper, which is now rare elsewhere in Shetland.

Birds
Counts of the breeding colonies in the late 1980s and 1990 have recorded 27,000 pairs of **fulmars** (5% of British), 1100 pairs of **shags** (3% of British), 105 pairs of **arctic skuas** (3% of British), 19,340 pairs of **kittiwakes** (4% of British), 32,300 individual **guillemots** (3% of British), 5100 individual **razorbills** (3.5% of British), 380 individual **black guillemots** (1% of British) and 20,200 individual **puffins** (3% of British).

Notable also are breeding gannet, storm petrel, great skua, herring gull, great black-backed gull, common tern and arctic tern.

There is an endemic race of wren *Troglodytes troglodytes fridariensis*. Between 1950 and the present the population has varied between a minimum of 10 and a maximum of 50 territory-holding males. Numbers were largest during the late 1950s and mid 1960s. In a full survey in 1987 a maximum of 33 males was recorded.

Fair Isle has for many years been internationally famous as a bird migration landfall and study site, and a bird observatory has operated here since 1947.

Conservation issues
Seabirds are sensitive to changes in the quality of the marine environment, especially to changes in fish stocks and to oil pollution. Arctic terns and puffins have proved extremely vulnerable to the crash in sandeel stocks of the 1980s.

Birds that use the site are vulnerable to agricultural changes, especially reseeding and changes in grazing pressure. There is occasional persecution of the arctic skua population.

Further reading
Aspinall, S J 1988 Fluctuating fortunes of the Fair Isle wren. *Fair Isle Bird Observatory Report for 1987*, 46–47.

Fair Isle Bird Observatory reports.
Williamson, K 1965 *Fair Isle and its birds*. Oliver and Boyd, Edinburgh and London.

West Westray

SPA/Ram Code	IBA Europe number
210A	052

County/Region	District(s)	OS sheet(s)	Grid Reference(s)	Map 2
Orkney	N/A	5	HY 4246	

Area (ha)	NNR	SPA		Ramsar	
1-999	No	Designated	N	Designated	N
		Candidate	Y	Candidate	N

Cliffs and maritime sedge heath with large colonies of breeding seabirds, especially kittiwakes and guillemots.

Site description
This site comprises 8 km of old red sandstone cliffs along the western coast of Westray, together with adjoining areas of grassland and heath. The latter habitats show a marked maritime influence and are species-rich, including plants such as the nationally scarce Scottish primrose. The exposed nature of the site is illustrated by the presence of typical montane plant species such as moss campion, alpine meadow-rue and alpine bistort.

Birds
The area supports internationally important numbers of breeding kittiwake and guillemot, and nationally important numbers of breeding arctic skua, arctic tern and razorbill.

A survey of the breeding seabirds on the cliffs in 1987 found 30,980 pairs of **kittiwakes** (1% of Western European, 6% of British), 60,670 individual **guillemots** (2% of Western European, 6% of British) and 1770 individual **razorbills** (1% of British). On the moors, there are colonies of 45 pairs of **arctic skuas** (1% of British) and 1600 individual **arctic terns** (1% of British). Notable also are breeding fulmar, shag, and black guillemot.

Conservation issues
Seabirds are sensitive to changes in the quality of the marine environment, especially to changes in fish stocks and to oil pollution. There may be a potential threat to this site through changes in the grazing regime.

Further reading
Meek, E R, Booth, C J, Reynolds, P and Ribbands, B 1985 Breeding skuas in Orkney. *Seabird* 8: 21-33.

Papa Westray
(North Hill and Holm)

SPA/Ram Code	IBA Europe number
211A	051

County/Region	District(s)	OS sheet(s)	Grid Reference(s)	Map 2
Orkney	N/A	5	HY 500550 (North Hill)	
			HY 508520 (Holm)	

Area (ha)	NNR	SPA		Ramsar	
254	No	Designated	N	Designated	N
		Candidate	Y	Candidate	N

Low-lying rocky coast and maritime sedge heath, important for breeding seabirds.

Site description
Rising to 48 m North Hill is the northern part of Papa Westray, and consists of a rocky coastline, backing on to maritime sedge heath. It is a large area of maritime heath, with a few small pools, and is botanically very rich, including the nationally scarce Scottish primrose. The Holm, an island of 48 ha off the east coast of Papa Westray, is dominated by maritime grassland.

Birds
The area supports nationally important numbers of breeding arctic skua, arctic tern, and black guillemot.

Recent counts of breeding seabirds include 145 pairs of **arctic skuas** (4% of British), 7200 individual **arctic terns** (2% of West and Central European, c. 6% of British) and 650 individual **black guillemots** (2% of British). Notable also are breeding storm petrel, eider, great black-backed gull, kittiwake, guillemot and razorbill, and wintering purple sandpiper.

Conservation issues
Seabirds are sensitive to changes in the quality of the marine environment, especially to changes in fish stocks and to oil pollution.

There may be a potential threat to this site from changes in the grazing regime.

Marwick Head

SPA/Ram Code	IBA Europe number
212A	057

County/Region	District(s)	OS sheet(s)	Grid Reference(s)	Map 2
Orkney	N/A	6	HY 226257	

Area (ha)	NNR	SPA		Ramsar	
9	No	Designated	N	Designated	N
		Candidate	Y	Candidate	N

A short section of sea cliffs, supporting large numbers of breeding seabirds.

Site description
On the west coast of Orkney Mainland, the eroded sandstone cliffs of Marwick Head rise to 85 m and provide suitable conditions for nesting seabirds. The cliff-top vegetation consists of maritime grassland, which includes species such as thrift, spring squill and kidney vetch.

Birds
The area supports nationally important numbers of breeding kittiwake and guillemot.

A complete survey of breeding seabirds in 1986 found 4750 pairs of **kittiwakes** (1% of British) and 25,200 individual **guillemots** (2% of British). Notable also are breeding fulmar, razorbill and raven.

Conservation issues
Seabirds are sensitive to changes in the quality of the marine environment, especially to changes in fish stocks and to oil pollution.

Further reading
Thomas, C J 1988 *Surveillance of cliff nesting seabirds in Orkney 1988*. NCC, CSD Report No. 872.

Lochs of Harray and Stenness

SPA/Ram Code	IBA Europe number
213A	060

County/Region	District(s)	OS sheet(s)	Grid Reference(s)	Map 2
Orkney	N/A	6	HY 2916	

Area (ha)	NNR	SPA		Ramsar	
1000-9999	No	Designated	N	Designated	N
		Candidate	Y	Candidate	Y

Two lochs, which attract large numbers of wintering wildfowl.

Site description

The drainage from a large part of Orkney's West Mainland enters the sea via these two lochs. The Loch of Harray (mean depth only 3 m) is a eutrophic freshwater loch, but conditions change around the Bridge of Brodgar which forms the junction with the Loch of Stenness. The latter has brackish conditions, with salinities close to sea water where it enters the sea via a tidal channel a few kilometres east of Stromness. This exceptional range of conditions is reflected in the flora and fauna, which include marine, brackish and freshwater species. The Loch of Harray is particularly notable for the occurrence of nine pondweed species, three of which, slender-leaved, flat-stalked, and long-stalked pondweeds are nationally scarce. The invertebrate community is similarly diverse.

The two lochs with their exceptional ranges of salt, brackish and eutrophic habitats attract a diverse population of wildfowl.

Birds

These lochs support internationally important numbers of wintering whooper swan and nationally important numbers of wintering mute swan, wigeon, pochard, tufted duck, scaup and goldeneye.

In the five-winter period 1985/86 to 1989/90 the average peak counts were 520 **mute swans** (3% of British), 490 **whooper swans** (3% of the world total, 8% of the number wintering in Britain, maximum 1010), 4370 **wigeon** (2% of British), 1310 **pochard** (3% of British), 1610 **tufted duck** (3% of British), 190 **scaup** (5% of British) and 290 **goldeneye** (2% of British). Notable also are wintering greylag goose, long-tailed duck and red-breasted merganser.

Conservation issues

The spread of Canadian waterweed within the Loch of Harray in recent years has led to an increase in the numbers of grazing wintering wildfowl. This spread does, however, threaten the long-term ecological balance of the loch.

Hoy

SPA/Ram Code	IBA Europe number
214A	062

County/Region	District(s)	OS sheet(s)	Grid Reference(s)	Maps 2, 5
Orkney	N/A	6, 7	HY 225010	

Area (ha)	NNR	SPA		Ramsar	
8186	No	Designated	N	Designated	N
		Candidate	Y	Candidate	N

islandmeansthatthevegetationatthesummitofWardHill(479m)iscomparabletothat onCairngormat1000m.Thearctic-alpineplantspresentincludebearberry,alpine bearberry,trailingazaleaanddwarfwillow.Someareashaverelativelyhighlevelsof calciuminthesoil,andheremorespecies-richcommunitiesarefound,withplantssuch asmountainavens,alpinemeadow-grass,alpinesaw-wort,hollyfern,starry,purpleand yellowmountainsaxifrages.Manyoftheseplantspecies,alongwithmountainhare,are confined in Orkney to Hoy.

The low intensity of burning and grazing on Hoy has allowed scrub regeneration to a much greater extent than on most British moors. At Berriedale is Orkney's one indigenous woodland; it consists of rowan, downy birch, aspen and hazel. The invertebrate interest of Hoy, which includes a number of species not found elsewhere on Orkney, is centred on this woodland.

On the west coast, old red sandstone cliffs reach 338 m in height, and include the famous 137 m rock stack, the Old Man of Hoy.

Birds
The area supports internationally important numbers of breeding arctic skua, great skua and great black-backed gull and nationally important numbers of breeding red-throated diver and fulmar.

Recent counts of breeding seabirds of the cliffs and rocky shores include **fulmar** (35,000 pairs in 1986, 6% of British) and **great black-backed gull** (1200 pairs 1% of Western European, 7% of British). On the moors are **red-throated diver** (c. 50 pairs in 1990, 4% British and EC population), **arctic skua** (220 pairs in 1982, 1% of Western European, 6.5% of British) and **great skua** (1230 pairs in 1982, 9% of Western European, 16% of British).

Notable also are breeding Manx shearwater, shag, golden plover, dunlin, common gull, kittiwake, common tern, guillemot, razorbill, black guillemot, puffin, stonechat and various raptors.

Conservation issues

Seabirds are sensitive to changes in the quality of the marine environment, especially to changes in fish stocks and to oil pollution.

Birds that use this site are vulnerable to agricultural improvement, overgrazing and the risk of moorland fires. A Forestry Grant Application has recently been approved to the south of the site.

Further reading

Meek, E R, Booth, C J, Reynolds, P and Ribbands, B 1985 Breeding skuas in Orkney. *Seabird* 8: 21–33.

Great skua

Copinsay

SPA/Ram Code	IBA Europe number
215A	065

County/Region	District(s)	OS sheet(s)	Grid Reference(s)	Map 2
Orkney	N/A	6	HY 605015	

Area (ha)	NNR	SPA		Ramsar	
152	No	Designated	N	Designated	N
		Candidate	Y	Candidate	N

A group of islands with important breeding seabird populations.

Site description
A main island with three islets and a rock stack. Copinsay, the main island, rises from a low rocky shore to sheer cliffs up to 70 m high on the south-east face. The rocky north shore has many plants of the splash zone, including much sea aster, and also sea spleenwort, common saltmarsh-grass, sea pearlwort and lesser sea-spurrey. The remainder of the island is grassland.

Corn Holm, an islet to the west of Copinsay, and linked by a storm beach at low water, is notable for its large colony of the nationally scarce oysterplant.

Birds
The area supports nationally important numbers of breeding great black-backed gull, kittiwake and guillemot.

Recent counts from the Seabird Colony Register include 520 pairs of **great black-backed gulls** (3% of British), 9550 pairs of **kittiwakes** (2% of British) and 31,000 individual **guillemots** (3% of British). Notable also are breeding fulmar, shag, arctic tern, razorbill, black guillemot and puffin.

Conservation issues
Seabirds are sensitive to changes in the quality of the marine environment, especially to changes in fish stocks and to oil pollution.

Sule Skerry and Sule Stack

SPA/Ram Code	IBA Europe number
218A	063

County/Region	District(s)	OS sheet(s)	Grid References(s)	Map 2
Orkney	N/A	6	HX 623241 (Sule Skerry)	
			HX 565177 (Sule Stack)	

Area (ha)	NNR	SPA		Ramsar	
19	No	Designated	N	Designated	N
		Candidate	Y	Candidate	N

Two remote islets, with large seabird colonies.

Site description
Sule Skerry lies about 60 km west of Orkney Mainland, while Sule Stack is another 8 km to the south-west. Sule Skerry is the larger of the two islands, covering an area of about 16 ha. It is low lying and covered by peaty soil with rocky outcrops. Vegetation is limited by the combination of salt spray and birds' activity, for example trampling, burrowing and guano deposition, but in summer, the central area is dominated by waist high scentless mayweed. Sule Stack is a higher, bare rock stack with no vascular plants.

Birds
The area supports internationally important numbers of breeding **gannet** and puffin, and nationally important numbers of breeding storm petrel and shag.

Sule Stack is Orkney's only gannetry, which at 5900 occupied sites in 1985 comprises 2% of the world population and 4% of British. Sule Skerry has a huge **puffin** colony, in burrows in the peaty soil; about 45,000 pairs are estimated (6% of the world population of the *grabae* race, 13% of British). There are also important colonies of **storm petrels** (at least 1000 pairs) and **shags** (870 pairs, 2% of British). Notable also are breeding kittiwake, arctic tern, guillemot and razorbill.

Conservation issues
Seabirds are sensitive to changes in the quality of the marine environment, especially to changes in fish stocks and to oil pollution. Ground-nesting seabirds on offshore islands are vulnerable to the introduction of predatory mammals.

Further reading
Murray, S and Wanless, S 1986 The status of the Gannet in Scotland 1984-85. *Scottish Birds* 14: 74-85.

Loch Spynie

SPA/Ram Code	IBA Europe number
220A	067

County/Region	District(s)	OS sheet(s)	Grid Reference(s)	Maps 5, 6
Grampian	Moray	28	NJ 234661	

Area (ha)	NNR	SPA		Ramsar	
1-999	No	Designated	N	Designated	N
		Candidate	Y	Candidate	Y

A shallow eutrophic loch with surrounding marshes which holds important numbers of wintering greylag geese.

Site description

The Loch of Spynie developed in the 16th century from the closure of a tidal inlet by a shingle spit, giving rise to a shallow, fertile lagoon. Since that time, the cutting of the Spynie canal and encroachment by reedbeds have reduced the loch area from 650 ha to its present 30 ha. The loch and its margins demonstrate classic features of succession of wetland plant communities, with open water grading into reed beds, fens, and alder and willow carr. The diversity of vegetation types supports a correspondingly wide range of plant and animal species. There are many plants which are typical of northern Scotland, but also some which have more southern distributions, for example water-violet, greater spearwort, hemlock water-dropwort, lesser water-parsnip, bulrush and slender spike-rush.

Birds

Loch Spynie supports internationally important numbers of wintering **greylag geese**. In the five-winter period 1985/86 to 1989/90 the average peak count was 7600 birds (8% of the world population of Icelandic greylags) and the maximum was 12,000 birds. Notable also are spring passage **pink-footed geese**, which reach levels of international importance, and wintering wigeon and goosander.

The loch holds an exceptional diversity of breeding wildfowl and other wetland birds. It is an important starling roost (up to 10,000 birds), and up to 2000 swallows roost in the reedbeds in autumn.

Conservation issues

The site is vulnerable to drainage, nutrient enrichment due to nitrate and phosphate run-off from surrounding agricultural areas, and increased wildfowling pressures. The management of reed and scrub succession and the control of visitors are important to safeguard the site. Wildfowl that use this site are vulnerable to lead poisoning resulting from ingestion of spent shotgun pellets.

Loch of Strathbeg

SPA/Ram Code	IBA Europe number
221A	071

County/Region	District(s)	OS sheet(s)	Grid Reference(s)	Map 6
Grampian	Banff and Buchan	30	NK 075590	

Area (ha)	NNR	SPA		Ramsar	
913	No	Designated	N	Designated	N
		Candidate	Y	Candidate	Y

A large eutrophic loch important for wintering wildfowl and breeding terns.

Site description

Situated inland from Rattray Head, the north-eastern point of the Buchan coast, the Loch of Strathbeg is the largest dune lake (200 ha) in Britain. It is a shallow eutrophic loch (mean depth only 1-1.5 m), with adjoining reedbeds, freshwater marshes, and alder and willow carr. In a district in which wetlands are scarce, it is of considerable interest. The calcareous dunes and dune slacks are relatively undisturbed and contain a rich flora. The diversity of plant communities supports a correspondingly diverse invertebrate fauna.

Birds

Loch of Strathbeg is a wetland of international importance by virtue of regularly supporting over 20,000 waterfowl. In the five-winter period 1985/86 to 1989/90 the average peak count was 40,900 wildfowl. The site is of international importance for wintering whooper swan, pink-footed goose and greylag goose and of national importance for wintering teal and breeding Sandwich tern.

Average peak counts for individual species were 300 **whooper swans** (2% of the world total and 5% of the number wintering in Britain), 27,500 **pink-footed geese** (25% of world), 6300 Icelandic **greylag geese** (6% of world) and 1200 **teal** (1% of British). Notable also are wintering mute swan, mallard, goldeneye and smew.

Breeding species include shoveler (5 pairs 1990), **Sandwich tern** (150 pairs, 1% of British) and common tern (78 pairs in 1990). Garganey breed and marsh harriers summer.

Conservation issues

This site is vulnerable to shooting pressure but the threat is declining due to RSPB reserve acquisitions. There has been a decrease in the number of diving ducks in recent years thought to be due to a decline in water quality. This is currently being investigated.

Ythan Estuary, Sands of Forvie, and Meikle Loch

	SPA/Ram Code	IBA Europe number
	222A	073

County/Region	District(s)	OS sheet(s)	Grid Reference(s)	Map 6
Grampian	Gordon	30, 38	NK 020275	

Area (ha)	NNR	SPA		Ramsar	
1006	Yes	Designated	N	Designated	N
		Candidate	Y	Candidate	Y

An undeveloped estuary and extensive sand dune system important for breeding, passage and wintering seabirds, wildfowl and waders. Meikle Loch is an important goose roost.

Site description

The long, narrow estuary of the River Ythan runs in a north–south direction entering the sea 18 km north of Aberdeen. At its mouth, the river splits an extensive area of sand dunes with the Foveran Links forming the west bank and the Sands of Forvie dune system on the east bank. Extensive mud flats in the upper reaches of the estuary are replaced by coarser gravels with mussel beds closer to the sea. The margins of the estuary are varied, and in addition to the dunes, there are areas of saltmarsh, reedbeds and poor fen.

Sands of Forvie exhibits a range of habitats from mobile dunes in the south, through fixed dunes to acidic dune heath with scrub to the north. It has large areas of lichen-rich heath that contains communities of crowberry/bell heather/common heather and lichen species, with creeping willow and cross-leaved heath in the damper dune slacks. There are also a number of burns, seasonal wet areas and permanent lochs within the site.

Meikle Loch is an important roost site for geese which feed on surrounding farmland in winter. It is eutrophic, but supports limited aquatic vegetation. It is joined by a burn to the smaller Little Loch.

Birds

The area supports internationally important numbers of breeding Sandwich tern and wintering pink-footed goose, together with nationally important numbers of breeding eider, common tern and little tern and wintering eider and redshank.

The Sands of Forvie hold the largest concentration of breeding **eider** in Britain (5500 birds with 1200 breeding pairs in 1987, 6% of British). A large tern colony includes **Sandwich tern** (1125 pairs 1990, 2.5% of Western European, 7% of British), **common tern** (265 pairs 1990, 2% of British) and **little tern** (31 pairs 1990, 1% of British). Other notable breeding species include shelduck, black-headed gull, herring gull and kittiwake.

In winter, the area is notable for large flocks of wildfowl and waders. In the five-winter period 1985/86 to 1989/90 the average peak count for **pink-footed goose** was 6350 birds (6% of the world total). Numbers are much larger in spring with an average for 1988 to 1990 of 24,300 birds (22% of world). Wintering **eider** average 1470 birds (3% of British) and **redshank** 760 birds (1% of British). Notable also are wintering greylag goose, light-bellied brent goose, common scoter, golden plover and snow bunting, and passage waders.

Conservation issues

Waterfowl that winter on estuaries are vulnerable to land-claim and other developments, such as the construction of barrages that would disturb or damage the existing ecology of these sites. Other human influences, such as recreational disturbance, commercial exploitation of shellfish and worms, and oil and industrial pollution, are also potentially damaging to the conservation interest of estuaries.

There is a problem of recreational disturbance to the site from anglers, walkers and windsurfers. Investigations into eutrophication, algal weed mats and depressed invertebrate populations are currently under way.

Further reading

Buckland, S T, Bell, M V and Picozzi, N (eds.) 1990 *The Birds of North-East Scotland.* North-East Scotland Bird Club, Aberdeen.

River Spey – Insh Marshes

SPA/Ram Code	IBA Europe number
223A	085

County/Region	District(s)	OS sheet(s)	Grid Reference(s)	Maps 5, 6, 8
Highland	Badenoch and Strathspey	35	NH 780013	

Area (ha)	NNR	SPA		Ramsar	
1177	No	Designated	N	Designated	N
		Candidate	Y	Candidate	Y

River, lochs and marshes with a diverse breeding and wintering bird community.

Site description

The Insh Marshes form the largest, most northerly, single-unit flood-plain mire of the poor fen type in Great Britain. They are 5 km in length and over 1 km wide. Although part of the area has been drained and claimed for pasture, there are over 3 square km of wet fenland remaining. Despite the land changes, the whole system remains a complete ecological and hydrological unit.

'Poor fen' develops in water which is poor in nutrients and bases, and generally has a pH between 4 and 6. This water quality is principally due to the local geology and the low level of eutrophication.

Of all the great flood-plain systems which once dominated the wide, often impassable, valleys of Britain, the Insh Marshes represent the last relatively natural example. While there are drainage ditches and impoundments within the system, it remains the epitome of the flood-plain fen, the type site by which others are judged.

The site lies within the flat valley floor of the River Spey between Kincraig and Kingussie at an altitude of c. 220 m. The low gradient of the wide valley of the River Spey, and the damming effects produced by Loch Insh, cause water velocities to be remarkably slow for an upland river. Such a large, sluggish river at so high an altitude is probably unique in Britain.

During periods of high rainfall and snow-melt the river floods extensively. The ponding of waters aided by the incomplete system of river embankments is a well-known feature and may occur for periods at any time between September and April. At other times of the year water tables are close to, and in places still above, the marsh surface. The consistently waterlogged nature of the valley floor has prevented the decomposition of plant material and resulted in the accumulation of peat, in some places to a depth of 7 m.

Within the peatland-riverine system are many typical flood-plain features; oxbow lakes, lochans, and tributary streams. In addition there are man-made features, such as ditches, which are nowadays largely unmanaged. These various natural and man-made features add to the total habitat diversity of the flood-plain mire by displaying different degrees of hydroseral succession. Open water areas are associated with aquatic life forms, with various stages of colonisation by submerged, floating and emergent plants. Naturally, this diversity is reflected in the diversity of invertebrate fauna.

Loch Insh is noted for its exceptionally rapid water turnover and is an excellent example of a mesotrophic loch, an uncommon type in Britain.

The Spey Valley, particularly the section from Kingussie to Grantown-on-Spey, has long been recognised as including areas of great importance for invertebrates, including species which have a boreo-alpine European distribution.

The distinctive arctic charr of Loch Insh display a breeding strategy found only in a few other populations in Britain. Instead of remaining in the lake to breed, they spawn in nearby streams.

The 1977-79 otter survey of Scotland showed that 76-90% of all the sites surveyed along the River Spey had evidence of otter. This makes the site comparable to the best otter areas in Scotland, namely Caithness, Sutherland, Wester Ross and the Islands.

Birds
The area supports nationally important numbers of breeding wigeon, pintail, goldeneye, and other species, and wintering whooper swan and hen harrier.

In summer, the area currently supports 20 pairs of **wigeon** (5% of British), 1 pair of **pintail** (3% of British), 29 pairs of **goldeneye** (33% of British), and other scarce breeding species. Insh Marshes provide foraging areas for up to 3 pairs of ospreys. In winter the area regularly supports 140 **whooper swans** (2% of British) and up to 14 **hen harriers** (2% of British).

Notable also are breeding lapwing, snipe, redshank and black-headed gull. Golden plover and other waders occur on passage.

Conservation issues
The birds that use this site are vulnerable to alterations in the hydrological regime resulting from river management, land drainage and agricultural intensification. The proposed River Spey Flood Alleviation Scheme could have serious effects on the whole system. Loch Insh is vulnerable to disturbance from canoeists, water skiers and commercial eel fishermen.

Cairngorms

SPA/Ram Code	IBA Europe number
224A	080

County/Region	District(s)	OS sheet(s)	Grid Reference(s)	Maps 5, 6, 8
Grampian	Kincardine and Deeside, Moray	35, 36, 43	NJ 0000	
Highland	Badenoch and Strathspey			

Area (ha)	NNR	SPA		Ramsar	
49,209	Yes	Designated	N	Designated	Y
		Candidate	Y	Candidate	N

The Cairngorms are of exceptional nature conservation and scientific importance within Britain and the EEC for a range of bird species associated with montane plateaux, open moorland and Caledonian pine forest. The Cairngorm lochs have been designated as a non-bird Ramsar site.

Site description
The Cairngorms massif rises from about 200 m to a high altitude plateau at over 1000 m, cut into separate areas by steep-sided glacial troughs. There are several summits exceeding 1000 m, the highest being Ben MacDui at 1309 m. The central core is granitic, giving rise to infertile acidic soils, but some peripheral areas are relatively base-rich. The size of the area, together with variation in such factors as aspect, exposure to wind or late snow-lie, mean that there is a great diversity of plant communities. Grazing by red deer, feral reindeer and, locally, sheep also affects the vegetation.

Woodland is present on some lower ground, up to about 550 m, though locally to 640 m, with scrub above this in the northern corries. Scots pine predominates, but there is some broad-leaved woodland, mostly of birch. The Rothiemurchus pinewoods are among the largest tracts of native pine forest remaining in Britain, and contain a characteristic association of woodland floor plants. Where grazing is at relatively low intensity, some natural regeneration of woodland is occurring. There are also some grasslands and valley mires at these lower altitudes.

Where the land has become deforested, the lower and middle slopes are clothed mainly in heather or bilberry heath, becoming prostrate and including a progressively greater proportion of lichens as altitude increases. On more gently sloping areas there is wet heath or blanket mire. Upper slopes and the plateaux have alpine type communities of fell-fields and snow-beds, including *Racomitrium* heaths, three-leaved rush and stiff sedge heaths, and mat-grass and moss-dominated snow-bed communities. There is some high altitude blanket mire, and further variety is found, for example, around alpine springs and in corrie wall grasslands dominated by hair-grass species.

The lichen, bryophyte and invertebrate communities are diverse, with pinewood and high altitude communities especially important. Mammals at this site include red squirrel, pine marten and wild cat. Arctic charr are present in Loch Builg.

Birds

Breeding birds of prey are particularly important and include **hen harrier** (up to 15 pairs, 2% of British), **golden eagle** (9 pairs, 2% of British), **osprey** (2 pairs, 2% of EC, 4% of British), **merlin** (25 pairs, 4% of British) and **peregrine** (10 pairs, 1% of British). On the montane plateaux are **ptarmigan** (1500 pairs, 15% of British), **dotterel** (about 240 pairs, 28% of EC and British) and **snow bunting** (up to 40 pairs, 57% of EC and British). Golden plover, snowy owl and short-eared owl also are present. Specialist pinewood birds include **capercaillie** (about 125 pairs, 11% of British), crested tit and **Scottish crossbill** (about 50 pairs, 14% of world population).

Conservation issues

The birds that use this site are vulnerable to human disturbance from increased public access to the high tops made possible by the skiing infrastructure. Non-skiing visitors during the summer months cause most of the damage; vegetation structure is also affected. Expansion of the skiing industry into Lurcher's Gully, which would have further increased public access to sensitive parts of the high tops, was ruled out in 1990 by the Secretary of State for Scotland during the review of the Highland Region Structure Plan. This should close for some years any hope the skiing industry may have for expansion westwards into Lurcher's Gully.

The native pinewoods of the Scottish Highlands have been reduced by felling and fire to occupy at present only about 1% of their natural range. Maintenance and good management of remaining areas is a strong conservation priority.

Further reading

Buckland S T, Bell M V, and Picozzi N (eds.) 1990 *The Birds of North-East Scotland*. North-East Scotland Bird Club, Aberdeen.

Nethersole-Thompson, D and Watson, A 1981 *The Cairngorms*. Melven Press, Perth.

Loch of Skene

SPA/Ram Code	IBA Europe number
226A	074

County/Region	District(s)	OS sheet(s)	Grid Reference(s)	Map 6
Grampian	Gordon	38	NJ 785075	

Area (ha)	NNR	SPA	Ramsar
1-999	No	Designated Y Candidate N/A	Designated Y Candidate N/A

A shallow loch attracting large numbers of wintering and breeding wildfowl.

Site description
The Loch of Skene, some 15 km west of Aberdeen, is a shallow, eutrophic loch (maximum depth <2 m). Eutrophication of the loch has led to a decline in the submerged flora. The fringing reedbed and birch–willow carr vegetation is largely undisturbed, and a number of uncommon plant species are present.

Birds
The loch supports internationally important numbers of wintering greylag goose and nationally important numbers of wintering whooper swan, goldeneye and goosander and breeding tufted duck.

In the five-winter period 1985/86 to 1989/90 the average peak counts were 105 **whooper swan** (2% of British), 9000 Icelandic **greylag geese** (9% of the world total; max. 13,300 birds), 190 **goldeneye** (1% of British) and 75 **goosander** (1% of British). In autumn, the lake forms a notable roost site for common gulls (up to 45,000).

The breeding bird community is diverse, and includes 50–100 pairs of **tufted duck** (1% of British).

Conservation issues
Formation of algal blooms has been caused by eutrophication of the loch from agricultural run–off and discharge from local sewage. As a result the submerged flora of the loch has declined.

The geese and other wildfowl on this site are vulnerable to disturbance particularly from shooting and sailing.

Further reading
Bell, M V and Riddoch, J F 1987 Wintering wildfowl at Loch of Skene. *North-east Scotland Bird Report 1987.*

Fowlsheugh

SPA/Ram Code	IBA Europe number
227A	075

County/Region	District(s)	OS sheet(s)	Grid References(s)	Maps 6, 9
Grampian	Kincardine and Deeside	45	NO 881799 to NO 881816	

Area (ha)	NNR	SPA		Ramsar	
8	No	Designated	N	Designated	N
		Candidate	Y	Candidate	N

Coastal cliffs with large seabird colonies.

Site description

Fowlsheugh is located on the east coast of Grampian Region in mainland north-east Scotland, overlooking the North Sea. The sheer cliffs, between 30 m and 60 m high, are cut mostly in basalt and conglomerate of old red sandstone age. They form a rock face with innumerable holes and ledges which provide ideal nesting sites for seabirds. The botanical interest is limited, with species-poor grassland occurring on top of the abrupt cliff edge.

Birds

Fowlsheugh supports internationally important numbers of breeding kittiwake and guillemot and nationally important numbers of razorbill.

The most recent complete count from the Seabird Colony Register was in 1986. This recorded 36,650 pairs of **kittiwakes** (2% of Western European, 7.5% of British), 56,450 individual **guillemots** (2.5% of Western European, 5% of British) and 5800 individual **razorbills** (4% of British).

Conservation issues

Seabirds are sensitive to changes in the quality of the marine environment, especially to changes in fish stocks and to oil pollution.

Lochnagar

	SPA/Ram Code	IBA Europe number
	228A	079

County/Region	District(s)	OS sheet(s)	Grid Reference(s)	Maps 6, 9
Grampian	Kincardine and Deeside	44	NO 250840	

Area (ha)	NNR	SPA		Ramsar	
1000-9999	No	Designated	N	Designated	N
		Candidate	Y	Candidate	N

A montane area with an important assemblage of upland breeding birds.

Site description
Rising to well over 1000 m, Lochnagar is the highest of the hills to the south of Deeside. Formed from granite, the hills support typical heath vegetation, with sub-arctic heaths and late snow-patch vegetation on the summit plateau. Corries and crags contain several nationally rare arctic-alpine flowering plants and bryophytes, including the largest British population of Alpine blue-sow-thistle.

Fragments of sub-montane birch woodland grow on the lower slopes near Loch Muick. In the same area, there are patches of herb-rich grassland on flushes, and in Corrie Chash, there is an unusually extensive area of relict dwarf birch scrub. The hills are drained by fast-flowing burns, and there are scattered lochs.

Birds
This area supports nationally important numbers of breeding **ptarmigan** and **dotterel**, and is notable for other breeding waders and for raptors, including golden eagle, merlin and peregrine.

Conservation issues
The birds that use this site are vulnerable to human disturbance from increased public access, particularly from hill-walkers, to the high tops.

Further reading
Buckland S T, Bell M V and Picozzi, N (eds.) 1990 *The Birds of North-East Scotland*. North-East Scotland Bird Club, Aberdeen.

Drumochter Hills

SPA/Ram Code	IBA Europe number
230A	118

County/Region	District(s)	OS sheet(s)	Grid Reference(s)	Map 8
Tayside	Perth and Kinross	42	NN 630765	
Highland	Badenoch and Strathspey			

Area (ha)	NNR	SPA		Ramsar	
9690	No	Designated	N	Designated	N
		Candidate	Y	Candidate	N

The Drumochter Hills are of exceptional nature conservation and scientific importance within Britain and the EC for a range of bird species associated with montane plateaux and open moorland.

Site description

The Drumochter Hills consist of rounded summits, generally between 900–950 m, on either side of the Drumochter Pass. The full altitudinal range within the area is 360–1010 m, with the plateaux divided by steep–sided stream gullies as well as the Pass.

The principal underlying rock is metamorphosed sandstone, and consequently the vegetation is dominated by acidic communities. The most extensive are the mid-altitude heather dominated heaths and the montane heaths and grasslands above 750 m, but there are also substantial areas of mire and wet heath on gently sloping or level ground. Some birch woodland and grassland with bracken and scattered trees is found, especially above the shores of Loch Ericht, with further variety provided by other habitats such as crags and screes, acidic and calcareous springs and flushes, and standing and running water.

Variation within the principal vegetation types depends on such factors as aspect, slope and exposure. The heath includes a dry type with hypnaceous mosses, and a damp type with *Sphagnum* mosses and cloudberry. There are also bilberry heaths. The lichen-rich variants of these heaths are a feature of the eastern highlands, as is bilberry dominated snow-bed vegetation.

The montane communities include heaths, grasslands, moss heaths and blanket mires, forming complex mosaics dependent on exposure and drainage. Of particular note are the extensive high altitude blanket mires, for which this is one of few such sites in the UK, and the widespread development, exceeding 100 ha, of stiff sedge-*Racomitrium* moss heath, which is typical of arctic regions.

Birds

The Drumochter Hills form one of the most important areas in Britain, and the EEC, for their assemblage of specialist montane plateaux bird species, which includes dotterel and ptarmigan. The site is of international importance for **dotterel** which use it both for breeding (70+ pairs, 8% of the British and EC population) and as a spring and autumn gathering ground for birds from a much wider area.

The Drumochter Hills are of importance also for wide-ranging birds of open ground, such as golden eagle, merlin, peregrine and hen harrier. Other breeding waders include golden plover, dunlin and greenshank. Ptarmigan are also present.

Conservation issues
The birds that use this site are vulnerable to human disturbance from increased public access to the tops. Visitors during the summer months cause most of the damage; vegetation structure is also affected. Trampling by red deer is a problem for some ground-nesting bird species.

Dotterel

West Mainland Moors

SPA/Ram Code	IBA Europe number
231A	059

County/Region	District(s)	OS sheet(s)	Grid Reference(s)	Map 2
Orkney	N/A	6	HY 3521	

Area (ha)	NNR	SPA		Ramsar	
1000-9999	No	Designated	N	Designated	N
		Candidate	Y	Candidate	N

An extensive area of moorland, important for its breeding birds of prey and other moorland birds.

Site description

The vegetation comprises wet and dry heaths and blanket mire. Although the hills rise to over 220 m, few alpine plant species are present. There are scattered oligotrophic lochans. The vegetation mainly reflects the acidic nature of the underlying rock, although more base-rich conditions occur at spring lines, where the vegetation is more species-rich. In sheltered dales, there is patchy scrub of eared and common willow, and stands of tall herb vegetation including such species as rosebay willowherb, common valerian and *Dryopteris* ferns.

Birds

The area supports nationally important numbers of breeding red-throated diver, hen harrier, arctic skua and short-eared owl.

Most notable among the breeding birds of prey are **hen harrier** (27 nests in 1989, 4% of British) and **short-eared owl** (up to 24 pairs, 2% of British). Other breeding birds include **red-throated diver** (15 pairs, 1% of British and EC) and **arctic skua** (37 pairs, 1% of British). Notable also are breeding merlin, golden plover, dunlin, curlew and great skua.

Hen harriers are also present in winter.

Conservation issues

Birds that use this site are vulnerable to agricultural intensification through reseeding, ploughing and overburning.

Further reading

Orkney Bird Reports.

North Mainland Coast

SPA/Ram Code	IBA Europe number
231B	058

County/Region	District(s)	OS sheet(s)	Grid Reference(s)	Map 2
Orkney	N/A	6	HY 4023	

Area (ha)	NNR	SPA		Ramsar	
1000-9999	No	Designated	N	Designated	N
		Candidate	Y	Candidate	Y

An area of rocky/sandy coast important for wintering waders.

Site description

Parts of the Orkney coast are considered to be of national/international importance for certain wintering wader species. Preliminary surveys have identified that the North Mainland coast is of special importance in this context, but further survey work is planned to delimit the precise areas of special interest.

North Mainland has a low lying rocky coastline, interspersed with sandy bays.

Birds

The area supports nationally important numbers of wintering purple sandpiper, curlew, redshank and turnstone.

North Mainland was included in a comprehensive winter shorebird survey carried out in Orkney and elsewhere in 1982/83 and 1983/84. This found 200 **purple sandpiper** (1% of British), 3200 **curlew** (3% of British), 770 **redshank** (1% of British) and 510 **turnstone** (1% of British).

Conservation issues

Birds that depend on these coastal habitats are vulnerable to land claim, oil pollution and human disturbance.

Further reading

The shorebirds of the Orkney Islands. Tay and Orkney Ringing Groups 1984, Perth.

South Westray Coast

SPA/Ram Code	IBA Europe number
232A	053

County/Region	District(s)	OS sheet(s)	Grid Reference(s)	Map 2
Orkney	N/A	5	HY 4643	

Area (ha)	NNR	SPA		Ramsar	
1-999	No	Designated	N	Designated	N
		Candidate	Y	Candidate	Y

An area with rocky/sandy shores, important for wintering waders.

Site description

Parts of the Orkney coast are considered to be of national/international importance for certain wintering wader species. Preliminary surveys have identified that the South Westray coast is of special importance in this context, but further survey work is planned to delimit the precise areas of special interest.

South Westray has a low-lying rocky coastline, interspersed with sandy bays.

Birds

The area supports internationally important numbers of wintering purple sandpiper, and nationally important numbers of wintering sanderling.

Westray was included in a comprehensive winter shorebird survey carried out in Orkney and elsewhere in 1982/83 and 1983/84. This found 180 **sanderling** (1% of British) and 640 **purple sandpiper** (1% of EAF, 4% of British). Notable also is wintering turnstone.

Conservation issues

Birds that depend on these coastal habitats are vulnerable to land claim, oil pollution and human disturbance.

Further reading

The shorebirds of the Orkney Islands. Tay and Orkney Ringing Groups 1984, Perth.

East Sanday

SPA/Ram Code	IBA Europe number
233A	049

County/Region	District(s)	OS sheet(s)	Grid Reference(s)	Map 2
Orkney	N/A	5	HY 7040	

Area (ha)	NNR	SPA		Ramsar	
1-999	No	Designated	N	Designated	N
		Candidate	Y	Candidate	Y

A rocky/sandy shore site holding nationally and internationally important numbers of wintering waders.

Site description

Parts of the Orkney coast are considered to be of national/international importance for certain wintering wader species. Preliminary surveys have identified that the coast of East Sanday is of special importance in this context, but further survey work is planned to delimit the precise areas of special interest.

This coastline is notable for the presence of sand dune and machair habitats which are rare outside the Hebrides, and for the extensive intertidal flats and saltmarshes. There are also shingle spits. The marram-dominated dunes have a variety of associated herbs including lady's bedstraw, common bird's-foot-trefoil and wild pansy. Species-rich fixed dune grassland occurs inland of the dunes and is characterised by plants such as lesser meadow-rue, autumn gentian and the scarce limestone bedstraw. Wetter areas have different plant communities with species including jointed rush, curved sedge and early marsh-orchid.

The Little Sea and Cata Sand have peripheral saltmarshes with large populations of sea aster and annual sea-blite, and form the largest area of such habitat on Orkney.

Birds

The area supports internationally important numbers of wintering purple sandpiper and turnstone, and nationally important numbers of wintering sanderling.

East Sanday was included in a comprehensive winter shorebird survey carried out in Orkney and elsewhere in 1982/83 and 1983/84. This found 420 **sanderling** (3% of British), 710 **purple sandpiper** (1% of EAF, 4% of British) and 760 **turnstone** (1% of EAF, 2% of British). Notable also are wintering whooper swan and bar-tailed godwit. The site also supports breeding Sandwich and arctic terns.

Conservation issues

Birds that depend on these coastal habitats are vulnerable to land claim, oil pollution and human disturbance.

Further reading

Bullock, I D and Gomersall, C H 1980 *The breeding populations of terns in Orkney and Shetland in 1980*. RSPB, Sandy.

The shorebirds of the Orkney Islands. Tay and Orkney Ringing Groups 1984, Perth.

Crussa Field and The Heogs

SPA/Ram Code 235A	IBA Europe number 036

County/Region	District(s)	OS sheet(s)	Grid Reference(s)	Map 1
Shetland	N/A	1	HP 6210	

Area (ha)	NNR	SPA		Ramsar	
1-999	No	Designated	N	Designated	N
		Candidate	Y	Candidate	N

An area of serpentine heathland of importance for breeding moorland birds including whimbrel and arctic skua.

Site description

This is an extensive area of herb-rich serpentine heathland in central Unst, partly influenced by former chromite workings. The varied maritime influenced vegetation includes much sedge-grass heath, with species such as alpine meadow-rue, mountain everlasting and fairy flax. The inland cliffs of the Heogs also support a serpentine-influenced community which includes the locally rare green spleenwort.

There are a number of disused chromite quarries scattered over the site.

Birds

The area supports nationally important numbers of breeding whimbrel and arctic skua.

The breeding bird community of 17 species includes more than 150 pairs of waders. Of particular significance are the relatively high numbers and densities of **whimbrel** (32 pairs, 7% of British and EC) and **arctic skua** (42 pairs, 1% of British). Notable also are breeding ringed plover and golden plover.

Conservation issues

Birds that use this site are vulnerable to changes in agricultural management, especially reseeding and changes in grazing pressure.

Mousa

SPA/Ram Code	IBA Europe number
236A	044

County/Region	District(s)	OS sheet(s)	Grid Reference(s)	Map 1
Shetland	N/A	4	HU 4624	

Area (ha)	NNR	SPA		Ramsar	
1-999	No	Designated	N	Designated	N
		Candidate	Y	Candidate	N

A low grassy island with important breeding populations of storm petrels, black guillemots and other seabirds.

Site description
Mousa is a low island, reaching only 55 m above sea level, and dominated by acidic grassland, with purple moorgrass and tormentil. There is also some maritime grassland and heathland, including plantain–thrift sward on the spray drenched south-west coast, and mesotrophic marsh. There are a few freshwater lochs and, in the south-east, tidal pools.

One of the largest concentrations of common seals hauls out and breeds, especially along the southern and eastern sides of the island.

Birds
The area supports nationally important numbers of breeding storm petrel and black guillemot.

The largest colony of **storm petrels** in Shetland breeds in dry stone dykes, boulder beaches and the broch. The breeding colony of **black guillemots** is also the largest in Shetland (350 individuals, 1% of British). Notable also are breeding fulmar, shag, arctic skua, great skua, common tern and arctic tern.

Conservation issues
Seabirds are sensitive to changes in the quality of the marine environment, especially to changes in fish stocks and to oil pollution. Ground–nesting seabirds on offshore islands are vulnerable to the introduction of predatory mammals.

Rousay (part)

SPA/Ram Code	IBA Europe number
237A	055

County/Region	District(s)	OS sheet(s)	Grid Reference(s)	Map 2
Orkney	N/A	6	HY 4031	

Area (ha)	NNR	SPA		Ramsar	
1000-9999	No	Designated	N	Designated	N
		Candidate	Y	Candidate	N

An area of moorland supporting an important breeding bird assemblage.

Site description
Central Rousay is mainly heather dominated moorland, including blanket mire, and with a number of nationally scarce species such as shady horsetail, round-leaved wintergreen and serrated wintergreen. On hill tops there are montane communities which support arctic-alpine plants notably dwarf willow, alpine bearberry and alpine saw-wort. There are a number of lochs, including the mesotrophic Muckle Water.

Maritime heaths and grasslands occur in the coastal areas of Brings in the north-west and Faraclett Head in the north-east. Numerous base-rich flushes are characterised by sedges, black bog-rush and a diversity of herbs including Scottish primrose.

Birds
The area supports nationally important numbers of breeding red-throated diver, hen harrier and arctic skua.

Breeding populations in 1990 were 13 pairs of **red-throated divers** (1% of British and EC), 7 nests of **hen harriers** (1% of British) and 120 pairs of **arctic skuas** (4% of British). Notable also are breeding shag, merlin, golden plover, curlew, great skua, kittiwake, arctic tern, guillemot, razorbill and short-eared owl, and wintering purple sandpiper.

Conservation issues
The birds that use this site are vulnerable to the loss of moorland and maritime heathland to agriculture, overgrazing and burning of moorland, and mechanical peat cutting.

North Ronaldsay Coast

SPA/Ram Code	IBA Europe number
241A	048

County/Region	District(s)	OS sheet(s)	Grid Reference(s)	Map 2
Orkney	N/A	5	HY 7244	

Area (ha)	NNR	SPA		Ramsar	
1-999	No	Designated	N	Designated	N
		Candidate	Y	Candidate	Y

Low-lying rocky/sandy coast important for breeding black guillemot and wintering purple sandpiper.

Site description
Parts of the Orkney coast are considered to be of national/international importance for certain wintering wader species. Preliminary surveys have identified that the North Ronaldsay coast is of special importance in this context, but further survey work is planned to delimit the precise areas of special interest.

North Ronaldsay has a low-lying rocky shoreline, interspersed with sandy bays. A large flock of semi-wild sheep are confined to this shore by the island's perimeter dyke, and feed on seaweed.

Birds
This area supports nationally important numbers of breeding black guillemot and wintering purple sandpiper.

A survey of **black guillemots** in 1987 found 460 individuals (1% of British). North Ronaldsay was included in a comprehensive winter shorebird survey carried out in Orkney and elsewhere in 1982/83 and 1983/84. This found 275 **purple sandpipers** (2% of British).

Conservation issues
Birds that depend on these coastal habitats are vulnerable to land-claim, oil pollution and human disturbance.

Further reading
Pennington, M G 1988 The breeding birds of North Ronaldsay. *Scottish Birds* 15: 83–89. *The shorebirds of the Orkney Islands.* Tay and Orkney Ringing Groups 1984, Perth.

South-eastern Stronsay

SPA/Ram Code	IBA Europe number
242A	050

County/Region	District(s)	OS sheet(s)	Grid Reference(s)	Map 2
Orkney	N/A	5	HY 6821	

Area (ha)	NNR	SPA		Ramsar	
1-999	No	Designated	N	Designated	N
		Candidate	Y	Candidate	Y

Rocky coastline important for breeding black guillemots and wintering purple sandpipers.

Site description
Parts of the Orkney coast are considered to be of national/international importance for certain wintering wader species. Preliminary surveys have identified that the coast of south-eastern Stronsay is of special importance in this context, but further survey work is planned to delimit the precise areas of special interest.

South-eastern Stronsay has a low-lying rocky coastline, interspersed with sandy bays.

Birds
The area supports nationally important numbers of breeding black guillemot and wintering purple sandpiper.

Stronsay was included in a comprehensive winter shorebird survey carried out in Orkney and elsewhere in 1982/83 and 1983/84. This found 300 **purple sandpipers** (2% of British). Breeding **black guillemots** were surveyed in 1983, when 330 birds were recorded (1% of British).

Conservation issues
Birds that depend on these coastal habitats are vulnerable to land-claim, oil pollution and human disturbance.

Further reading
The shorebirds of the Orkney Islands. Tay and Orkney Ringing Groups 1984, Perth.

Eday

SPA/Ram Code	IBA Europe number
243A	054

County/Region	District(s)	OS sheet(s)	Grid References	Map 2
Orkney	N/A	5	HY 581391 (Calf of Eday)	
			HY 565368 (Mill Loch)	
			HY 560347 (Doomy)	
			HY 547322 (Whitemaw Hill)	

Area (ha)	NNR	SPA		Ramsar	
475	No	Designated	N	Designated	N
		Candidate	Y	Candidate	N

Coastal, moorland and freshwater habitats, with notable breeding populations of seabirds and upland breeding species.

Site description

The site includes three separate parts of Eday, and the off-lying Calf of Eday to the north. Mill Loch, towards the north end of Eday, is an oligotrophic loch of about 10 ha, and is surrounded by marshy grassland. In addition there are two areas of moorland at Doomy and Whitemaw Hill, further south on the island, either side of London Airfield; rising to only 25 m and 95 m respectively, these have a sub-montane character.

The Calf of Eday is a low island of 242 ha, rising to 54 m, vegetated with maritime grassland and moorland.

Birds

The area supports internationally important numbers of breeding great black-backed gull, and nationally important numbers of breeding cormorant, whimbrel, arctic skua and guillemot, and wintering purple sandpiper.

Counts of seabirds on the Calf of Eday in the late 1980s include 185 pairs of **cormorants** (average of five counts in 1980s, 3% of British), 1000 pairs of **great black-backed gulls** (1% Western European, 5% of British) and 25,000 individual **guillemots** (2% of British). The moorland areas attract breeding **whimbrel** (6-7 pairs, 1% of British and EC), and **arctic skua** (min. 54 pairs, 1% of British). Notable also are breeding red-throated diver, fulmar, shag, kittiwake, razorbill and black guillemot.

In winter, **purple sandpiper**s (250 birds, 1.5% British population) occur on Eday.

Conservation issues

Seabirds are sensitive to changes in the quality of the marine environment, especially to changes in fish stocks and to oil pollution. Birds that use this site are vulnerable to intensification of agriculture, burning and overgrazing of moorland, drainage and mechanical peat-cutting.

Troup, Pennan and Lion Heads

SPA/Ram Code	IBA Europe number
247A	069

County/Region	District(s)	OS sheet(s)	Grid Reference(s)	Map 6
Grampian	Banff and Buchan	29, 30	NJ 824673	

Area (ha)	NNR	SPA		Ramsar	
322	No	Designated	N	Designated	N
		Candidate	Y	Candidate	N

A 15-km length of sea cliffs, with large seabird colonies notably of kittiwakes and guillemots.

Site description
The cliffs, along the north Buchan coast, are generally below 125 m, and are broken with many ledges and steep vegetated slopes. There is a diverse maritime grassland and heathland flora, and the more sheltered dens near Gardenstown and Pennan Head contain herb-rich grassland, flushes and scrub reflecting more base-rich conditions. The flora of the cliffs include montane species such as purple and mossy saxifrages and roseroot. The nationally scarce species oysterplant and sea pea grow on shingle beaches in the area.

Birds
The site holds nationally important numbers of herring gull, kittiwake and guillemot. A census in 1986 found 2580 pairs of **herring gulls** (2% of British), 16,300 pairs of **kittiwakes** (3% of British) and 16,200 individual **guillemots** (2% of British). Troup Head has the only mainland gannetry in Scotland. Breeding was first confirmed in 1988 and in 1990 the site held 14+ pairs (maximum of 140 individuals present), but is increasing rapidly.

Conservation issues
Seabirds are sensitive to changes in the quality of the marine environment, especially to changes in fish stocks and to oil pollution.

Further reading
Mudge, G P 1986 Trends of population change at colonies of cliff-nesting seabirds in the Moray Firth. *Proc. Roy. Soc. Edin.* 91B: 73–80.
Lloyd, C S and North, S G 1987 The seabirds of Troup and Pennan Heads 1979–86. *Scottish Birds* 14: 199–204.

St Cyrus

SPA/Ram Code	IBA Europe number
248A	077

County/Region	District(s)	OS sheet(s)	Grid Reference(s)	Maps 6, 9
Grampian	Kincardine and Deeside	45	NO 745630	
Tayside	Angus			

Area (ha)	NNR	SPA		Ramsar	
1-999	Yes	Designated	N	Designated	N
		Candidate	Y	Candidate	N

A sand dune system and associated estuary with an important little tern colony.

Site description

The small dynamic estuary of the River North Esk, a few kilometres north of Montrose, has a frequently changing pattern of sand banks and intertidal flats. On either side of the mouth of the river are extensive sand dunes. The fore-dune is dominated by marram and lyme grass. Dune communities further inland include grasslands with red fescue, sweet vernal-grass, sand sedge and wild thyme, and, south of the river, heather-dominated lichen heath.

There is a small saltmarsh, currently seldom inundated, but which is the only saltmarsh in the district.

The diverse invertebrate fauna includes species, such as the shore wainscot moth, at their northern limit in Britain. St Cyrus is one of few Scottish localities for the small blue butterfly.

Birds

A breeding area for nationally important numbers of **little tern**, St Cyrus has held up to 158 pairs (6% of British) but numbers have fluctuated considerably and are currently smaller. The largest count in recent years was 60 pairs in 1984 (3% of British). Notable also is a large colony of herring gulls (900 pairs).

Conservation issues

Seabirds are sensitive to changes in the quality of the marine environment, especially to changes in fish stocks and to oil pollution. Nesting terns are vulnerable to disturbance from people and losses from foxes and high spring tides.

Buchan Ness to
Collieston Coast

SPA/Ram Code	IBA Europe number
249B	072

County/Region	District(s)	OS sheet(s)	Grid Reference(s)	Map 6
Grampian	Banff and Buchan, Gordon	30	NK 133419 to NK 042285	

Area (ha)	NNR	SPA		Ramsar	
213	No	Designated	N	Designated	N
		Candidate	Y	Candidate	N

Seacliffs and offshore stacks with large seabird colonies.

Site description

Facing south-east, these cliffs of granite, quartzite and other rocks run for over 15 km south from Peterhead, broken only by the sandy beach of Cruden Bay. The low, broken cliffs (generally less than 50 m) show many erosion features such as stacks, arches, caves and blowholes. There is varied coastal vegetation on ledges and at the cliff top, including maritime heaths and grasslands, and brackish flushes. The cliff flora includes local species such as Scots lovage and roseroot, and, in richer soils, plants which are local in north-east Scotland such as carline thistle, cowslip and sea wormwood.

Birds

These cliffs hold nationally important numbers of breeding shag, herring gull, kittiwake, and guillemot.

Recent counts from the Seabird Colony Register include 440 pairs of **shags** (1% of British), 3600 pairs of **herring gulls** (2% of British), 19,100 pairs of **kittiwakes** (4% of British) and 12,900 individual **guillemots** (1% of British). Notable also are breeding fulmar, razorbill and puffin.

Conservation issues

Seabirds are sensitive to changes in the quality of the marine environment, especially to changes in fish stocks and to oil pollution. Large numbers of auks are killed in fixed salmon nets along this stretch of coast.

Sumburgh Head

SPA/Ram Code	IBA Europe number
251A	047

County/Region	District(s)	OS sheet(s)	Grid Reference(s)	Map 1
Shetland	N/A	4	HU 408091	

Area (ha)	NNR	SPA		Ramsar	
41	No	Designated	N	Designated	N
		Candidate	Y	Candidate	N

Cliffs and boulder beaches supporting colonies of breeding seabirds.

Site description
The area includes the boulder-strewn beaches and cliffs, up to 100 m high, along the east side of Sumburgh Head, the southerly tip of the Shetland mainland.

Birds
This cliff colony supports nationally important numbers of breeding **shag**, with 490 pairs recorded in 1985 (1% of British). Notable also are fulmar, kittiwake, arctic tern, guillemot, razorbill and puffin.

Conservation issues
Seabirds are sensitive to changes in the quality of the marine environment, especially to changes in fish stocks and to oil pollution. Kittiwakes, arctic terns and puffins have proved extremely vulnerable to the crash in sandeel stocks of the 1980s.

Monadhliath

SPA/Ram Code	IBA Europe number
253A	N/A

County/Region	District(s)	OS sheet(s)	Grid Reference(s)	Maps 4, 5, 8
Highland	Badenoch and Strathspey Inverness	35	NH 6303	

Area (ha)	NNR	SPA		Ramsar	
1000-9999	No	Designated	N	Designated	N
		Candidate	Y	Candidate	N

A montane area with an important assemblage of upland breeding birds.

Site description

The Monadhliaths comprise a large area of high altitude tableland. The underlying Dalradian and Moine schists largely give rise to acidic soils, but in one glen there is an extensive calcareous outcrop on which the calcareous soils add to the biological diversity. The diversity is further enhanced by the steep-sided gullies and large cliff-fringed corries with species-poor lochs that punctuate the plateau.

A large proportion of the area above 600 m is dominated by blanket bog on which there is considerable erosion through gullying. The site supports a mosaic of upland plant communities. A variety of grass, heath and flush communities occur, changing with altitude and drainage. The lower slopes are dominated by a ling/hare's-tail cottongrass community grading with increasing altitude through a number of communities to be replaced by crowberry-blaeberry heath. The highest areas show an interesting mix of continental and oceanic heaths, with lichen-rich *Vaccinium-Empetrum* heath occurring on the same areas as the woolly-hair moss (*Racomitrium*) heath. A wide range of late snow-bed communities also occur.

Birds

This site is important for its assemblage of specialist montane bird species. In particular it holds over 1% of the British and EC breeding population of dotterel.

Conservation issues

The birds that use this site are vulnerable to human disturbance from increased public access, particularly from hill-walkers, to the high tops, and to habitat degradation through high livestock levels.

Further reading

Nethersole-Thompson, D 1973 *The dotterel*. Collins, London.

Alvie

SPA/Ram Code	IBA Europe number
254A	084

County/Region	District(s)	OS sheet(s)	Grid Reference(s)	Maps 5, 6, 8
Highland	Badenoch and Strathspey	35	NH 8709	

Area (ha)	NNR	SPA		Ramsar	
1-999	No	Designated	N	Designated	N
		Candidate	Y	Candidate	N

Lochs, marshes and birch woodland, important for breeding waterfowl.

Site description

Situated near the River Spey, this is a complex area consisting of the wooded Torr Alvie (358 m) sloping down to the north to a series of lochs and marshes. Loch Alvie is a shallow mesotrophic loch, while the smaller Loch Beag and the Bogach are eutrophic. The lochs are linked by a chain of mires, fens and marshes.

The woodland consists mainly of birch, but with aspen, rowan, Scots pine, oak and juniper in places. The pine is locally dominant, and a stand of pure oak woodland is one of few examples in the middle Spey valley. Stands of willow, birch and alder occur in wetter areas, and around the lochs.

The invertebrate fauna includes several rare species in a number of different groups, including true flies, caddis-flies and beetles.

Birds

This site is nationally important for breeding waterfowl.

Conservation issues

Alvie is highly vulnerable to disturbance by visitors.

Ben Alder

SPA/Ram Code	IBA Europe number
255A	N/A

County/Region	District(s)	OS sheet(s)	Grid Reference(s)	Map 8
Highland	Badenoch and Strathspey	42	NN 4974	

Area (ha)	NNR	SPA		Ramsar	
1000-9999	No	Designated	N	Designated	N
		Candidate	Y	Candidate	N

A montane area with an important assemblage of upland breeding birds.

Site description

This site lies in a remote area between Lochs Ericht and Laggan. It supports a great diversity of vegetation and fine examples of the vegetation complexes associated with prolonged snow cover. It is geographically and ecologically intermediate between the mountains of the western and eastern Highlands. Geologically it is composed largely of acidic Moine schists, but a band of limestone outcrops at one place between 900 and 1000 m and this supports a rich upland flora. These hills have suffered less from heavy grazing than many high hills of western Inverness-shire and this, together with the position and geology, has resulted in one of the most ecologically varied mountain systems in the western Grampians.

The large summit plateaux support a range of high level plant communities including the widespread woolly-fringe moss – stiff sedge heath which has a variety of different sub-types. The high altitude limestone outcrops increase the species diversity. Alpine species found here include mountain avens and cyphel. Other interesting and typical plant communities include bearberry – heather heath and extensive heather heath grading into heather – deer-grass blanket bog.

Birds

This site is important for its assemblage of specialist montane bird species. In particular it holds over 1% of the British and EC breeding population of dotterel.

Conservation issues

The birds that use this site are vulnerable to human disturbance from increased public access, particularly from hill-walkers, to the high tops, and to habitat degradation through high livestock levels.

Further reading

Nethersole-Thompson, D 1973 *The dotterel*. Collins, London.

Abernethy Forest

SPA/Ram Code	IBA Europe number
256A	081

County/Region	District(s)	OS sheet(s)	Grid Reference(s)	Maps 5, 6, 8
Highland	Badenoch and Strathspey	36	NJ 010165	

Area (ha)	NNR	SPA	Ramsar
5796	Part	Designated Y Candidate N/A	Designated N Candidate N

The largest tract of remnant native pinewood in Britain, important for various pinewood specialist bird species.

Site description

Lying on undulating glacial deposits to the north of the Cairngorms, Abernethy Forest is the largest tract of native pinewood in Britain, and represents part of a once continuous tract of woodland around the lower slopes of the Cairngorms. It forms part of the eastern group of pinewoods which includes Rothiemurchus (site 224A), Ballochbuie and Glen Tanar (site 277A). Parts of Abernethy consist of almost completely undisturbed high forest, but much of the northern area is semi-natural. Although much of the woodland is managed, it retains a high degree of naturalness, in terms of age and vertical structure, and the presence of a shrub layer of juniper. Some parts of the woodland are partly or completely dominated by broad-leaved tree species, especially birch.

Within the forest area, there is a series of oligotrophic to mesotrophic valley mires with many pools, and in free-draining areas dry heather-bearberry heath. The River Nethy flows through the forest, and together with lochs and lochans adds to the diversity of habitats.

Both plant and animal communities include many highly localised species, including those which are restricted to or characteristic of native pinewoods. These include flowering plants such as intermediate wintergreen, serrated wintergreen and twinflower. Abernethy is the only known British locality for nine species of microfungi, and 28 very rare species of lichen have been recorded from the old Scots pine and juniper woodland. The invertebrate fauna includes rare and scarce insects; over 400 species of beetle have been recorded from the area, including 15 species that are grade 1 indicators of ancient woodland. Scotch argus and dark green fritillary butterflies occur here and the rare northern damselfly breeds in the forest mires and lochans. Many species of mammal breed or use the site, notable amongst which are wildcat, badger and red squirrel.

Birds

Abernethy Forest supports important breeding populations of **goldeneye** (23 pairs, 26% of British), **capercaillie** (30-60+ pairs, 4% of British), **crested tit** (115-150 pairs, c. 4% of British) and **Scottish crossbill** (75-100 pairs, 25% of the world total). Other notable breeding species include golden eagle, osprey, black grouse, long-eared owl and siskin.

Conservation issues

The native pinewoods of the Scottish Highlands have been reduced by felling and fire to occupy at present only about 1% of their natural range. Maintenance and good management of remaining areas is a strong conservation priority.

The site is vulnerable to overgrazing by deer and sheep, preventing the natural regeneration of the native pinewoods, and is sensitive to visitor disturbance.

Capercaillie

Kinveachy

SPA/Ram Code	IBA Europe number
258A	082

County/Region	District(s)	OS sheet(s)	Grid Reference(s)	Maps 5, 6, 8
Highland	Badenoch and Strathspey	35, 36	NH 8517	

Area (ha)	NNR	SPA		Ramsar	
1000-9999	No	Designated	N	Designated	N
		Candidate	Y	Candidate	N

An important area of Caledonian pine forest and moorland, notable for native pinewood breeding bird species.

Site description
The principal stands of this remnant Caledonian pine forest lie south-west of Carrbridge on either side of the river Dulnain. The stocking is irregular, with dense stands of mature woodland separated by open moorland with scattered trees. Woodland to the south of the river is dominated by Scots pine, whilst on the north side, there are areas of broadleaved woodland, mostly of birch and alder; juniper scrub is extensive in places. Wet heathland and poor fen communities dominated by purple moor-grass, deer-grass and cotton-grass also occur.

Birds
The pinewood supports nationally important numbers of breeding **capercaillie, crested tit** and **Scottish crossbill**. Notable also in the woods and adjacent moorland are breeding merlin and black grouse.

Conservation issues
The native pinewoods of the Scottish Highlands have been reduced by felling and fire to occupy at present only about 1% of their natural range. Maintenance and good management of remaining areas is a strong conservation priority.

The site is vulnerable to overgrazing by deer and sheep, preventing the natural regeneration of the native pinewoods, and is sensitive to visitor disturbance.

Creag Meagaidh

SPA/Ram Code	IBA Europe number
261A	N/A

County/Region	District(s)	OS sheet(s)	Grid Reference(s)	Maps 4, 5, 8
Highland	Badenoch and Strathspey Lochaber	34, 35, 42	NN 4488	

Area (ha)	NNR	SPA		Ramsar	
1000-9999	Yes	Designated N		Designated N	
		Candidate Y		Candidate N	

A montane area with an important assemblage of upland breeding birds.

Site description
This is an outstanding upland site with a wide range of characteristic plant communities and some notable montane plants. A feature of the site is the uninterrupted transition of natural and semi-natural vegetation from the shores of Loch Laggan at 250 m to the summit of Creag Meagaidh at 1130 m.

The lower slopes of the site support a range of grass, heath and flush plant communities interspersed with extensive birchwoods. Above these slopes there is a broad summit plateau with large areas of *Racomitrium* heath and swards of stiff sedge. In places, communities associated with late snow patches are well represented. There are magnificent cliffs on the site; especially notable are the massive 400 m cliffs of Corrie Ardair and ungrazed cliff vegetation of both acidic and basic rocks is fully developed with, for example, wood vetch at lower levels and downy willow at higher altitudes.

Birds
This site is important for its assemblage of specialist montane bird species. In particular it holds over 1% of the British and EC breeding population of dotterel.

Conservation issues
The birds that use this site are vulnerable to human disturbance from increased public access, particularly from hill-walkers, to the high tops.

Further reading
Nethersole-Thompson, D 1973 *The dotterel*. Collins, London.

Lochs of Spiggie and Brow

SPA/Ram Code	IBA Europe number
265A	045

County/Region	District(s)	OS sheet(s)	Grid Reference(s)	Map 1
Shetland	N/A	4	HU 374160	

Area (ha)	NNR	SPA		Ramsar	
145.7	No	Designated	N	Designated	N
		Candidate	Y	Candidate	Y

The largest eutrophic 'machair type' lochs in Shetland, which attract large numbers of wintering and passage whooper swans.

Site description
The Loch of Spiggie was formed through the closure of a shallow voe from the sea by a sand bar. Both the Loch of Spiggie and the Loch of Brow have slightly brackish conditions, as indicated by the presence of invertebrates such as the crustacean *Neomysis integer*. The sand and mud substrates of the lochs support communities dominated by stoneworts *Chara aspersa* and *Nitella opaca*, slender-leaved pondweed, and the moss *Fontinalis antipyretica*.

Birds
These lochs support internationally important numbers of wintering **whooper swan**. In the five-winter period 1985/86 to 1989/90 the average peak count was 180 birds (1% of the world total, 3% of the number wintering in Britain), with a maximum of 384 birds in October 1986. Peak numbers usually occur here in early winter.

Conservation issues
The birds that use this site are vulnerable to drainage, agricultural run-off, pollution and to disturbance by wildfowlers.

Further reading
Berry, R J and Johnson, J L 1980 *The natural history of Shetland*. Collins, New Naturalist, London.

Mill Dam, Shapinsay

SPA/Ram Code	IBA Europe number
267A	056

County/Region	District(s)	OS sheet(s)	Grid Reference(s)	Map 2
Orkney	N/A	6	HY 4817	

Area (ha)	NNR	SPA		Ramsar	
1-999	No	Designated	N	Designated	N
		Candidate	Y	Candidate	Y

A man-made lake important for breeding pintail and wintering whooper swan.

Site description
An artificial water body now largely encroached by vegetation, but with open water mainly after heavy rain.

Birds
The site holds nationally important numbers of breeding **pintail** (2-3 pairs, 5% of British) and wintering **whooper swan** (120 birds, 2% of British).

Conservation issues
Birds that use this site are vulnerable to loss of open water through natural vegetation succession exacerbated by fertiliser run-off.

Rosehearty to
Fraserburgh Coast

SPA/Ram Code	IBA Europe number
268A	070

County/Region	District(s)	OS sheet(s)	Grid Reference(s)	Map 6
Grampian	Banff and Buchan	30	NJ 967675	

Area (ha)	NNR	SPA		Ramsar	
1-999	No	Designated	N	Designated	N
		Candidate	Y	Candidate	Y

A length of rocky and sandy shore, attracting wintering waders.

Site description

This exposed north-facing coast running west from the town of Fraserburgh has fairly extensive intertidal mud and sand flats interspersed with low rocky outcrops. There are some coastal lagoons, backed by a narrow fringe of sand dunes and saltmarsh. The littoral zone has a rich invertebrate fauna, important as prey for wintering birds; the mollusc fauna is particularly noteworthy.

Birds

This stretch of coast supports internationally important numbers of wintering turnstone and nationally important numbers of purple sandpiper.

Counts during the 1980s have regularly found over 250 **purple sandpiper** (2% of British; up to 620) and over 750 **turnstone** (1% of EAF, 2% of British; up to 1200). Notable also are wintering eider, curlew and redshank. Divers and other seaduck are often present.

Conservation issues

Birds that depend on these coastal habitats are vulnerable to land–claim, oil pollution and human disturbance. Illegal dumping of waste occurs on this site, and it is necessary to monitor the effects this may have on wader populations.

Further reading

North East Scotland Bird Report 1975-89. Aberdeen University Bird Club.

Orphir and Stenness Hills

SPA/Ram Code	IBA Europe number
269A	061

County/Region	District(s)	OS sheet(s)	Grid Reference(s)	Map 2
Orkney	N/A	6	HY 3308	

Area (ha)	NNR	SPA		Ramsar	
1000-9999	No	Designated	N	Designated	N
		Candidate	Y	Candidate	N

An area of moorland important for breeding birds of prey and other species.

Site description
This area of moorland on the Orkney Mainland, rising to 275 m at Mid Hill, is dominated by various heath communities, including dwarf shrub (heather), deer grass, and lichen heaths. A colony of the nationally scarce pyramidal bugle is present. Small burns run along the numerous dales, and these sheltered areas hold tall herb and flush vegetation.

Birds
This area supports nationally important numbers of breeding **hen harrier**. In 1989 a total of 22 nests was recorded in this area, representing 3.5% of the current British breeding population. Notable also are breeding kestrel, merlin, red grouse, golden plover, and short-eared owl.

Conservation issues
Birds that use this site are vulnerable to agricultural intensification through reseeding, ploughing, overburning and mechanical peat-cutting.

Keelylang

SPA/Ram Code	IBA Europe number
270A	N/A

County/Region	District(s)	OS sheet(s)	Grid Reference(s)	Map 2
Orkney	N/A	6	HY 3909	

Area (ha)	NNR	SPA		Ramsar	
1-999	No	Designated	N	Designated	N
		Candidate	Y	Candidate	N

Moorland supporting important numbers of breeding hen harriers.

Site description
An area of typical Orkney moorland dominated by heather and bog cotton, with extensive stands of greater woodrush.

Birds
The site supports nationally important numbers of breeding **hen harrier**, regularly in excess of 7 females (1% of British).

Notable also are breeding merlin, curlew and short–eared owl.

Conservation issues
Birds that use this site are vulnerable to changes in agricultural management, especially changes in grazing pressure.

Loch of Isbister

SPA/Ram Code	IBA Europe number
271A	N/A

County/Region	District(s)	OS sheet(s)	Grid Reference(s)	Map 2
Orkney	N/A	6	HY 2524	

Area (ha)	NNR	SPA		Ramsar	
1-999	No	Designated	N	Designated	N
		Candidate	Y	Candidate	N

A basin mire and eutrophic lochs supporting breeding and wintering wildfowl and breeding waders.

Site description
The basin mire is separated from the eutrophic Loch of Isbister by low ridges of glacial till. Encroachment by peripheral vegetation has resulted in the development of Orkney's best basin-mire complex. There are excellent examples of open-water transition plant communities while the mosaic of bog habitats supports a very rich assemblage of wetland plants. The site includes the Loch of Banks (90 ha), a partially drained loch, with its southern end drying out in summer. There is luxuriant growth of marginal vegetation, and an extensive reedbed.

Birds
The area supports nationally important numbers of breeding pintail.

In recent years 6-10 pairs of **pintail** have bred (20% of British). A colony of arctic terns is present and up to 250 pairs have been recorded. Notable also are breeding wigeon, shoveler, dunlin, snipe, curlew and redshank, and wintering Greenland white-fronted goose, greylag goose, wigeon, teal and hen harrier.

Conservation issues
Birds that use this site are vulnerable to drainage, but various conservation measures including reserve acquisition by the RSPB have reduced this threat.

In recent years shooting had been a problem. However, creation of a no-shooting buffer zone by the RSPB in conjunction with local landowners is succeeding.

Blackpark and Gutcher, Yell

SPA/Ram Code	IBA Europe number
272A	038

County/Region	District(s)	OS sheet(s)	Grid Reference(s)	Map 1
Shetland	N/A	1	HU 5399	

Area (ha)	NNR	SPA		Ramsar	
1000-9999	No	Designated	N	Designated	N
		Candidate	Y	Candidate	N

Areas of blanket bog supporting an important assemblage of breeding birds.

Site description
This is an area of blanket bog on deep peat, dominated by heather, cotton-grass and deer-grass, which has been partly drained in the past. There are a number of fresh water lochs. Black Park also has areas of acid grassland and *Sphagnum*-rich mire.

Birds
The area supports nationally important numbers of breeding red-throated diver, whimbrel and arctic skua.

A comprehensive breeding season survey in 1986 recorded 13 pairs of **red-throated divers** (1% of British and EC population), 28 pairs of **whimbrels** (6% of British and EC), and 32 pairs of **arctic skuas** (1% of British). Notable also are breeding golden plover.

Conservation issues
Birds that use the site are vulnerable to agricultural changes, especially reseeding and changes in grazing pressure.

Further reading
Rothwell, A, Stroud, D A and Shepherd, K B 1988 *Shetland Moorland Bird Surveys 1986*. NCC CSD Report No. 775.

Loch Oire

SPA/Ram Code	IBA Europe number
274A	068

County/Region	District(s)	OS sheet(s)	Grid Reference(s)	Maps 5, 6
Grampian	Moray	28	NJ 2860	

Area (ha)	NNR	SPA		Ramsar	
1-999	No	Designated	N	Designated	N
		Candidate	Y	Candidate	Y

A small mesotrophic loch, important for breeding waterfowl.

Site description
Located about 7 km east of Elgin, Loch Oire is one of the few lochans remaining in the hummocky glacial deposits of lowland Moray. It has an undisturbed aquatic plant community, with diverse submerged and emergent vegetation, sedge fen and marginal carr woodland.

Birds
The site is of international importance for a variety of breeding waterfowl.

Conservation issues
Birds that use this site are vulnerable to nutrient enrichment and human disturbance from adjacent roads and lay-bys. Management of fisheries poses a potential problem.

Loch Vaa

SPA/Ram Code	IBA Europe number
275A	083

County/Region	District(s)	OS sheet(s)	Grid Reference(s)	Maps 5, 6, 8
Highland	Badenoch and Strathspey	36	NH 9117	

Area (ha)	NNR	SPA		Ramsar	
1-999	No	Designated Candidate	N Y	Designated Candidate	N N

A loch, surrounded by woodland, important for breeding waterfowl.

Site description

Loch Vaa is a small mesotrophic, spring–fed loch, of about 500 m diameter. The shore line forms a series of small bays and inlets and is vegetated with fen and bog communities. The loch is surrounded by deciduous woodland, comprising mainly birch to the south and plantation Scots pine to the north. Small ephemeral pools around the loch are important for insects, notably water beetles and the northern damselfly.

Birds

Loch Vaa supports nationally important numbers of breeding waterfowl. Crested tit and Scottish crossbill breed in surrounding Scots pine.

Conservation issues

Birds that rely on northern freshwater lochs are vulnerable to changes in water quality and the consequent impacts on food resources. Damage can be caused by the acidic run-off from conifer plantations in the catchment area and from fish farm developments. The site is vulnerable to recreational disturbance, particularly from anglers and birdwatchers.

Glen Tanar

SPA/Ram Code	IBA Europe number
277A	078

County/Region	District(s)	OS sheet(s)	Grid Reference(s)	Maps 5, 6
Grampian	Kincardine and Deeside	44	NO 460930	

Area (ha)	NNR	SPA		Ramsar	
1000-9999	Yes	Designated	N	Designated	N
		Candidate	Y	Candidate	N

A large area of native pinewood, with some heather moorland, important for several characteristic pinewood bird species.

Site description

The Forest of Glen Tanar covers the slopes of Glen Tanar and tributary valleys, rising to the present tree line at about 450 m. It is the third largest expanse of native pinewood in Britain. Broad-leaved species are uncommon. Much of the forest is fenced against deer, and regeneration is occurring, giving a more varied range of age classes than in most native pinewoods. The woodland field layer is typically a bilberry-moss or bilberry-heather community on the free-draining soils. Characteristic pinewood plants include twinflower, creeping lady's-tresses, and toothed and intermediate wintergreens. The fungus flora and invertebrate fauna are diverse.

Above the tree line, there is heather moorland, with a series of mires and flushes. In places, the pinewood is extending into the moorland.

Birds

The forest contains nationally important populations of **capercaillie** (80-90 birds, 8% of British) and **black grouse,** and is one of the most important localities for the endemic Scottish crossbill. This area is also important for raptors including hen harrier, golden eagle and merlin.

Conservation issues

The native pinewoods of the Scottish Highlands have been reduced by felling and fire to occupy at present only about 1% of their natural range. Maintenance and good management of remaining areas is a strong conservation priority.

Further reading

Buckland S T, Bell M V and Picozzi N (eds.) 1990 *The Birds of North-East Scotland.* North-East Scotland Bird Club, Aberdeen.

Muir of Dinnet

SPA/Ram Code	IBA Europe number
279A	076

County/Region	District(s)	OS sheet(s)	Grid Reference(s)	Maps 5, 6
Grampian	Kincardine and Deeside	37, 44	NO 433000	

Area (ha)	NNR	SPA		Ramsar	
1000-9999	Yes	Designated	N	Designated	N
		Candidate	Y	Candidate	Y

A complex of heath, woodland and mire, with two sizable lochs of high importance for greylag geese in autumn and winter.

Site description

The open water areas are of prime interest to greylag geese which use them for roosting. Adjacent land supports a mosaic of communities located on granite overlain by glacial drift. Classic vegetational succession from open water to fen habitat is found at Loch Kinord and includes fens of bottle sedge, slender sedge, and stands of bog-myrtle. Other habitats include wet heath at Black Moss which is dominated by cross-leaved heath, purple moor grass, heather and *Sphagnum* moss. Swamps, such as that at Ordie Moss, are dominated by bottle sedge or common reed. There is also carr woodland of willow and birch around the Lochs Kinord and Davan, together with other wetland vegetation.

Birds

An internationally important autumn passage and wintering area for Icelandic **greylag geese**, which roost on the lochs. In the five-winter period 1985/86 to 1989/90 the average peak count was 13,000 birds (13% of the world total). Up to 25,300 birds have been recorded in autumn (November 1988).

Moorland Areas, Central Shetland

SPA/Ram Code	IBA Europe number
280A	N/A

County/Region	District(s)	OS sheet(s)	Grid Reference(s)	Map 1
Shetland	N/A	3,4, 5	HU 4040	

Area (ha)	NNR	SPA		Ramsar	
10,000+	No	Designated	N	Designated	N
		Candidate	Y	Candidate	N

Areas of blanket bog supporting an important assemblage of breeding birds.

Site description
This area supports a variety of plant communities, especially *Calluna/Tricophorum/Eriophorum* mire, with *Sphagnum* mire in the wetter areas. Heathland and acid grassland communities occur in drier areas. Marshy areas adjacent to lochans support stands of yellow iris, bogbean, spike-rush *Eleocharis* species and rush *Juncus* species.

Birds
The area supports nationally important numbers of breeding whimbrel and arctic skua.

A breeding season survey in 1986 in parts of this area recorded 48 pairs of **whimbrels** (10% of British and EC) and 63 pairs of **arctic skuas** (2% of British). Notable also are breeding red-throated diver, merlin, oystercatcher, golden plover and curlew.

Conservation issues
Birds that use the site are vulnerable to agricultural changes, especially reseeding and changes in grazing pressure.

Further reading
Rothwell, A, Stroud, D A and Shepherd, K B 1988 *Shetland Moorland Bird Surveys, 1986.* NCC CSD Report No. 775.

West Burrafirth

SPA/Ram Code	IBA Europe number
283A	N/A

County/Region	District(s)	OS sheet(s)	Grid Reference(s)	Map 1
Shetland	N/A	3	HU 2754	

Area (ha)	NNR	SPA		Ramsar	
1000-9999	No	Designated	N	Designated	N
		Candidate	Y	Candidate	N

Areas of blanket bog supporting an important assemblage of breeding birds.

Site description
Heather moorland, bordered to the south by degraded areas of *Nardus* grassland and with extensive blanket bog in the east. There are many lochs and several small areas of upland mire.

Birds
The area supports nationally important numbers of breeding red-throated diver and whimbrel.

A comprehensive breeding season survey in 1986 recorded 25 pairs of **red-throated divers** (2% of British and EC) and 13 pairs of **whimbrels** (3% of British and EC). Notable also are breeding merlin, oystercatcher, golden plover, lapwing, curlew, greenshank and arctic skua.

Conservation issues
Birds that use the site are vulnerable to agricultural changes, especially reseeding, moor (muir) burn and changes in grazing pressure.

Further reading
Rothwell, A, Stroud, D A and Shepherd, K B 1988 *Shetland moorland bird surveys, 1986*. NCC CSD Report No. 775.

Hill of Colvadale and Sobul

SPA/Ram Code	IBA Europe number
284A	N/A

County/Region	District(s)	OS sheet(s)	Grid Reference(s)	Map 1
Shetland	N/A	1	HP 6105	

Area (ha)	NNR	SPA		Ramsar	
1-999	No	Designated	N	Designated	N
		Candidate	Y	Candidate	N

An area of serpentine heathland in east Unst with a rich assemblage of breeding birds including whimbrel and arctic skua.

Site description
The area contains a range of vegetation types. In the northern and western parts of the site there is herb-rich sedge-grass heath over serpentinite. In the southern and eastern parts of the site there are relatively species-poor dry and wet heaths dominated by *Calluna vulgaris* and *Racomitrium lanuginosum* over the metagabbro. There are areas of deeper peat, wet flush and mire throughout the site. A number of notable arctic alpine species such as three-flowered rush and alpine saussurea have been recorded from the Colvadale area. The main land-use is sheep grazing.

Birds
The area supports nationally important numbers of breeding whimbrel and arctic skua.

A breeding survey of this area in 1985 revealed 43 pairs of **whimbrel**s (9% British and EC) and 90 pairs of **arctic skua**s (3% of British). Notable also are breeding red-throated diver, merlin, golden plover, great skua and greylag goose.

Conservation issues
Birds that use this site are vulnerable to changes in agricultural management, especially reseeding and changes in grazing pressure. This site is also vulnerable to mineral exploration and extraction.

An Socach – Carn a Gheoidh

SPA/Ram Code	IBA Europe number
285A	N/A

County/Region	District(s)	OS sheet(s)	Grid Reference(s)	Map 6
Grampian	Perth and Kinross Kincardine and Deeside	43	NO 1278	

Area (ha)	NNR	SPA		Ramsar	
1-999	No	Designated	N	Designated	N
		Candidate	Y	Candidate	N

A montane area with an important assemblage of upland breeding birds.

Site description
An area of upland montane plateaux and associated habitats. Geologically this area comprises Dalradian limestone and calcareous schist. Cairnwell is of particular importance on account of its sugar limestone grassland/heath vegetation which is uncommon in Britain. Glas Tulaichean has a rich, although somewhat localised, cliff flora. It also has a representative range of summit vegetation, including montane heaths.

Birds
This site is important for its assemblage of specialist montane bird species. In particular it holds over 1% of the British and EC breeding population of dotterel.

Conservation issues
The birds that use this site are vulnerable to human disturbance from increased public access, particularly from hill-walkers, to the high tops, and to habitat degradation through high livestock levels.

Further reading
Nethersole-Thompson, D 1973 *The dotterel*. Collins, London.

Loch Lomond

SPA/Ram Code	IBA Europe number
302A	104

County/Region	District(s)	OS sheet(s)	Grid Reference(s)	Maps 8, 10
Strathclyde	Dumbarton	56, 57	NS 4389	
Central	Stirling			

Area (ha)	NNR	SPA		Ramsar	
1-999	Part	Designated	N	Designated	Y
		Candidate	Y	Candidate	Y

An area of marshland in the south-east corner of the loch, important for wintering Greenland white-fronted and greylag geese, together with wooded islands used by capercaillie.

Site description

Loch Lomond is the largest freshwater body in Britain, measuring over 36 km in length and up to 7 km wide. The loch is located across the Highland Boundary Fault and displays a gradation in water chemistry from the oligotrophic north to mesotrophic or eutrophic conditions in the south. Fish in the loch include powan which are only found in Scotland in Loch Lomond and the nearby Loch Eck.

The larger islands are clustered in the southern part of the loch. Some are inhabited, others are more natural. The principal habitat on most islands is woodland.

Marshes are most extensively developed in the south-east corner of the loch, where the River Endrick flows into the loch. They include rough grassland, and swamps dominated by reed sweet-grass, bladder-sedge and other species, some cut as a bog hay meadow. These marshes are adjoined by woodland, grading from alder and willow carr to dry oak-birch woodland.

Birds

The area of Loch Lomond at the mouth of the River Endrick is an internationally important wintering site for Greenland white-fronted and greylag geese. In the five-year period 1984/85 to 1988/89 the average peak count for Greenland **white-fronted goose** was 240 birds (1% of the world population, 2% of British) and for **greylag goose** was 1450 birds (1.5% of the world and British total of the Icelandic population). Other wintering wildfowl of note include whooper swan, wigeon (440), teal (290) and shoveler. Breeding species include shoveler (>6 pairs) together with goosander and red-breasted merganser in the environs. Small numbers of capercaillie breed on some of the Loch Lomond islands and on the eastern shore; a census in 1991 located a total of 13 adult birds.

Conservation issues

The birds of Loch Lomond are vulnerable to intensive and increasing human recreational use (water sports activity, including water-skiing and jetskis, is increasing, particularly in the southern part) and to changes in water quality through agricultural run-off, sewage pollution and through afforestation of surrounding land. The water level of the loch has been raised to allow greater water abstraction. Common scoter formerly bred on the loch but have not occurred in recent years, probably due to increasing levels of human disturbance.

Further reading

Mitchell, J 1984 The birds of the Endrick Mouth, Loch Lomond. *The Scottish Naturalist*, 1984, 3–47.

Jones, A M 1990 Capercaillie numbers on three Loch Lomond islands. *Scottish Birds* 16: 47.

Tiree and Coll

SPA/Ram Code	IBA Europe number
303A	087

County/Region	District(s)	OS sheet(s)	Grid Reference(s)	Map 7
Strathclyde	Argyll and Bute	46	NM 0045 (Tiree), NM 2758 (Coll)	

Area (ha)	NNR	SPA		SPA		Ramsar	
1000-9999	No	Designated	N	Wider		Designated	N
		Candidate	Y	Countryside Measures Candidate		Candidate	Y

The Inner Hebridean islands of Tiree and Coll are of major international importance for a range of bird species associated with wetlands and low intensity agricultural lands on machair. These include one of the very few healthy populations of breeding corncrakes in Britain, and assemblages of wintering and breeding waders and wildfowl.

Site description

Coll is a whale-backed island with an underlying nutrient-poor gneissic geology. Rock outcrops occur throughout the island which is largely covered by a variety of peaty and acidic plant communities. Large areas are covered in blanket bog, dry and wet heaths, and other acidic plant communities. Low-intensity cultivation is confined to limited coastal areas (although nowhere is far from the sea), particularly where blown sand has resulted in formation of richer soils. There are many lochs, particularly in the northern part of the island. These act as roosting areas for Greenland white-fronted geese and also hold rare plant species.

South Coll is lower lying and dominated by dune grasslands and machair. A large area of sand-dunes occurs near Breachacha while near the western point of the island is an extensive area of sandy grassland, which contains wetter areas prone to seasonal flooding.

Tiree is a low flat island overlooked by three hills (Ben Hynish, Beinn Hough and Ceann a' Mhara), all towards the west. There is a central, extensive area of wetland and freshwater marsh north and east of the Reef, parts of which used to be more brackish when the watercourse, An Fhaodhail, was directly connected to the sea and regular salt-water incursions occurred, especially at spring tides. As a consequence, the area was important for a variety of rare plants associated with these mild brackish conditions. A pipe now takes the water from the Reef under the road and a sluice prevents seawater flowing inland. The result has been to allow the Reef to change to more freshwater conditions, to the detriment of some of the flora. Waders nest here in extraordinarily high densities.

Unlike Coll, virtually all peat deposits on Tiree have been cut away in the past to provide domestic fuel and the few peaty areas that remain are much modified and very different from those found under undisturbed conditions. Indeed, such acidic habitats are restricted to only a few central areas of Tiree (where they are important breeding areas for native greylag geese). Elsewhere the large amounts of blown shell sand has made Tiree soils markedly base-rich.

Lochs are fewer, and generally larger and shallower than on Coll. Several particularly large lochs (Loch Riaghain, Loch a'Phuill, Loch Bhasapoll and Loch an Eilean) occur with fringing areas of wet croftlands. As in the Uists, such lochs lie between inland areas of more acidic, heathy vegetation and coastal areas with more calcareous machair soils. The particular nature of these lochs means that they are of conservation importance both to breeding and wintering ducks, geese and swans and to breeding waders.

Long, sandy beaches more or less encircle Tiree and these are important for many wintering and migrant waders, as well as breeding terns. Large amounts of seaweed on the driftline are particularly important feeding areas for some waders. Cliffs at Ceann a' Mhara are also important for breeding terns and other seabirds.

On the tops of small cliffs, and just inland from dunes and rocky shores in the north of the island (between Balephetrish and Caoles), areas of wind-clipped maritime turf occur. These exposed, spray-drenched short swards are dominated by salt-tolerant plants such as red fescue and sea plantain, and are highly favoured feeding areas for barnacle geese.

On Tiree there are extensive areas of machair. The island machairs of western Scotland have developed from coastal landforms and a long history of low intensity cultivation. Grazing by sheep and cattle occurs throughout machair habitats and is an important factor in their development. Most of Tiree is crofted. The maintenance of this system of agriculture is of particular importance for nature conservation.

SSSI/SPA designation is appropriate for the core areas of bird interest within this extensive tract of land, while 'wider countryside' conservation measures are appropriate in other parts.

Birds
The two islands support a total of 12 Annex 1 species, including internationally important populations of breeding red-throated diver, greylag goose, corncrake and dunlin and wintering Greenland white-fronted goose, greylag goose, Greenland barnacle goose, ringed plover and turnstone. The figures given below are minima and relate to areas of the islands currently proposed for site-based protection.

In summer Tiree and Coll hold large numbers of breeding **corncrakes**, with about 117 calling birds recorded (about 3% of the declining western European population and 20% of British). Numbers on Tiree have been sustained throughout recent decades whilst elsewhere in Scotland numbers have declined markedly. Up to 14 pairs of **red-throated divers** occur on freshwater lochs on Coll (about 1% of the British and EC breeding populations). Also breeding are 90 pairs of **greylag geese** (5% of the North Scottish biogeographical population), at least 4 pairs of **pintail** (11% of British), over 225 pairs of **dunlin** (2% of the temperate population of the *schinzii* race; 2·5% of British) and about 80 pairs of **little terns** (3% of British).

Notable also are breeding fulmar, shoveler, merlin, peregrine, oystercatcher, ringed plover, lapwing, snipe, redshank, arctic skua, kittiwake, common tern, arctic tern, guillemot and razorbill.

Tiree and Coll are important as staging areas for certain migratory bird species in spring and autumn. This is especially the case for whooper swan, golden plover, lapwing, dunlin and snipe.

In winter the area supports an average of 145 **whooper swans** (2% of British), 980 Greenland **white-fronted geese** (5% of the world population and 11% of the number wintering in Britain), 380 **greylag geese** (>5% of the north Scottish biogeographical population), 770 Greenland **barnacle geese** (2% of the world population and 4% of British), 1025 **ringed plover** (2% of the EAF population, 4% of British), 380 **sanderling** (3% of British), 180 **purple sandpiper** (1% of British) and 1040 **turnstone** (1.5% of the EAF population, 2% of British).

Conservation issues
Many of the bird species, such as corncrake and breeding waders, on Tiree and Coll are associated with managed landscapes. The persistence of traditional agricultural practices in these areas, particularly pastoralism, is crucial to the maintenance of this special wildlife interest.

The birds that use Tiree are vulnerable to changes in agricultural practices and to increased disturbance through recreation and tourism.

On Coll, large scale burning of heather moorland has reduced the availability of habitat for some breeding moorland bird species.

Further reading
Stroud, D A (ed.) 1989 *Birds on Coll and Tiree: Status, Habitats and Conservation.* NCC and SOC, Edinburgh.

Dunlin

Treshnish Isles

SPA/Ram Code	IBA Europe number
304A	088

County/Region	District(s)	OS sheet(s)	Grid Reference(s)	Map 7
Strathclyde	Argyll and Bute	46	NM 2741	

Area (ha)	NNR	SPA		Ramsar	
208	No	Designated	N	Designated	N
		Candidate	Y	Candidate	N

A string of islands and skerries with breeding seabird colonies, and attracting internationally important numbers of barnacle geese in winter.

Site description

The islands are notable geomorphologically for the high-level shore platform, which is particularly striking on Bac Mor (Dutchman's Cap). The islands are rocky, with cliffs and screes. There is a strong maritime influence on the grassland and heath vegetation, and there are marked contrasts between islands. Large numbers of common seal and grey seal breed on Lunga.

Birds

Especially important for breeding storm petrels and wintering Greenland barnacle geese.

The islands support a large breeding colony of **storm petrels**, estimated to hold about 2000 pairs (c. 3% of British). Other notable breeding seabirds include fulmar (750 AOS), Manx shearwater (estimated 300 pairs), shag (155 pairs), herring gull (345 pairs), great black-backed gull (95 pairs), guillemot (4780 individuals), razorbill (240 individuals), black guillemot (40 individuals) and puffin (750 individuals). The most important colonies, including the majority of auks and the Manx shearwaters and storm petrels, are on Lunga.

The grasslands are grazed in winter by large numbers of **barnacle geese**. The mean number recorded during the last five spring aerial surveys was 565 birds (Fox et al 1990), representing 2% of the world and British wintering populations.

Conservation issues

Seabirds are sensitive to changes in the quality of the marine environment, especially to changes in fish stocks and to oil pollution. Ground-nesting seabirds on offshore islands are vulnerable to the introduction of predatory mammals.

Appropriate grazing management of the grassland is important for the maintenance of the wintering goose population.

This site is vulnerable to disturbance from increasing numbers of uncontrolled visitors landed on Lunga by commercial operators during the summer.

Further reading

Fox, A D, Ogilvie, M A, Easterbee, N, and Bignal E M 1990 East Greenland Barnacle Geese in Scotland, Spring 1988. *Scottish Birds* 16: 1-10.

Islay: Loch Gruinart

SPA/Ram Code	IBA Europe number
305A	093

County/Region	District(s)	OS sheet(s)	Grid Reference(s)	Map 7
Strathclyde	Argyll and Bute	60	NR 285665	

Area (ha)	NNR	SPA	Ramsar
3170	No	Designated Y Candidate N/A	Designated Y Candidate N/A

Intertidal and coastal habitats attracting internationally important numbers of wintering barnacle geese and other species.

Site description

Loch Gruinart is a north-facing sea loch, over 5 km long, with wide intertidal mud and sand flats. There is some saltmarsh on the loch margins, and extensive areas of sand dunes at the mouth of the loch. The hinterland is predominantly grassland, cut for hay and silage and grazed by cattle and sheep, but attracting geese in winter. Much of it is intensified agricultural land, but some rush-rich swards remain, including both acidic and base-rich examples. To the south, there is an area of heathland and blanket mire. Other habitats include drainage channels and lochs, and woodlands.

Both Loch Gruinart and Nave Island, hold grey and common seals, the latter site having a sizeable grey seal colony.

Birds

This site supports internationally important numbers of Greenland white-fronted goose and Greenland barnacle goose, together with nationally important numbers of breeding hen harrier and chough.

Loch Gruinart is of major importance to wintering barnacle geese from the population that breeds in Greenland. They use the site for feeding, loafing and as a night-time roost. Daytime numbers in recent winters have averaged 14,550 birds (45% of the world population, 54% of the number wintering in Britain). Numbers are swollen at night when birds that feed elsewhere on Islay gather to roost. Virtually the whole of the Greenland population of **barnacle geese** (>95%) stage at Loch Gruinart in autumn before dispersing more widely within the wintering range in Britain and Ireland. Also present are feeding flocks of wintering Greenland **white-fronted geese**, with an average of 930 birds recorded in recent winters (4% of the world population, 9% of the number wintering in Britain).

The area supports up to 10 breeding pairs of **chough** (4% of British) and is also used as a winter feeding area with, for example, up to 44 choughs (6% of the British wintering population) recorded in 1990. Other breeding species include **hen harrier**, corncrake, lapwing, redshank, arctic tern, little tern and barn owl.

211

Notable also are wintering hen harrier, buzzard, golden eagle, merlin, peregrine and barn owl, and passage whooper swan (up to 480 birds), light-bellied brent goose and ringed plover (up to 300 birds).

Conservation issues

Wintering barnacle geese are vulnerable to changes in grassland management regimes and to human disturbance.

Pastures on RSPB's Loch Gruinart Reserve are specifically managed for the benefit of the geese. Outside the reserve farmers have entered into management agreements with NCC/SNH to maintain areas for the geese and not to scare birds from the land. Shellfish farming has recently been introduced to the area and needs to be monitored.

Further reading

Bignal, E M, Curtis, D J and Matthews, J 1988 *Islay: Land types, bird habitats and nature conservation. Part 1. Land types and birds on Islay*. NCC CSD Report No. 809, Part 1.

Ogilvie, M A 1983 Wildfowl of Islay. *Proceedings of the Royal Society of Edinburgh*, 83B: 473-489.

Easterbee, N, Stroud, D A, Bignal, E M and Dick, T D 1987 The arrival of Greenland Barnacle geese at Loch Gruinart, Islay. *Scottish Birds* 14: 175-179.

Islay: Bridgend Flats

SPA/Ram Code	IBA Europe number
305B	094

County/Region	District(s)	OS sheet(s)	Grid Reference(s)	Map 7
Strathclyde	Argyll and Bute	60	NR 330620	

Area (ha)	NNR	SPA	Ramsar
331	No	Designated Y Candidate N/A	Designated Y Candidate N/A

Saltmarsh and intertidal flats, important for wintering geese and other waterfowl.

Site description

Despite its south-western aspect, the inner part of Loch Indaal is sheltered to an extent by Laggan Point and the Rinns. This has allowed sand and mud flats, backed by saltmarsh, to develop at Bridgend, giving rise to one of the few extensive areas of intertidal flats in the Inner Hebrides. These flats provide a feeding and roosting ground for a wide range of wintering wildfowl and waders and other waterfowl.

Birds

Bridgend Flats are used for roosting by internationally important numbers of barnacle geese from the population that breeds in Greenland.

Barnacle geese that winter on Islay roost at night in two main areas – Bridgend Flats and Loch Gruinart. The Bridgend Flats roost regularly holds up to 6700 birds (21% of the world population, 25% of the number wintering in Britain). These geese feed on the merse (saltmarsh) to some extent, but their main feeding sites are on farmland inland. Offshore, the area also holds nationally important numbers of wintering **scaup** (mean 1040 birds, 26% of British) and **red-breasted merganser** (mean 115 birds, 1% of British).

Other species of note include wintering whooper swan, eider, peregrine, oystercatcher, ringed plover, golden plover, dunlin, bar-tailed godwit and redshank.

Conservation issues

Waterfowl that winter on estuaries are vulnerable to land-claim and other developments that would disturb or damage the existing ecology of these sites. Other human influences such as recreational disturbance, commercial exploitation of shellfish and worms, and oil and industrial pollution, are also potentially damaging to the conservation interest of estuaries. The impacts of shellfish cultivation need to be monitored. Bridgend Flats have been threatened recently by proposals to construct a road across the flats and merse.

Further reading

Bignal, E M, Curtis, D J and Matthews, J 1988 *Islay: Land types, bird habitats and nature conservation. Part 1. Land types and birds on Islay.* NCC CSD Report No. 809, Part 1.

Ogilvie, M A 1983 Wildfowl of Islay. *Proceedings of the Royal Society of Edinburgh*, 83B: 473–489.

Islay: Laggan

SPA/Ram Code	IBA Europe number
305C	095

County/Region	District(s)	OS sheet(s)	Grid Reference(s)	Map 7
Strathclyde	Argyll and Bute	60	NR 297555	

Area (ha)	NNR	SPA	Ramsar
1270	No	Designated Y	Designated N
		Candidate N/A	Candidate N

Peatland, dunes and other coastal habitats important for wintering geese.

Site description

This area includes the rocky headland of Laggan Point, backed by blanket mire, and the broad, sandy sweep of Laggan Bay with its dunes and dune grassland. There is also an extensive area of intensified and rush-rich grassland used for feeding by the wintering geese.

Birds

The area supports internationally important numbers of wintering Greenland white-fronted goose and Greenland barnacle goose, together with nationally important numbers of breeding and wintering chough.

In recent years barnacle goose numbers have averaged 3190 birds (10% of the world population, 12% of the number wintering in Britain). They feed on the intensified fields, but occur widely elsewhere on the site, especially when disturbed. The majority move to Bridgend Flats to roost at night. Greenland **white-fronted goose** numbers have averaged 320 birds in recent years (1.5% of the world population, 3% of the number wintering in Britain). They feed principally on the more rush-rich pastures, but like barnacle geese are found throughout the site, including the dune grassland and peatland areas. The Greenland white-fronted geese roost principally on Eilean na Muice Duibh.

Choughs breed (3 pairs, 1% of British) with larger numbers (20, 3% of the British wintering population) occurring in winter. The strands support breeding colonies of arctic and little terns.

Conservation issues

Wintering barnacle and white-fronted geese are vulnerable to changes in grassland management regimes and to human disturbance. Part of the Laggan area is managed as a goose refuge with payments to farmers for appropriate grassland management. Tern colonies on beaches, and other nesting birds are vulnerable to human disturbance.

Further reading

Bignal, E M, Curtis, D J and Matthews, J 1988 *Islay: Land types, bird habitats and nature conservation. Part 1. Land types and birds on Islay.* NCC CSD Report No. 809, Part 1.

Ogilvie, M A 1983 Wildfowl of Islay. *Proceedings of the Royal Society of Edinburgh,* 83B: 473-489.

Islay: Eilean na Muice Duibh (Duich Moss)

	SPA/Ram Code	IBA Europe number
	305D	096

County/Region	District(s)	OS sheet(s)	Grid Reference(s)	Map 7
Strathclyde	Argyll and Bute	60	NR 320550	

Area (ha)	NNR	SPA	Ramsar
574	Proposed	Designated Y Candidate N/A	Designated Y Candidate N/A

An area of low level blanket mire, important especially in winter as a roost, and night feeding area, for Greenland white-fronted geese.

Site description
Bounded by the Duich River, the River Laggan, and two roads, Eilean na Muice Duibh is a relatively undisturbed expanse of patterned mire, of a transitional type, incorporating elements of both blanket mire and raised mire. This highly oceanic type is characterised by its structure, and, for example, by hummocks of mosses *Sphagnum imbricatum* and *S. fuscum*, and frequent stands of white beak-sedge. There are scattered peaty pools and lochans, including deep watershed pools, a feature otherwise known only from true blanket mires further north. Locally, the vegetation has become modified by gulls (nutrient input and trampling).

Birds
Duich Moss forms a night-time roosting and feeding area for internationally important numbers of Greenland **white-fronted geese**. Up to 1800 birds are known to use the roost (8% of the world population, 18% of the number wintering in Britain). Recently Greenland **barnacle geese** have also roosted there with up to 1530 present in January 1990 (5% of world, 6% of British). Notable also in winter are merlin, peregrine and short-eared owl.

Breeding species include red-throated diver, teal, hen harrier, dunlin, redshank, common gull, lesser black-backed gull and herring gull.

Conservation issues
Eilean na Muice Duibh was recently threatened by a major proposal to extract peat on a commercial basis. This would have had a damaging effect on the hydrology of the site and directly affected the wintering geese. The proposal was dropped following legal intervention by the European Commission. The site is also vulnerable to drainage and the disturbance of roosting geese, and would benefit from restorative management, including the damming of drainage channels, the control of the burning regime and control of invasive rhododendron.

Further reading
Bignal, E M, Curtis, D J and Matthews, J 1988 *Islay: Land types, bird habitats and nature conservation. Part 1. Land types and birds on Islay.* NCC CSD Report No. 809, Part 1.

Greenland White-fronted Goose Study 1986 Duich Moss: a minor administrative hitch....*Ecos* 7(2): 24–31.

Penford, N 1985 *Islay peatlands: a survey and evaluation of selected sites.* MSc thesis, University College, London.

Islay: Rinns

SPA/Ram Code 305G	IBA Europe number 090

County/Region	District(s)	OS sheet(s)	Grid Reference(s)	Map 7
Strathclyde	Argyll and Bute	60	NR 235620	

Area (ha) 8961	NNR No	SPA Designated Y Candidate Y	SPA Wider Countryside Measures Candidate	Ramsar Designated Y Candidate Y

This site includes the former sites Glac na Criche (305E) and Feur Lochain (305F), both of which have been individually designated as Special Protection Areas and Ramsar sites.

A site of special importance for a range of bird species associated with wetlands, open moorlands and low intensity agricultural land. These include chough, corncrake, common scoter, various raptors, breeding waders, and two species of wintering geese.

Site description

The area is a mosaic of natural and semi-natural habitats including bog, moorland, dune grassland, marsh, maritime grassland, and intensive and low intensity farmland. Much of the natural vegetation forms rough grazing for sheep and cattle and is managed in a generally low-intensity fashion. These habitats are linked by their differing daily and seasonal use by an assemblage of wide ranging bird species.

Exposed to the prevailing south-western weather, the Rinns of Islay have a highly oceanic climate with closer ecological affinities to western Ireland than to the rest of Britain. The area consists of low hills (to 250 m) running down to a rocky coastline. Much is covered by peat of varying depths, with rough pasture, dry and wet heathland, and mires. Locally, more base-rich conditions have given rise to fens. The higher hills and the coast are craggy, and there are numerous lochans. Around the coast, there is heathland and grassland enriched by sea spray and blown sand; these communities tend to be more species-rich than those inland. They include juniper/bearberry heath, unimproved acidic grasslands, and sand dunes and machair. Locally there are woodlands, including the unusual eared willow scrub woodland.

The complex of habitats supports many plant and animal species, including some uncommon ones, such as meadow thistle, great fen-sedge and the nationally rare Irish lady's-tresses in fens. Oysterplant and sea-holly grow on the coast, and tubular and parsley water-dropworts, both very localised in Scotland, occur in coastal marshes. The mires have important invertebrate communities, including scarce dragonflies and water beetles.

SSSI/SPA designation is appropriate for the core areas of bird interest within this extensive tract of land, while 'wider countryside' conservation measures are appropriate in other parts.

Birds

The area supports a total of 15 Annex 1 species, including internationally important numbers of wintering Greenland white-fronted goose and Greenland barnacle goose, as well as nationally important numbers of breeding common scoter, hen harrier, corncrake and chough and passage whooper swan

Whooper swans occur on the Rinns of Islay mainly during the spring and autumn passage periods when total numbers may be in the order of 120-160 birds (2% of the British wintering population). The site may in fact be used by larger numbers of individuals due to turnover of birds during the passage periods.

The average peak count of Greenland **white-fronted geese** from comprehensive daytime surveys on the Rinns peninsula in the three winters 1984/85, 1986/87 and 1987/88 was 1820 birds (about 8% of the world population and 18% of the number wintering in Britain). They generally feed in small flocks in various parts of the site, utilising a range of grasslands including intensively managed agricultural fields, rough pastures, bogs and rushy fields. They are joined at night by birds from other parts of Islay to roost and feed on the peatland areas. The complex of peatland systems comprising Feur Lochain, associated lochans and pools to the east, Loch Corr, and Glac na Criche form an ecologically dependent unit supporting up to 1600 geese which roost and feed there at various times through the winter.

The average peak count of **barnacle geese** from comprehensive daytime surveys on the Rinns peninsula in the three winters 1984/85, 1986/87 and 1987/88 was 2970 birds (10% of the world population and 15% of the number wintering in Britain). Barnacle geese do not roost at night on the Rinns peninsula but move to roosts on Loch Gruinart and elsewhere on Islay.

Breeding populations include hen harrier, about 14 pairs of **corncrake**s (2% + of British) and 10 pairs of **common scoter**s (10% of British).

In summer about 56 pairs of **choughs** nest on the Rinns (21% of British). Nesting locations are widely dispersed in both coastal and inland parts. In addition, 105 or more non-breeding choughs occur on the site. Choughs are resident throughout the year and the total number of individuals present is in excess of 295 birds (40% of the British wintering population). In summer, breeding pairs feed within a home range which may be coastal or inland. A great variety of habitats are used, including maritime turf, heathland, dunes, stubble, machair, peatlands and pastures, particularly insect-rich permanent pastures. In winter, birds move further afield and large flocks build up in the vicinity of communal roost sites. Birds then favour dune areas for feeding as well as grasslands, and range widely within the overall site, as do non-breeding sub-adult birds in summer. Three or four regular communal roosting sites are used.

Notable also are red-throated diver, golden eagle, merlin, peregrine, golden plover, dunlin, curlew, arctic tern and short-eared owl. The cliffs of the Rinns, particularly in the north and west, support colonies of breeding seabirds.

Conservation issues

Many of the bird species on the Rinns of Islay, such as corncrake and chough, are associated with managed landscapes. The maintenance of traditional agricultural practices in these areas, particularly pastoralism, is crucial to the conservation of the special wildlife interest.

The birds that use this site are also vulnerable to drainage, afforestation, agricultural intensification and disturbance from recreational activities. They are also vulnerable to dereliction/degradation of agricultural land and property (chough especially).

Further reading

Bignal, E M, Curtis, D J and Matthews, J 1988 *Islay: Land types, bird habitats and nature conservation. Part 1. Land types and birds on Islay.* NCC CSD Report No. 809, Part 1.

Easterbee, N and Bignal, E M 1989 Status and distribution of chough in Scotland, 1986, and some recent changes. In: *Choughs and Land-use in Europe: Proceedings of an international workshop on the conservation of the chough (*Pyrrhocorax pyrrhocorax*) in the EC. 11-14 November 1988,* pp 15-18.

Ogilvie, M A 1983 Wildfowl of Islay. *Proceedings of the Royal Society of Edinburgh,* 83B: 473-489.

Stroud, D A 1985 A preliminary list of Greenland White-fronted Goose roost sites in Argyll. *The Second Argyll Bird Report*: 20-29.

Lindsay, R A, Riggall, J and Bignal, E M 1983 Ombrogenous mires in Islay and Mull. *Proc. Roy. Soc. Edin.* 83B: 341-371.

Barnacle goose

Islay: The Oa

SPA/Ram Code	IBA Europe number
305H	097

County/Region	District(s)	OS sheet(s)	Grid Reference(s)	Map 7
Strathclyde	Argyll and Bute	60	NR 3045	

Area (ha)	NNR	SPA		SPA		Ramsar	
1000-9999	No	Designated	N	Wider		Designated	N
		Candidate	Y	Countryside Measures Candidate		Candidate	N

Rocky coastland, blanket mire, heathland and traditionally managed farmland, important for breeding choughs, birds of prey and wintering Greenland white-fronted geese.

Site description

A peninsula in the south-west of Islay, the Oa comprises a mosaic of habitats including rocky coastland, blanket mire, heathland and traditionally managed farmland with extensive stock-rearing. In common with the Rinns, the site, being exposed to the prevailing south-western weather, has a highly oceanic climate with closer ecological affinities to western Ireland than to the rest of Britain. The component habitats, individually and collectively, support the assemblage of bird species that depends on these conditions.

SSSI/SPA designation is appropriate for the core areas of bird interest within this extensive tract of land, while 'wider countryside' conservation measures are appropriate in other parts.

Birds

The Oa supports internationally important numbers of wintering Greenland white-fronted goose and nationally important numbers of breeding and wintering chough.

A total of 23 pairs of **chough**s breed on the coastal cliffs of the Oa (9% of British). Also breeding are hen harrier, golden eagle, peregrine and short-eared owl.

In recent years the numbers of wintering Greenland **white-fronted geese** feeding by day on the Oa have averaged 1490 birds (7% of the world population, 15% of the number wintering in Britain).

Conservation issues

Many of the bird species on the Oa, but especially chough, are associated with managed landscapes. The persistence of traditional agricultural practices in these areas, particularly pastoralism, is crucial to the maintenance of this special wildlife interest.

The birds are also vulnerable to afforestation, drainage of wetlands and human disturbance at nesting and roosting localities. They are also vulnerable to dereliction/degradation of agricultural land and property (chough especially).

Further reading

Bignal, E M, Curtis, D J and Matthews, J 1988 *Islay: Land types, bird habitats and nature conservation. Part 1. Land types and birds on Islay*. NCC CSD Report No. 809, Part 1.

Easterbee, N and Bignal, E M 1989 Status and distribution of the chough in Scotland, 1986, and some recent changes. In: *Choughs and Land-use in Europe: Proceedings of an International workshop on the conservation of the Chough* (Pyrrhocorax pyrrhocorax) *in the EC. 11-14 November 1988*. Eds. E M Bignal and D J Curtis.

Inner Clyde Estuary

SPA/Ram Code	IBA Europe number
306A	105

County/Region	District(s)	OS sheet(s)	Grid Reference(s)	Maps 8, 10
Strathclyde	Inverclyde (south shore), Renfrew (south shore), Dumbarton (north shore), Clydebank (north shore)	63, 64	NS 350760	

Area (ha)	NNR	SPA		Ramsar	
1500+	No	Designated	N	Designated	N
		Candidate	Y	Candidate	Y

An area of extensive intertidal mudflats attracting important numbers of wintering waders and wildfowl.

Site description
Although heavily industrialised along much of its length, the estuary of the Clyde above Gourock Bay and Helensburgh contains some very extensive intertidal sand- and mud-flats. There is an abundant invertebrate fauna, the species composition of which has been changing in recent years with the improving water quality of the estuary. There are *Zostera* beds and mussel beds also occur in places, for example at Pillar Bank. These provide a food source for eiders and other seaducks. There are a few small areas of saltmarsh adjoining the mudflats, with species including sea rush and English scurvy-grass which are scarce in Scotland.

Birds
The Inner Clyde supports internationally important numbers of wintering redshank and nationally important numbers of wintering cormorant, scaup, eider, goldeneye, red-breasted merganser, oystercatcher and curlew.

In the five-winter period 1985/86 to 1989/90 the average peak counts were as follows: 220 **cormorant** (1% of British), 150 **scaup** (4% of British), 3850 **eider** (8% of British), 570 **goldeneye** (4% of British), 175 **red-breasted merganser** (2% of British), 4100 **oystercatcher** (1% of British), 1070 **curlew** (1% of British) and 2410 **redshank** (2% of the EAF population, 3% of British).

Notable also is wintering greenshank, the largest wintering population in Scotland.

Conservation issues
Waterfowl that winter on estuaries are vulnerable to land-claim and other developments, such as the construction of barrages that would disturb or damage the existing ecology of these sites. Other human influences, such as recreational disturbance, commercial

exploitation of shellfish and worms, and oil and industrial pollution, are also potentially damaging to the conservation interest of estuaries.

Wildfowling, clay pigeon shooting and bait-digging all occur on the estuary. There are currently threats of land-claim and leisure developments, and also motorbike riding on the foreshore.

Further reading

Allen, J A, Barnett, P R O, Boyd, J M, Kirkwood, R C, Mackay, D W and Smyth, J C (eds.) 1986 The Environment of the estuary and Firth of Clyde. *Proc. Roy. Soc. Edin.* 90B. Royal Society of Edinburgh, Edinburgh.

Halliday, J B, Curtis, D J, Thompson, D B A , Bignal, E M and Smyth, J C 1982 The abundance and feeding distribution of Clyde Estuary shorebirds. *Scottish Birds* 12: 3.

Rhunahaorine Point

SPA/Ram Code	IBA Europe number
307A	098

County/Region	District(s)	OS sheet(s)	Grid Reference(s)	Maps 7, 8,
Strathclyde	Argyll and Bute	62	NR 695493	10

Area (ha)	NNR	SPA		SPA		Ramsar	
326	No	Designated	N	Wider		Designated	N
		Candidate	Y	Countryside Measures Candidate		Candidate	N

A shingle foreland with coastal heath and grassland, attracting large numbers of wintering Greenland white-fronted geese.

Site description
Located on the west side of Kintyre, Rhunahaorine is one of the largest vegetated shingle forelands in Britain. The foreland consists of ridges laid down in two distinct sequences: the older ridges run south-west to north-east and are some 3 m higher than the younger ridges which run north-west to south-east. The area is generally level. The western part is mainly short, grazed, dry heath, while the larger eastern section is wetter. The site also holds a significant area of managed farmland, some of which is farmed in an intensive fashion. The open grassland areas are much used for feeding by wintering geese, while the heath and shingle areas are used for roosting and as a refuge from disturbance.

SSSI/SPA designation is appropriate for the core areas of bird interest within this extensive tract of land, while 'wider countryside' conservation measures are appropriate in other parts.

Birds
Rhunahaorine is of special importance within Britain and the EC as a wintering area for internationally important numbers of Greenland **white-fronted goose**. In the five-winter period 1985/86 to 1989/90 the average peak count was 930 birds (4% of the world population, 9% of the number wintering in Britain). Preferred feeding areas include fields of rough and intensified pasture. Rhunahaorine also holds a small wintering flock of greylag geese. Substantial numbers of red-breasted mergansers (over 400) gather along the coast during the autumn moulting period.

Also of note are breeding arctic and common terns.

Conservation issues
Wintering Greenland white-fronted geese are vulnerable to changes in grassland management regimes and to human disturbance.

At Rhunahaorine there is agricultural conflict with wintering geese, and some disturbance to nesting terns from visitors to the nearby caravan park. Adjacent shingle areas have been lost to conifer plantations.

Further reading
Greenland White-fronted Goose Study 1988 *Greenland White-fronted Geese in Britain: 1986/87*. Greenland White-fronted Goose Study Research Report No.6. Aberystwyth.

Machrihanish and Tangy Loch

SPA/Ram Code	IBA Europe number
308A	099

County/Region	District(s)	OS sheet(s)	Grid Reference(s)	Maps 7, 8,
Strathclyde	Argyll and Bute	68	NR 6523 (Machrihanish) NR 6928 (Tangy Loch)	10

Area (ha)	NNR	SPA		SPA	Ramsar	
1-999	No	Designated N Candidate Y		Wider Countryside Measures Candidate	Designated N Candidate Y	

Grassland and a separate loch, used, respectively, as feeding and roosting areas by Greenland white-fronted geese.

Site description

Towards the south end of the west coast of Kintyre, an area of intensively managed pasture and arable farmland is used by wintering geese.

Tangy Loch is about 4 km to the north-east, at about 135 m above sea level. The surrounding land is extensively afforested, but some rough grazing and an area of bog remain around the loch. The shore plant community of common spike-rush and shoreweed, and some of the open water communities, for example, alternate water-milfoil, are typical of nutrient-poor waters with lime input. The nationally rare slender naiad, which prefers such conditions, is present.

SSSI/SPA designation is appropriate for the core areas of bird interest within this extensive tract of land, while 'wider countryside' conservation measures are appropriate in other parts.

Birds

The site supports internationally important numbers of wintering Greenland **white-fronted geese**. In the period 1987/88 to 1989/90 the average peak count was 950 birds representing 4% of the world population and 10% of the numbers wintering in Britain. These feed at Machrihanish and roost at Tangy Loch. Notable also are wintering greylag geese. Along the coast there are substantial numbers of wintering **red-breasted mergansers** (200 birds, 2% of British).

Conservation issues

The geese that winter here are vulnerable to changes in agricultural practices on their feeding areas. Fish-farm proposals for Tangy Loch may pose a threat to the loch and the geese.

Further reading

The Argyll Bird Club. *Argyll Bird Club Reports.*

Greenland White-fronted Goose Study 1988 *Greenland White-fronted Geese in Britain: 1986/87.* Greenland White-fronted Goose Study Research Report No. 6. Aberystwyth.

Ailsa Craig

SPA/Ram Code	IBA Europe number
309A	103

County/Region	District(s)	OS sheet(s)	Grid Reference(s)	Map 10
Strathclyde	Kyle and Carrick	76	NX 020998	

Area (ha)	NNR	SPA	Ramsar
104	No	Designated Y Candidate N/A	Designated N Candidate N

An island with steep, high cliffs, important for its seabird colonies, especially gannets.

Site description

Ailsa Craig is a cone-shaped granitic island, rising to 338 m, situated in the outer part of the Firth of Clyde. Cliffs up to 100 m in height encircle most of the island and provide nesting sites for seabirds.

Birds

Ailsa Craig supports one of the largest breeding colonies of **gannets** in the world with 22,500 pairs recorded in 1985 (9% of the world population, 14% of British). Breeding gulls are present in nationally important numbers with 1800 pairs of **lesser black-backed gulls** (2% of British) and 2250 pairs of **herring gulls** (2% of British). Notable also are breeding kittiwake (3100 pairs), guillemot (5000 individuals), razorbill (1000 individuals) and black guillemot (4-5 pairs).

Conservation issues

Seabirds are sensitive to changes in the quality of the marine environment, especially to changes in fish stocks and to oil pollution. Ground-nesting seabirds on offshore islands are vulnerable to the introduction of predatory mammals. Common rats are known to be having a detrimental effect on the breeding success of Ailsa Craig's seabirds, and an attempt is currently being made to exterminate the rats from the island.

Further reading

Wanless, S and Murray, S 1986 The status of the Gannet in Scotland. 1984-85. *Scottish Birds* 14: 74-85.

Loch Ken and Dee Marshes

SPA/Ram Code	IBA Europe number
311A	109

County/Region	District(s)	OS sheet(s)	Grid Reference(s)	Maps 10, 11
Dumfries and Galloway	Stewartry	77, 83, 84	NX 7068	

Area (ha)	NNR	SPA		Ramsar	
1-999	No	Designated	N	Designated	N
		Candidate	Y	Candidate	Y

An extensive and varied wetland in the Dee valley, important especially for wintering Greenland white-fronted geese.

Site description

This highly complex system of loch, swamps, fens, grassland and carr stretches for about 20 km. The River Dee follows a meandering course with islands and oxbows at the northern and southern ends. The goose flocks roost out on the open water. Loch Ken was dammed in the 1930s, resulting in the re-formation of marshes. The marshes are dominated by reed and sedge beds and adjoined by fens and marshy grassland where Greenland white-fronted geese occasionally feed.

Birds

An important feeding and roosting site for wintering Greenland **white-fronted geese** with a five-year average peak for 1985/86 to 1989/90 of 360 birds (2% of the world population and 3.5% of the number wintering in Britain).

Notable also are wintering mute swan (mean of 45 birds), whooper swan, greylag goose, wigeon, teal, pintail, shoveler, goldeneye and goosander.

Conservation issues

Greenland white-fronted geese at this site are vulnerable to changes in agricultural practices and to human disturbance.

Lochinch and Torrs Warren

SPA/Ram Code	IBA Europe number
312A	106

County/Region	District(s)	OS sheet(s)	Grid Reference(s)	Map 10
Dumfries and Galloway	Wigtown	82	NX 1060 (Lochinch) NX 1454 (Torrs Warren)	

Area (ha)	NNR	SPA		Ramsar	
1000-9999	No	Designated Candidate	N Y	Designated Candidate	N Y

A freshwater loch and extensive sand dune system important for wintering geese.

Site description

Lochinch (also known as White Loch) is a shallow, eutrophic loch. The vegetation includes the nationally scarce six-stamened waterwort, and there is a rich invertebrate fauna. The open water is used for roosting by the geese.

Torrs Warren lies to the south, at the head of Luce Bay. It is the largest acidic dune system in western Scotland, and has a highly varied dune morphology, with areas of both accretion and erosion, and well developed slacks. Behind the dune system are large areas of heathland and marshy grassland both of which have formed over the underlying gravel banks. These two habitats are important roosting areas for the geese, and the marshy grassland is occasionally utilised by feeding Greenland white-fronted geese.

Birds

The site holds internationally important numbers of wintering Greenland **white-fronted geese**. In the period 1987/88 to 1989/90 the average peak count was 505 birds representing 2% of the world population and 5% of the numbers wintering in Britain. These feed inland on agricultural land and roost both on the loch and on the foreshore of the dunes. There are also substantial numbers of **greylag geese** (average peak 1500), although a large proportion of these are of feral origin. Hen harriers roost in winter at this site.

Conservation issues

Roosting and feeding geese are vulnerable to human disturbance and changes in agricultural practices.

Further reading

Greenland White-fronted Goose Study 1990 *Greenland White-fronted Geese in Britain: 1987/88 – 1989/90*. Greenland White-fronted Goose Study Research Report No. 7, Aberystwyth.

Wigtown Bay

SPA/Ram Code	IBA Europe number
316A	108

County/Region	District(s)	OS sheet(s)	Grid Reference(s)	Map 10
Dumfries and Galloway	Wigtown	83	NX 465545	

Area (ha)	NNR	SPA		Ramsar	
3465	No	Designated	N	Designated	N
		Candidate	Y	Candidate	Y

A large area of intertidal mudflats with adjacent saltmarsh, attracting large numbers of wintering wildfowl and waders.

Site description

This is a large estuary into which drain the Rivers Cree and Bladnoch, and several burns. The extensive invertebrate-rich mud- and sand-flats are bordered by grazed saltmarsh.

The short, grazed turf of the saltmarsh is dominated by red fescue and common saltmarsh-grass, with abundant thrift, sea-milkwort and sea aster. This grazed turf provides important feeding areas for geese and duck, while the mudflats are important for feeding waders and roosting geese.

Birds

This site holds internationally important numbers of wintering whooper swan, pink-footed goose and greylag goose, and nationally important numbers of pintail and curlew.

Wigtown Bay is a wetland of international importance by virtue of regularly supporting over 20,000 waterfowl. In the five-winter period 1985/86 to 1989/90 the average peak count was 23,828 birds, comprising 6875 waders and 16,953 wildfowl. Average peak counts for individual species were as follows : 240 **whooper swan**s (1% of the world population, 4% of British), 290 **pintail** (1% of British), 9600 **pink-footed geese** (9% of the world and British population), 1400 **greylag geese** (1% of the world and British population) and 1540 **curlew** (2% of British).

Conservation issues

Waterfowl that winter on estuaries are vulnerable to land-claim and other developments, such as the construction of barrages that would disturb or damage the existing ecology of these sites. Other human influences such as recreational disturbance, commercial exploitation of shellfish and worms, and oil and industrial pollution, are also potentially damaging to the conservation interest of estuaries.

North Colonsay and Western Cliffs

	SPA/Ram Code	IBA Europe number
	317A	089

County/Region	District(s)	OS sheet(s)	Grid Reference(s)	Map 7
Strathclyde	Argyll and Bute	61	NR 4198	

Area (ha)	NNR	SPA		SPA		Ramsar	
1-999	No	Designated	N	Wider		Designated	N
		Candidate	Y	Countryside Measures Candidate		Candidate	N

An area of rocky coast, cliffs and maritime heath supporting nationally important numbers of choughs and seabirds; the island also supports nationally important numbers of corncrakes.

Site description

The core area includes the northern promontory of Colonsay, and a 2 km section of cliffs on the western coast. The hills rise to about 140 m above sea level, and the cliffs include some almost sheer sections up to 100 m in height. The whole area is craggy, and the mainly acidic rocks support dry and wet heathland over the northern hills. Especially on the west coast, there is strong influence of sea spray, giving a herb-rich sward with abundant spring squill. Locally blown sand dunes, including the 60-m high Leac Bhuidhe dune, are found in two areas in the north, and are rich in characteristic plant species.

SSSI/SPA designation is appropriate for the core areas of bird interest within this extensive tract of land, while 'wider countryside' conservation measures are appropriate in other parts.

Birds

The site supports about 8 pairs of breeding **choughs** (3% of British). With the exception of one pair on Mull these are the most northerly breeding choughs in the world. Breeding seabird populations censused in 1986 include **kittiwakes** 5650 pairs (1% of British), **guillemots** 14,400 individuals (1% of British) and **razorbills** 1380 individuals (1% of British). The island as a whole also supports nationally important numbers of **corncrakes** (12 calling birds, 2% of British).

Notable also are breeding red-throated diver (1-2 pairs), fulmar (770 AOS), storm petrel (up to 70 birds), shag (115 pairs), herring gull (2200 individuals), arctic tern (275 pairs) and black guillemot (170 individuals).

Conservation issues

The well-being of choughs and corncrakes is dependent upon the maintenance of traditional low intensity farming methods and appropriate grazing regimes. Seabirds are sensitive to changes in the quality of the marine environment, especially to changes in fish stocks and to oil pollution.

Sensitive sites, including tern colonies, are under increasing pressure from disturbance by tourists.

Further reading

Easterbee, N and Bignal, E M 1989 Status and distribution of chough in Scotland, 1986, and some recent changes. In: *Choughs and Land-use in Europe: Proceedings of an international workshop on the conservation of the chough* (Pyrrhocorax pyrrhocorax) *in the EC.* 11–14 November 1988, pp 15–18.

Jardine, D C, Clarke, J and Clarke, P M 1986 *The Birds of Colonsay and Oronsay; their history and distribution.*

Sanda

SPA/Ram Code	IBA Europe number
318A	100

County/Region	District(s)	OS sheet(s)	Grid Reference(s)	Map 10
Strathclyde	Argyll and Bute	68	NR 725045	

Area (ha)	NNR	SPA		Ramsar	
210	No	Designated	N	Designated	N
		Candidate	Y	Candidate	N

An island with breeding seabirds, including nationally important numbers of shag.

Site description
A grassy island with cliffs and associated islets.

Birds
Sanda supports a nationally important breeding colony of **shags** with 950 pairs counted in 1987 (3% of British). Other breeding seabirds of note include Manx shearwater (50–100 pairs), storm petrel (50–100 pairs), cormorant (25 pairs), herring gull (900 pairs), guillemot (1250 individuals), razorbill (750 individuals) and black guillemot (65 pairs).

Conservation issues
Seabirds are sensitive to changes in the quality of the marine environment, especially to changes in fish stocks and to oil pollution. Ground-nesting seabirds on offshore islands are vulnerable to the introduction of predatory mammals.

Further reading
The Argyll Bird Club. *Argyll Bird Club Reports.*

Castle Loch, Dumfries

SPA/Ram Code	IBA Europe number
319A	107

County/Region	District(s)	OS sheet(s)	Grid Reference(s)	Map 10
Dumfries and Galloway	Annandale and Eskdale	78	NY 0881	

Area (ha)	NNR	SPA		Ramsar	
1-999	No	Designated	N	Designated	N
		Candidate	Y	Candidate	Y

Important numbers of geese and other wildfowl winter at this eutrophic loch.

Site description
This is a shallow loch with large stands of emergent vegetation, dominated by common reed and reed sweet-grass. These swamps merge into marshy grassland, and there is a wide range of wetland plants. In places these open habitats grade into stands of willow, birch and alder carr, and there are some areas of mature woodland.

Birds
The loch is of international importance in winter as a roost site for pink-footed and greylag geese. In the five-winter period 1985/86 to 1989/90 the average peak counts were 4270 **pink-footed geese** (4% of the world population, max. 13,400) and 1240 **greylag geese** (1% of the world population, max. 2850). The loch also holds nationally important numbers of wintering **goosander** (mean 85 birds, 1.5% of British).

Conservation issues
Roosting geese are vulnerable to human disturbance. There have been various proposals for recreational developments on the loch in recent years. A Local Nature Reserve permit system allows shooting on part of the loch.

Further reading
Scottish Ornithologists' Club. *Dumfries and Galloway Bird Reports*.
Shimmings, P *Local Nature Reserve Annual Bird Reports*

Caenlochan

SPA/Ram Code	IBA Europe number
401A	110

County/Region	District(s)	OS sheet(s)	Grid Reference(s)	Maps 6, 9
Tayside	Angus, Perth	43, 44	NO 210770	
	and Kinross			
Grampian	Kincardine			
	and Deeside			

Area (ha)	NNR	SPA		Ramsar	
6619	Part	Designated	N	Designated	N
		Candidate	Y	Candidate	N

A large area of montane plateau holding important populations of dotterel, raptors and other upland birds.

Site description

There is considerable habitat variety in the area, due to the varied topography and the presence of both acidic and calcareous rocks. The hills rise from the glen floors to plateaux at over 900 m, and there are many crags and steep rocky slopes. The main vegetation types are dwarf-shrub communities and blanket mire, each occupying about one-third of the area. Substantial areas of grasslands and bryophyte heath are also present, as are smaller areas of herb-rich communities, soligenous mires, open water and birch woodland.

The area is notable for the extent of high-altitude bog, lichen-rich communities and snow-bed vegetation, in particular stiff sedge-*Polytrichum alpinum* snow-bed heath. Also at high altitude, base-rich flushing gives rise to mires which range from eutrophic to mesotrophic; the latter especially include local communities with rare *Sphagnum* mosses. Much of the area is grazed by deer and, locally, sheep, but on inaccessible crags there are important alpine willow scrub and tall-herb communities. Other unusual vegetation types, such as those around high altitude springs in the corries, are also present.

There is a high diversity of plants, including many national rarities. The presence of high altitude calcareous rocks is particularly important in the occurrence of several of these rarities.

Birds

The site is of major international importance holding a montane/upland bird assemblage found in few other areas and considered to be amongst the most important of such sites in the EEC.

Caenlochan is of international importance as a nesting area for **dotterel**, supporting 25-40 pairs (depending on year). These constitute 3-5% of the British and EC total. Dotterels use the site also as a gathering ground during migration, with up to 70 birds recorded. It forms part of a network of suitable sites for breeding dotterel with birds moving between them at various stages of the breeding season.

The lower parts of the site support breeding **golden eagles** (5 pairs, 1% of British). Notable also are breeding merlin, peregrine, ptarmigan, golden plover, dunlin and a range of upland passerine species.

Conservation issues

The birds that use this site are vulnerable to human disturbance from increased public access made possible by the skiing infrastructure. Visitors during the summer months cause most of the damage; vegetation structure is also affected.

Golden eagle

Montrose Basin

SPA/Ram Code	IBA book number
403A	111

County/Region	District	OS sheet(s)	Grid Reference(s)	Maps 6, 9
Tayside	Angus	45, 54	NO 685580	

Area (ha)	NNR	SPA		Ramsar	
921 ha	No	Designated	N	Designated	N
		Candidate	Y	Candidate	Y

Montrose Basin is an estuary which supports large numbers of wintering wildfowl and waders.

Site description
Montrose Basin is almost circular, about 3 km across, forming the estuary of the river South Esk. At low tide, extensive mud flats are exposed, which contain abundant invertebrates, including annelid worms, the spire snail *Hydrobia* and the crustacean *Corophium*, which are important as prey for birds. There are also mussel beds. The flora of several species of algae, and all three British species of eel grass, are grazed by certain wildfowl.

On the periphery of the mud flats are marshes which range from freshwater to saline, and support a correspondingly diverse variety of plants. These include species such as saltmarsh flat-sedge, long-bracted sedge and beaked tasselweed which are scarce in the district.

Duns Dish is a lowland loch, about 4 km north-west of Montrose Basin. It is nutrient-rich, and is surrounded by mires which grade into fens and carrs. These habitats contain several plant species which are local in Angus.

Birds
Montrose Basin holds internationally important numbers of wintering pink-footed goose, knot and redshank and nationally important numbers of wintering wigeon, eider and oystercatcher.

The Basin is a wetland of international importance by virtue of regularly supporting over 20,000 waterfowl. In the five-winter period 1985/86 to 1989/90 the average peak count was 43,100 birds, comprising 12,800 waders and 30,300 wildfowl. Totals for individual species include: 18,700 **pink-footed geese** (17% of the world population), 5170 **wigeon** (2% of British), 2360 **eider** (5% of British), 3550 **oystercatcher** (1% of British), 3700 **knot** (1% of the EAF population, 2% of British) and 1770 **redshank** (2% of EAF and British). Notable also are wintering mute swan, shelduck and dunlin. The Basin supports a large breeding colony of **eider** (400 pairs and increasing, 2% of British).

The nearby Duns Dish supports breeding black-headed gulls, common terns and various duck species.

Conservation issues

Waterfowl that winter on estuaries are vulnerable to land-claim and other developments, such as the construction of barrages that would disturb or damage the existing ecology of these sites. Other human influences such as recreational disturbance, commercial exploitation of shellfish and worms, and oil and industrial pollution, are also potentially damaging to the conservation interest of estuaries.

Shooting has been restricted in the basin since the creation of the Local Nature Reserve in 1981; this led to a dramatic rise in the numbers of wildfowl, particularly pink-footed geese using the area.

Loch of Kinnordy

SPA/Ram Code	IBA Europe number
405A	233

County/Region	District(s)	OS sheet(s)	Grid Reference(s)	Maps 6, 9
Tayside	Angus	54	NO 361539	

Area (ha)	NNR	SPA		Ramsar	
94	No	Designated	N	Designated	N
		Candidate	Y	Candidate	Y

A loch with associated wet meadows and marshes, important for wintering geese and breeding waterfowl.

Site description

A eutrophic loch covering 22 ha with 40 ha of associated wetland communities, notably basin mire, swamp and fen. Submerged aquatic plant communities are absent. There is also an incomplete grassland and woodland fringe.

The loch was formerly much larger in extent, but a series of drainage attempts were made, initially to facilitate marl removal. However it has been increasing in extent in recent years due to the silting of the loch's current outflow stream, the Garrie Burn.

Many fen communities have been identified including those dominated by common reed and yellow iris in places. A stand of bogbean is found in the main lochan. Scarce plant species present include cowbane, water sedge, lesser tussock-sedge and swamp meadow-grass.

Carr woodland includes willow, alder and birch communities, which are thought to be natural. The remainder of the woodland is planted.

A range of grassland types are present, including a species-rich damp *Molinia*-dominated area. Northern brown argus and pearl-bordered fritillary butterflies have been recorded at this site. Mammalian interest includes otter and red squirrel.

Birds

The site holds internationally important numbers of wintering pink-footed and greylag geese and nationally important numbers of various breeding waterfowl species.

The loch acts as a roost for wintering geese. In the five-winter period 1985/86 to 1989/90 the average peak numbers recorded were 2600 **pink-footed geese** (2% of the world and British population) and 1400 Icelandic **greylags** (1% of the world and British population).

There is a breeding colony of **black-headed gulls** (7000 pairs, 3% of British). Breeding wildfowl include **black-necked grebe** (4 pairs, 14% of British), **gadwall** (7 pairs, 1% of British), **shoveler** (18 pairs, 1% of British), **pochard** (11 pairs, 3% of British) and ruddy duck (8 pairs).

Conservation issues

Fluctuating water levels caused by flash flooding are believed to affect the breeding success of waterfowl, particularly grebes. The decline in area of bogbean islands on the main lochan, used by many nesting birds, may be attributable to increasing water levels during the last few decades. It is desirable to regulate water levels to retain nesting habitat for breeding waterfowl.

Wintering wildfowl, particularly geese, are vulnerable to human disturbance. Breeding wildfowl are vulnerable to disturbance by fishermen.

Important mere and fen communities may degenerate into scrub and carr woodland and current monitoring may show that management is necessary.

The lochan and fen communities are fragile and vulnerable to further eutrophication through fertiliser run-off from the catchment and from the faeces of up to 14,000 gulls in summer and 8000 geese in winter. The effects of this need to be closely monitored.

Loch of Lintrathen

SPA/Ram Code	IBA Europe number
406A	112

County/Region	District(s)	OS sheet(s)	Grid Reference(s)	Maps 6, 9
Tayside	Angus	53	NO 278549	

Area (ha)	NNR	SPA	Ramsar
1-999	No	Designated N	Designated Y
		Candidate Y	Candidate N/A

A eutrophic loch attracting internationally important numbers of greylag geese to roost in winter.

Site description
The Loch of Lintrathen is situated in the foothills above Strathmore, at about 200 m altitude. It occupies a glacial basin, and is now used as a reservoir. There is no emergent vegetation.

Birds
The roost of wintering Icelandic **greylag geese** is of international importance with an average peak during the five winters 1985/86 to 1989/90 of 1400 birds (1% of the world and British population) and a maximum of 2500.

Conservation issues
Roosting geese are vulnerable to human disturbance.

Tay-Isla Valley

SPA/Ram Code	IBA Europe number
407A	113

County/Region	District(s)	OS sheet(s)	Grid Reference(s)	Maps 6, 9
Tayside	Perth and Kinross	53	NO 1440	

Area (ha)	NNR	SPA		Ramsar	
1-999	No	Designated	N	Designated	N
		Candidate	Y	Candidate	Y

A series of shallow lochs and rivers, with adjoining fens and pastures, important for feeding and roosting greylag and pink-footed geese in winter.

Site description
The confluence of the rivers Tay and Isla is about 15 km north of Perth; the valley floors in this area include a complex of wetland habitats.

A series of lochs is found along the Lunan Burn, a tributary of the River Isla, and are of particular interest for birds.

Lochs Clunie, Marlee and Lowes are moderate-sized mesotrophic lochs, each about 1 km across, linked by the Lunan Burn, to the west of Blairgowrie. They are rich in aquatic plants, with several nationally rare species present and have varied marginal fens including one area in the north-west of Loch Marlee where the influence of calcareous groundwater gives rise to an especially diverse community. The Lunan Burn itself is notable for its lack of disturbance and diversity of vegetation. South of Blairgowrie lies a group of smaller lochs and fens along tributaries of the Lunan Burn and River Isla, including Monk Myre, Stormont Loch and Hare Myre. These habitats also hold scarce plant species.

Fens also exist beside the river Tay, where additional unusual vegetation types include unimproved lowland pasture and riverine shingle beds.

Birds
The area supports internationally important numbers of wintering Icelandic **greylag goose** (c. 3000 birds, 3% of the world and British population). The area has recently proved attractive to pink-footed geese and numbers are rising rapidly.

Notable also is breeding great crested grebe.

Conservation issues
Roosting and feeding geese are vulnerable to human disturbance and changes in agricultural practices.

Loch Leven

SPA/Ram Code	IBA Europe number
411A	117

County/Region	District(s)	OS sheet(s)	Grid Reference(s)	Maps 6, 9
Tayside	Perth and Kinross	58	NO 145015	

Area (ha)	NNR	SPA	Ramsar
1612	Part	Designated N Candidate Y	Designated Y Candidate N/A

A large eutrophic loch, surrounded by farmland, of major importance for both breeding and wintering wildfowl.

Site description

Loch Leven measures about 5 km by 3 km, lying midway between the estuaries of the Forth and the Tay, and is the largest eutrophic lake in Britain. It contains several islands, the largest of which, St Serf's Island, has an area of about 46 ha.

The loch is of considerable interest for its aquatic plants. Even though the diversity of the flora has been reduced by pollution, there is still a wide range of plant species present, including a number which are nationally uncommon. The damp, unimproved pasture surrounding the loch contains several plants of national and local rarity. The loch and its surrounds are also of entomological interest, especially for rare beetles and flies.

Birds

Loch Leven is a wetland of international importance by virtue of regularly supporting over 20,000 waterfowl. In the five-winter period 1985/86 to 1989/90 the average peak count was 22,147 wildfowl. Loch Leven supports internationally important numbers of wintering whooper swan, pink-footed goose, greylag goose, gadwall and shoveler, nationally important numbers of wintering teal, pochard, tufted duck, goldeneye and coot and nationally important numbers of breeding wigeon, gadwall, mallard, shoveler, tufted duck and black-headed gull.

Large numbers of waterfowl use the loch as both a feeding and roosting site in autumn and winter. Averages for individual species were: 80 great crested grebe, 200 **whooper swan** (1% of the world population, 3% of British), 8500 **pink-footed geese** (8% of world and British), 1950 Icelandic **greylags** (2% of world and British), 180 **gadwall** (1.5% of NW Europe, 3% of British), 1760 **teal** (2% of British), 430 **shoveler** (1% of NW Europe, 5% of British), 920 **pochard** (2% of British), 2570 **tufted duck** (4% of British), 270 **goldeneye** (2% of British) and 1500 **coot** (2% of British). Notable also are wintering wigeon and mallard.

Loch Leven is of major importance for its assemblage of breeding duck which include **wigeon** (6 pairs, 1.5% of British), **gadwall** (60-70 pairs, 12% of British), **mallard** (400-600 pairs, 1% of British), **shoveler** (12-20 pairs, 1% of British) and **tufted duck** (500-600 pairs, 8% of British). A large colony of **black-headed gulls** also breeds here

(8000 pairs, 3% of British). Notable also are breeding shelduck (30–50 pairs) and pochard (1 pair).

Conservation issues

Eutrophication from agricultural run-off from surrounding agricultural land and industrial and domestic effluent, including sewage effluent from Kinross and Milnathort, led to increased algal blooms, at their worst in the late 1960s. These blooms have been less severe in recent years, and some aquatic vegetation has returned. Shoreline erosion is a problem at the loch.

Firth of Tay

SPA/Ram Code	IBA Europe number
412A	121

County/Region	District(s)	OS sheet(s)	Grid Reference(s)	Maps 6, 9
Tayside	Perth and Kinross, Dundee	53, 54	NO 330260	
Fife	North East Fife			

Area (ha)	NNR	SPA		Ramsar	
5613	No	Designated	N	Designated	N
		Candidate	Y	Candidate	Y

The Tay estuary has extensive intertidal flats, reedbeds and saltmarshes, and is important for passage and wintering wildfowl and waders, and breeding reedbed species.

Site description
The Firth of Tay site stretches some 35 km along the estuary from near Newburgh to the estuary mouth. The flats on either side of the mouth, including those at Tayport, Tentsmuir Point and Abertay Sands are included in the Eden Estuary site (SPA/Ram 414A). The Firth of Tay consists of the inner estuary (above Invergowrie and Balmerino) and Monifieth Bay.

For much of its length, the main channel of the estuary lies close to the southern shore, and the most extensive intertidal flats are consequently on the north side, west of Dundee. In Monifieth Bay, to the east of Dundee, the substrate becomes more sandy and there are also mussel beds. The south shore consists mainly of fairly steeply shelving mud and shingle.

The inner Tay estuary is particularly noted for the continuous dense stands of reed along its north shore. These reedbeds, inundated during high tides, are among the largest in Britain. Eastwards, as conditions become more saline, there are areas of saltmarsh, a relatively scarce habitat in eastern Scotland.

Birds
The Firth of Tay is important for wintering and passage waterfowl, and breeding reedbed specialists.

For wintering waterfowl the following average peaks have been recorded in recent years: 1120 **pink-footed geese** (1% of world total), 595 **sanderling** (4% of British) and 1180 **redshank** (1% of EAF, 2% of British). Notable also are wintering oystercatcher, golden plover and dunlin, and autumn passage redshank (average of 1640 birds).

Breeding reedbed species include **water rail** (100+ pairs, c. 4% of British), sedge warbler (1000+ pairs) and large numbers of reed bunting.

Conservation issues
Waterfowl that winter on estuaries are vulnerable to land-claim and other developments,

such as the construction of barrages that would disturb or damage the existing ecology of these sites. Other human influences such as recreational disturbance, commercial exploitation of shellfish and worms, and oil and industrial pollution, are also potentially damaging to the conservation interest of estuaries.

The dumping of rubbish, which can support large rat populations, in the reedbed along the edge of the estuary, may pose a threat to breeding birds. Land-claim of the remainder of Invergowrie Bay remains a possibility, and the Firth is vulnerable to sewage pollution.

Large numbers of wildfowlers visit the inner estuary and at present there are no specific controls or limitations over the amount or location of shooting.

It is necessary to ensure continued management and monitoring of the reedbed to maintain suitable breeding habitat for birds.

Cameron Reservoir

SPA/Ram Code	IBA Europe number
413A	123

County/Region	District(s)	OS sheet(s)	Grid Reference(s)	Maps 6, 9
Fife	North East Fife	59	NO 4812	

Area (ha)	NNR	SPA		Ramsar	
1-999	No	Designated	N	Designated	N
		Candidate	Y	Candidate	Y

A reservoir, important as an autumn and winter roost for pink-footed geese.

Site description

Situated about 5 km south-west of St Andrews, this reservoir was formed through the impounding of the Cameron Burn. The reservoir is mesotrophic in nature and supports beds of aquatic and marginal macrophyte vegetation. This grades into willow carr along the southern shore, and on parts of the northern shore, where areas of coarse grassland also occur.

Birds

Cameron Reservoir provides a roost site for internationally important numbers of wintering **pink-footed goose**. In the five-winter period 1985/86 to 1989/90 the average peak count was 7600 birds, representing 7% of the world population. Notable also is wintering Icelandic greylag goose (average of 700 birds).

Conservation issues

Roosting geese are vulnerable to human disturbance. At Cameron, recently increasing levels of shooting in the vicinity of the roost may be discouraging the geese. Also the reservoir is no longer required for public water supply and is due to be de-commissioned. Its future as an open water body may then be in doubt.

Eden Estuary, Tentsmuir
Point and Abertay Sands

SPA/Ram Code	IBA Europe number
414A	122

County/Region	District(s)	OS sheet(s)	Grid Reference(s)	Maps 6, 9
Fife	North East Fife	54, 59	NO 500200	
Tayside	Angus			

Area (ha)	NNR	SPA		Ramsar	
2250+	Part	Designated	N	Designated	N
		Candidate	Y	Candidate	Y

A small estuary and coastal sand flats, which attract large numbers of wintering waders and wildfowl, including offshore seaduck.

Site description

The Eden Estuary in the southern part of this area, just north of St Andrews is fairly small compared with other Scottish east coast estuaries, but still contains a wide diversity of habitats. The extensive mudflats have abundant invertebrate fauna, and also hold beds of mussels, brown algae and all three British species of eelgrass. Around the estuary are saltmarshes, the largest in Fife, which range from pioneer communities of glasswort to upper level marshes with saltmarsh rush, saltmarsh flat-sedge and slender spike-rush. There are also brackish swamps, dominated by sea club-rush, and freshwater swamp or fen communities.

At the head of the estuary, the area includes woodland, scrub and freshwater marshes along the River Eden. These habitats include alder–willow swamp woodland.

At the estuary mouth there are intertidal sand and mud flats which extend northwards along the coast to Tayport to include the shore of Buddon Ness. Backing the shore are strandline and dune communities which have some scarce plants and animals, such as oak-leaved goosefoot and the grayling butterfly.

Tayport Bay comprises a relatively undisturbed area of mudflats, fragments of saltmarsh and eroding sand dunes. At Tentsmuir Point the dune system is rapidly accreting and supports some 300 plant species including some rarities. The outer sandflats are a major haul-out site for both common and grey seals, and common seals also breed there.

Birds

The area is of importance principally for the passage and wintering waterfowl, especially eider, red-breasted merganser and bar-tailed godwit.

Large flocks of wintering sea ducks occur, especially in St Andrews Bay. Notably well represented are **eider** (10,000–15,000, c. 28% of British). Also present are scaup, long-tailed duck, **common scoter** (1100 birds, 3% of British) and velvet scoter. Large numbers of **shelduck** (1600, 2% of British), **red-breasted merganser** (720, 7% of British) and **goosander** (60, 1% of British) also winter here. The Eden Estuary is used as a nocturnal roost by large numbers of pink-footed and greylag geese.

Wintering waders include 3800 **oystercatcher** (1% of British), 610 **grey plover** (3% of British), 90 **black-tailed godwit** (2% of British), 1400 **bar-tailed godwit** (1% of EAF, 2% of British) and 940 **redshank** (1% of British).

Conservation issues

Waterfowl that winter on estuaries are vulnerable to land-claim and other developments, such as the construction of barrages that would disturb or damage the existing ecology of these sites. Other human influences such as recreational disturbance, commercial exploitation of shellfish and worms, and oil and industrial pollution, are also potentially damaging to the conservation interest of estuaries.

The Eden Estuary suffers some disturbance from wildfowling, but its declaration as a Local Nature Reserve (1978) has been of benefit in regulating this. Coastal erosion and the pressure for piecemeal protection measures is a threat to the semi-natural habitats. Flights from the adjacent Leuchars airfield cause some disturbance to birds, but this may be unimportant except during hard weather.

Forth Islands

SPA/Ram Code	IBA Europe number
417A	125

County/Region	District(s)	OS sheet(s)	Grid Reference(s)	Maps 6, 9
Lothian	Edinburgh,	59, 66, 67	NT 207805	
	East Lothian		(Inchmickery) NT	
Fife	North East Fife		207811 (Cow and	
			Calves), NT 513868	
			(Fidra), NT 535866	
			(Lamb), NT 553870	
			(Craigleith), NT 602873	
			(Bass Rock), NT 655995	
			(Isle of May)	

Area (ha)	NNR	SPA	Ramsar
92	Part	Designated Y	Designated N
		Candidate N/A	Candidate N

Rocky islands in the Firth of Forth, which have large seabird breeding colonies.

Site description

The islands included within this area comprise Inchmickery, together with the nearby Cow and Calves, off Edinburgh; Fidra, Lamb and Craigleith plus the Bass Rock off North Berwick, and the much larger Isle of May in the outer part of the Firth. There are other small islands in the Firth, but those named are the ones with greatest ornithological interest.

The inner islands are very low lying, while those in the outer Firth are higher, steeper and rockier. This applies especially to the Bass Rock, which is an impressive volcanic plug rising to over 100 m, and to the Isle of May which has cliffs up to almost 50 m.

These islands characteristically support patchy, rank vegetation, typically of sea mayweed, scurvygrass and nettles, enriched with guano from breeding and roosting seabirds. The nationally scarce tree-mallow occurs on several of the islands. Tussocky grassland dominated by red fescue is found in less enriched areas. In June, most islands are ablaze with flowering thrift and, to a lesser extent, sea campion. The Isle of May supports the most extensive maritime clifftop grasslands in Fife, and has the largest breeding colony of grey seals off the east coast of Britain.

Birds

The islands are important for breeding seabirds with internationally important numbers of gannet, shag and lesser black–backed gull and nationally important numbers of many other species.

Recent counts from the Seabird Colony Register include **gannet** (21,600 pairs, 8% of the world population, 14% of British), **cormorant** (430 pairs, 6% of British), **shag** (2840 pairs, 2% of Western European, 8% of British), **lesser black–backed gull** (4300 pairs, 2% of Western and Central European population, 5% of British), **herring gull** (10,300 pairs, 7% of British), **kittiwake** (12,300 individuals, 2.5% of British), **guillemot** (26,500 individuals, 2.5% of British), **razorbill** (3100 pairs, 2% of British) and **puffin** (17,700 pairs, 5% of British). Four species of terns breed on the islands with nationally important populations of **Sandwich tern** (270 pairs, 2% of British), **roseate tern** (13 pairs 1990, 15% of British) and **common tern** (340 pairs, 3% of British).

Conservation issues

Seabirds are sensitive to changes in the quality of the marine environment, especially to changes in fish stocks and to oil pollution. Ground-nesting seabirds on offshore islands are vulnerable to the introduction of predatory mammals. Recreational disturbance by the public can also be a threat, for example, power boating can affect auk colonies.

All species of breeding terns have undergone a decline in recent years, although there has been notable success on the Isle of May, where terns have returned following the control of gull numbers. Gulls have not been culled in recent years but this may become necessary again at some time in the future.

Further reading

Campbell, L H (Ed.) 1978 *Report of the Forth Ornithological Working Party*. Nature Conservancy Council, Edinburgh.

Ratcliffe, D A (Ed.) 1977 *A Nature Conservation Review*. Cambridge University Press, Cambridge.

Flanders Moss and Lake of Menteith

SPA/Ram Code	IBA Europe number
419A	120

County/Region	District(s)	OS sheet(s)	Grid Reference(s)	Maps 8, 10
Central	Stirling	57	NS 630985	

Area (ha)	NNR	SPA		Ramsar	
1-999	Part	Designated	N	Designated	N
		Candidate	Y	Candidate	Y

A large, lowland raised mire and adjacent lake, important for wintering swans and geese.

Site description
The Lake of Menteith is a shallow water body with fringing reedbeds in some bays. The nearby Flanders Moss is the largest remaining intact lowland raised mire in the United Kingdom, and the largest remnant of the lowland raised mire system that formerly covered the Carse of Stirling, west of the Menteith moraine. It is of international importance for its biological and geomorphological features.

The relatively undisturbed plant communities on the drier areas of the dome of the bog itself are dominated by heather, cross-leaved heath and cotton grass. Where the surface peat is wetter, communities dominated by actively growing *Sphagnum* moss species occur. An exceptionally large number of vascular plants for a raised bog occur on the Moss, including several species, such as white-beaked sedge and bog-rosemary, that are locally rare or on the limits of their British range. The Moss is a locality for the nationally rare northern mire plant, Labrador-tea.

The rich invertebrate fauna is characterised by species of moths, beetles, flies and spiders normally associated with lowland areas, as well as those of northern temperate regions. There are breeding populations of adder and mountain hare (one of the few lowland breeding sites for this species).

Birds
The Lake of Menteith is internationally important as a winter roost for **pink-footed geese**, with a five-winter average peak count for 1985/86 to 1989/90 of 1700 birds (1.5% of the world and British population). They feed on neighbouring farmland with lesser numbers of greylag geese. Whooper swans (up to 191 birds) winter on the Carse of Stirling, and some occasionally roost on the Lake of Menteith. There are also wintering raptors.

Conservation issues
The birds that use this site are vulnerable to recreational pressure, for example, fishing, shooting and other disturbance. Afforestation, peat winning and drainage on the Moss itself could reduce the habitat value of mosslands and mires. The Lake of Menteith has also suffered algal blooms.

Gladhouse Reservoir

SPA/Ram Code	IBA Europe number
423A	126

County/Region	District(s)	OS sheet(s)	Grid Reference(s)	Map 9
Lothian	Midlothian	73	NT 299535	

Area (ha)	NNR	SPA	Ramsar
187	No	Designated Y Candidate N/A	Designated Y Candidate N/A

A mesotrophic reservoir, attracting important numbers of roosting pink-footed geese in winter.

Site description
Lying at the foot of the Moorfoot Hills, about 20 km south of Edinburgh, Gladhouse Reservoir is a large loch, with several small islands. There is limited development of aquatic and marginal vegetation, notably shoreweed and amphibious bistort. Small areas of marginal fen have developed, with canary-grass and species of willow.

Birds
The principal importance of Gladhouse Reservoir for birds is as a roost for wintering **pink-footed geese**. In the five-winter period 1985/86 to 1989/90 the average peak count was 3050 birds (3% of the world population). This site, and the alternative roost at Fala Flow (SPA/Ram 424A), are two of the major pink-footed goose roosts in the Lothians. Smaller numbers of greylag geese also occur.

Conservation issues
Roosting geese are vulnerable to human disturbance. Peak numbers of pink-footed geese have dropped considerably on this site over recent years. The reasons for the decline in numbers are unclear although shooting disturbance at the roost and/or at nearby feeding areas may be a factor.

Fala Flow

SPA/Ram Code	IBA Europe number
424A	127

County/Region	District(s)	OS sheet(s)	Grid Reference(s)	Map 9
Lothian	Midlothian	73	NT 432586	

Area (ha)	NNR	SPA	Ramsar
323	No	Designated Y Candidate N/A	Designated Y Candidate N/A

An area of blanket mire which is a major wintering roost site for pink-footed geese.

Site description
Fala Flow (325 m) is in the Lammermuir Hills, to the south-east of Edinburgh. It is a blanket mire, with some pools, developed at a lower altitude than most blanket mires in Midlothian. The vegetation comprises heather/cottongrass blanket mire, with other characteristic species including crowberry, common cottongrass and *Sphagnum* mosses. Such mires are scarce and declining in Midlothian, and this example is relatively undisturbed.

Birds
Fala Flow is important as a winter roost site for **pink-footed geese**. In the five-winter period 1985/86 to 1989/90 the average peak count was 1580 birds (1% of the world population). This area and Gladhouse Reservoir (SPA/Ram 423A) are used alternately as roost sites. The flow supports small numbers of breeding golden plover and dunlin.

Conservation issues
Roosting geese are vulnerable to human disturbance.

Westwater

SPA/Ram Code	IBA Europe number
425A	128

County/Region	District(s)	OS sheet(s)	Grid Reference(s)	Map 9
Borders	Tweeddale	72	NT 117523	

Area (ha)	NNR	SPA		Ramsar	
1-999	No	Designated	N	Designated	N
		Candidate	Y	Candidate	Y

An upland reservoir of outstanding importance as a winter roost for pink-footed geese.

Site description
Westwater Reservoir is an artificial water body, situated in the Pentland Hills, at 320 m above sea level. There is no emergent vegetation.

Birds
Westwater is a wetland of international importance by virtue of regularly supporting over 20,000 waterfowl. In the five-winter period 1984/5 to 1989/90 the average peak count was 21,412 wildfowl. The site is of major importance for **pink-footed geese** in early autumn as an arrival area, and throughout the winter. In the five-winter period 1985/86 to 1989/90 the average peak count was 21,100 birds (19% of the world population). Since 1985 there has been a continuing, regular increase in use (especially during post-migration) of the loch, with a maximum count of 40,000+ pink-feet having been recorded.

Conservation issues
Roosting geese are vulnerable to human disturbance. This water body is part of Lothian Regional Council's water supply to which byelaws and regulations apply regarding access and conservation.

Further reading
Newton, S F, Bell, M V, Brown, A W, and Murray, R 1990 Pink-footed goose numbers at arrival sites in eastern and central Scotland. *Scottish Birds* 16: 35-36.

St Abb's Head to Fast Castle

SPA/Ram Code	IBA Europe number
427A	132

County/Region	District(s)	OS sheet(s)	Grid Reference(s)	Map 9
Borders	Berwickshire	67	NT 880699	

Area (ha)	NNR	SPA		Ramsar	
1-999	Part	Designated	N	Designated	N
		Candidate	Y	Candidate	N

Sea cliffs with large colonies of breeding seabirds.

Site description
These cliffs extend for over 10 km along the Berwickshire coast and comprise old red sandstone and silurian rock, locally reaching over 150 m in height. In addition to exposed cliff, and cliff ledges, there are areas of scrub-woodland, grassland, open water, flushes and splash zone communities.

The diversity of vegetation types holds a large number of plants, with over 360 species of flowering plants recorded, including several which are scarce in the region, such as Scots lovage, knotted hedge-parsley and early marsh-orchid. Butterflies present include the northern brown argus.

Birds
The area supports nationally important breeding populations of shag, kittiwake, guillemot and razorbill.

Counts carried out for the Seabird Colony Register in the late 1980s recorded 620 pairs of **shag**s (2% of British), 25,250 pairs of **kittiwake**s (5% of British), 33,000 individual **guillemot**s (3% of British) and 1480 pairs of **razorbill**s (1.5% of British). Notable also are breeding fulmar, cormorant and herring gull.

The area is also a noted landfall for passage migrant landbirds, with over 240 species recorded in total.

Conservation issues
Seabirds are sensitive to changes in the quality of the marine environment, especially to changes in fish stocks and to oil pollution.

Greenlaw Moor and Hule Moss

SPA/Ram Code	IBA Europe number
428A	131

County/Region	District(s)	OS sheet(s)	Grid Reference(s)	Map 9
Borders	Berwickshire	74	NT 705500	

Area (ha)	NNR	SPA		Ramsar	
1000-9999	No	Designated	N	Designated	N
		Candidate	Y	Candidate	Y

An extensive area of moorland with pools, which are important as a pink-footed goose roost.

Site description

This area, in the southern Lammermuir Hills, consists of heather moorland to the east, and a raised mire to the west. The heath, rising to less than 300 m, is the largest remaining example of moorland at mid altitude in the Borders. It contains the two pools of Hule Moss which are of importance for geese.

Dogden Moss is a well developed example of a raised moss, with a fairly typical flora, including some regionally uncommon bryophytes.

On the eastern fringe of the area, there is a small area of secondary woodland which adds to habitat diversity, as do water courses and peripheral areas of grassland.

Birds

This site holds internationally important numbers of pink-footed geese.

Hule Moss is particularly significant as an early autumn arrival area for **pink-footed geese**, with a maximum of 25,700 geese recorded here (October 1989). Wintering pink-feet roost at Hule Moss. In the five-winter period 1985/86 to 1989/90 the average peak count there was 4350 birds (4% of world population).

Conservation issues

Roosting and feeding geese are vulnerable to human disturbance.

Further reading

Newton, S F, Bell, M V, Brown, A W and Murray, R 1990 Pink-footed Goose numbers at arrival sites in eastern and central Scotland. *Scottish Birds* 16: 35-36.

Hoselaw Loch

SPA/Ram Code	IBA Europe number
429A	130

County/Region	District(s)	OS sheet(s)	Grid Reference(s)	Map 9
Borders	Roxburgh	74	NT 806315	

Area (ha)	NNR	SPA	Ramsar
46	No	Designated Y Candidate N/A	Designated Y Candidate N/A

A loch with associated fen and raised mire, important as a winter roost for greylag and pink-footed geese.

Site description
Hoselaw Loch is a fairly small loch (approximately 15 ha) located on the northern slopes of the Cheviot Hills at about 180 m above sea level. There is little emergent vegetation.

Adjoining the loch is Din Moss, an area of raised mire with associated lagg fens. This is the most complete example of a raised mire in the district.

Birds
The loch supports internationally important wintering numbers of roosting pink-footed geese and Icelandic greylag geese.

In the five-winter period 1985/86 to 1989/90 the average peak counts were 1300 **pink-footed geese** (1% of world population) and 2680 **greylags** (3% of world population).

Conservation issues
Roosting geese are vulnerable to human disturbance. Numbers have dropped severely in the last two seasons as a result of adjacent shooting consequent on a change of ownership.

South Tayside Goose Roosts

SPA/Ram Code	IBA Europe number
440A	114, 115, 116

County/Region	District(s)	OS sheet(s)	Grid Reference(s)	Maps 6, 8
Tayside	Perth and Kinross	52, 58	NO 030205 NN 853185 NN 861097	10

Area (ha)	NNR	SPA		Ramsar	
1-999	No	Designated	N	Designated	N
		Candidate	Y	Candidate	Y

This site comprises three former sites with SPA/Ram codes 408A, 409A and 410A.

A group of freshwater lochs important as roosts for wintering pink-footed and greylag geese.

Site description
This site to the west of Perth comprises seven lochs, a number of smaller water bodies and other wetland habitats. Some of the lochs are eutrophic and support rich emergent vegetation at the loch edges.

Other wetland habitats associated with the lochs include one of the largest raised mires in the Tayside region, base rich flushes and fen communities. These diverse habitats support a correspondingly high number of plants, including some scarce species.

Ancient woodland is adjacent to one loch and consists mainly of oak, but also has some stands of alder/ash, and is notable for its lichen flora, including many species characteristic of old woodland. The woodland also contains several suboceanic epiphytic bryophytes, and higher plants of restricted distribution. Other woodland surrounding some lochs includes conifer plantations.

Birds
The area holds internationally important numbers of wintering Icelandic greylag geese and pink-footed geese.

In the five-winter period 1985/86 to 1989/90 the average peak count was 20,550 **pink-footed geese** (18% of the world and British population) and 6550 **greylags** (7% of the world and British population). Notable also are wintering mute swan and tufted duck.

Conservation issues
Roosting geese are vulnerable to human disturbance.

Firth of Forth

SPA/Ram Code	IBA Europe number
441A	124

County/Region	District(s)	OS sheet(s)	Grid Reference(s)	Maps 6, 8,
Central	Clackmannan (north shore), Falkirk (south shore), Stirling,	58, 59, 65, 66, 67	NT 1080	9, 10
Fife	Dunfermline, Kirkcaldy, North East Fife (all north shore),			
Lothian	East Lothian, Edinburgh, West Lothian (all south shore)			

Area (ha)	NNR	SPA		Ramsar	
5734+	No	Designated	N	Designated	N
		Candidate	Y	Candidate	Y

Firth of Forth includes the following IBAs as listed in the IBA Europe book: Inner Firth of Forth (SPA/Ram 415A) and Outer Firth of Forth (SPA/Ram 416A).

A vast area of intertidal flats and inshore water important for wintering wildfowl and waders.

Site description

The Firth of Forth is a complex estuarine site, stretching for a distance of over 100 km from the River Forth at Stirling eastwards past Edinburgh, and along the coasts of Fife and East Lothian to a wide estuary mouth. A wide range of coastal and intertidal habitats is found within the site, including saltmarshes, dune systems, maritime grasslands, heath and fen, cliff slopes, shingle and brackish lagoons. The Forth is heavily developed in parts, for example along the southern shore at Grangemouth and Edinburgh.

Extensive mudflats are found particularly in the Inner Firth, notably at Kinneil Kerse and Skinflats on the south shore and Torry Bay on the north shore. Sheltered bays such as those found at Blackness and Aberlady Bays also have intertidal flats. Typically the flats support a rich invertebrate fauna, with eelgrass species growing on the main mudflats; both of these act as an important food source for the large numbers of wintering birds that use the estuary.

In the Inner Firth both shores of the river are fringed by saltmarsh which in places shows succession to upper marsh, with areas of scrub, woodland and freshwater communities above the marsh. A range of other habitats includes reedbeds (at Tullibody Inch), brackish fen and natural improved grasslands.

Coastal lagoon systems back the saltmarsh at Skinflats and ash settling pools are present on former mudflats at Torry Bay (Inner Firth); these act as spring high tide wader roosts.

To the east of the bridges in the Outer Firth, the shoreline diversifies, with sandy shores, some rocky outcrops, mussel beds and some artificial sea walls. The North Berwick coast includes cliffs and dune grassland, with extensive dune systems at Aberlady (the largest in SE Scotland) and from Gullane to Broad Sands. These dune areas and associated dune slacks support particularly rich floras.

The north Outer Firth shore shows a similar range of habitats. The coastline from Burntisland to Kirkcaldy supports cliffs and areas of floristically rich coastal grassland. Calcareous, herb-rich neutral and thyme-rich maritime grassland types are found here, along with areas of mixed burnet rose/blackthorn scrub. The northern brown argus butterfly is an uncommon feature of these grasslands.

The sheltered Largo Bay is fringed by several stretches of species-rich coastal grassland, dune grassland and cliff slopes. Beach head saltmarsh occurs at scattered localities. The shallow waters of the Bay attract large numbers of wintering sea duck.

Birds
The Firth of Forth is a wetland of international importance by virtue of regularly supporting 61,400 wintering waterfowl, comprising 23,800 wildfowl and 37,600 waders.

The Firth of Forth is of international importance for wintering pink-footed geese, knot, bar-tailed godwit, redshank and turnstone. It is of national importance for wintering great crested grebe, cormorant, seven species of wildfowl and two species of wader, and for breeding common and little terns.

In the five-winter period 1985/86 to 1989/90 the following average peak counts were recorded: **great crested grebe** (650, 6% of British), **cormorant** (555, 3% of British), **pink-footed goose** (7880, 7% of the world total, notably at Aberlady), **shelduck** (2405, 3% of British plus large post-breeding flock of moulting birds at Kinneil), **teal** (2010, 2% of British, 1988-89), **scaup** (875, 17% of British, notably in Largo Bay), **eider** (5620, 8% of British), **long-tailed duck** (680, 3% of British), **common scoter** (2110, 6% of British, 1988-89, mainly in Largo Bay), **goldeneye** (1375, 9% of British, notably in Kirkcaldy Bay), **red-breasted merganser** (430, 4% of British), **oystercatcher** (7590, 3% of British), **knot** (9450, 5% of British), **bar-tailed godwit** (3135, 5% of British), **curlew** (2170, 2% of British), **redshank** (3505, 3% of EAF, 5% of British) and **turnstone** (1255, c. 2% of EAF, 3% of British).

The Firth of Forth supports nationally important numbers of breeding **common tern** (600 pairs 1990, 5% of British) and **little tern** (24 pairs 1990, 1% of British).

Conservation issues
Waterfowl that winter on estuaries are vulnerable to land-claim and other developments, such as the construction of barrages that would disturb or damage the existing ecology of these sites. Other human influences such as recreational disturbance, commercial exploitation of shellfish and worms, and oil and industrial pollution, are also potentially damaging to the conservation interest of estuaries.

The Firth of Forth is vulnerable to industrial expansion from the Grangemouth refinery. Threats to the mudflats of Kinneil have recently occurred (1989) in the form of land-fill and refuse disposal (successfully averted). Final land-claim of the ash lagoons in Torry Bay will result in the loss of wader roosting areas. There may be pressure for further expansion of such areas onto mudflats in future. There is a proposed barrage scheme at Kincardine Bridge and the expansion of an oil terminal at Hound Point is expected. There is increasing recreational use throughout the whole of the estuary.

Further reading

Hawarth, D and Bryant, D M (1988). *Spatial and temporal changes in the bird populations on the estuary and Firth of Forth*. NCC Chief Scientist Directorate commissioned research report No. 841.

McLusky, D S (ed.) 1987 The natural environment of the estuary of the Firth of Forth. *Proc. Roy. Soc. Edin.* 93B, Edinburgh.

SITE ACCOUNTS: ENGLAND

Upper Solway Flats and Marshes

SPA/Ram Code	IBA Europe number
501A	133

County/Region	District(s)	OS sheet(s)	Grid Reference(s)	Maps 10, 11
Cumbria	Allerdale, Carlisle	84, 85	NY 160610	
Dumfries and Galloway	Annandale and Eskdale, Nithsdale, Stewartry			

Area (ha)	NNR	SPA		Ramsar	
29,951	Part	Designated	Y	Designated	Y
		Candidate	Y	Candidate	Y

A large estuary complex, with extensive areas of grazed saltmarsh, important for wintering wildfowl and waders with 15 species occurring in numbers of international or national significance.

Site description

The flats and marshes of the Upper Solway Firth form one of the largest and most important continuous areas of intertidal habitat in Britain, exceeded only by Morecambe Bay (site 508A) and the Wash (site 802A). The estuarine system of flats and marshes is a dynamic one with shifting channels and phases of erosion and accretion. Sand is the predominant substrate although there are areas of mud and silt as well as a number of boulder-strewn mussel beds.

The most extensive areas of saltmarsh in the Solway are the Rockcliffe and Burgh marshes towards the head of the estuary, the Caerlaverock and Kirkconnell Merses on the Scottish side and the marshes of Moricambe on the south shore. These saltmarshes include the finest example in Britain of marsh terraces and provide excellent evidence of saltmarsh development over the last six thousand years. The saltmarsh vegetation is particularly noteworthy for its broad transition to mature upper marsh; its seaward edge is typified by pioneer species such as common saltmarsh-grass and glasswort, and gives way to a grassy saltmarsh dominated by red fescue, thrift and saltmarsh rush. On the landward side, the sward is dominated by species of bent and fescue.

The site is noted for its populations of invertebrates and amphibians and holds breeding great crested newts, and 11-23% of the British population of natterjack toads.

Birds

The area supports internationally important numbers of wintering whooper swan, pink-footed goose, barnacle goose, scaup, oystercatcher, knot, bar-tailed godwit, curlew and redshank, and nationally important numbers of wintering shelduck, pintail, goldeneye, golden plover, grey plover and dunlin.

In the five-winter period 1985/86 to 1989/90 the average peak count of total waterfowl was 109,795 birds, comprising 37,675 wildfowl and 72,120 waders. Totals for individual species were: 290 **whooper swan** (2% of the world total, 5% of British), 11,600 **pink-footed geese** (11% of world), 11,220 **barnacle geese** from the Svalbard population (100% of the world population), 1400 **shelduck** (2% of British), 770 **pintail** (3% of British), 2300 **scaup** (2% of NW European, 58% of British, including the largest assembly in the UK at Carse Bay), 150 **goldeneye** (1% of British), 21,860 **oyster-catcher** (2.5% of EAF, 8% of British), 2400 **golden plover** (1% of British), 440 **grey plover** (2% of British), 5650 **knot** (2% of EAF, 3% of British), 11,000 **dunlin** (3% of British), 2600 **bar-tailed godwit** (2% of EAF, 4% of British), 6500 **curlew** (2% of EAF, 7% of British) and 1800 **redshank** (2% of EAF and British). Notable also are wintering Bewick's swan, wigeon, mallard, lapwing and turnstone.

The Solway complex is a vital link in a chain of west coast estuaries used by migrating birds, and is one of the most important in Britain. It is especially important for ringed plover and sanderling.

The intertidal areas of the estuary are of value to geese as safe nocturnal roosts, with most of the feeding occurring on the marshes or inland. The most important intertidal wader feeding areas are Mersehead Sands, Blackshaw and Priestside Banks, Cardurnock Flats and the mouth of Moricambe bay. Species preferring muddy substrates are most numerous on the inner, sheltered parts of the estuary. The main goose roosts are at Blackshaw and Priestside Banks, Mersehead Sands and Rockcliffe and Moricambe bay. Dabbling ducks concentrate in the Caerlaverock area, in the channels of the Nith and Eden, and at the mouth of Moricambe bay.

The marshes at Rockcliffe and Caerlaverock support large populations of breeding birds, including oystercatcher, lapwing, redshank, black-headed gull, lesser black-backed gull, herring gull, and common and arctic terns.

Conservation issues
Waterfowl that winter on estuaries are vulnerable to land-claim and other developments, such as the construction of barrages that would disturb or damage the existing ecology of these sites. Other human influences such as recreational disturbance, commercial exploitation of shellfish and worms, and oil and industrial pollution, are also potentially damaging to the conservation interest of estuaries.

Industrial gathering of shellfish is a serious and growing concern on the Solway, and local problems occur from shooting on goose roosts and shooting of protected species on the north shore.

Further reading
Cumbria Naturalists Union. *Cumbria Bird Reports. Birds in Cumbria 1970-90.*

Duddon Estuary

SPA/Ram Code	IBA Europe number
503A	134

County/Region	District(s)	OS sheet(s)	Grid Reference(s)	Map 11
Cumbria	South Lakeland, Copeland, Barrow-in-Furness	96	SD 200800	

Area (ha)	NNR	SPA		Ramsar	
5122	Part	Designated	N	Designated	N
		Candidate	Y	Candidate	Y

Intertidal flats, saltmarshes, dunes and lagoons, important for wintering wildfowl and waders and for breeding terns.

Site description

Situated to the north-west of Morecambe Bay, the Duddon estuary is a complex area. Extensive mud- and sandflats are surrounded by saltmarshes, especially in the inner, northern parts of the estuary, and by sand dunes to the south including the north end of Walney Island. There are a number of settlements and industrial areas on the periphery; the former iron ore workings at Hodbarrow now comprise a 200-acre lagoon of considerable wildlife interest.

The intertidal sand and silt contains abundant invertebrates, which are important prey for the overwintering birds. Bordering the intertidal area, the saltmarsh is mostly grazed, and dominated by common saltmarsh-grass often with much red fescue. However, there is considerable variation, dependent on the intensity of grazing pressure as well as the degree of inundation. Pioneer marsh of glasswort, annual sea-blite and common cord-grass is present at the lowest levels, while at the other extreme sea rush is frequent at the upper limit.

Ungrazed saltmarsh is found on the eastern side of Walney Island, and is richer in species than elsewhere in the estuary.

There are three large dune systems around the mouth of the estuary, at Haverigg on the north side, and Sandscale Haws and North Walney on the south side. Dunes also occur as narrow belts backing some saltmarshes further up the estuary. A full range of dune types is present, from the strandline and fore-dune communities based on highly mobile sand, through progressively more fixed yellow and grey dunes, to dune grasslands and slacks. The calcareous nature of the sand has given a very diverse flora with many scarce species, and there is a rich associated invertebrate fauna. The dune slacks have a quite different flora, characterised by species such as marsh pennywort and creeping willow. Seasonal pools in wetter slacks, and ditches and ponds elsewhere around the estuary support 18-24% of the British breeding population of natterjack toads. Most of the British population of natterjacks is found at only five English estuaries, of which this is one. The

Duddon's population contributes to its international importance as a wetland. The toads feed on the upper shore and in short grass swards during the breeding and post-breeding seasons.

Particularly on North Walney, there is some vegetated shingle, an unusual plant community in Britain.

On each of the main dune systems, dune heath occupies small areas, where heather, bell heather, cross-leaved heath, and locally western gorse or mosses characterise the vegetation.

In poorly-drained areas, the dune systems in some places give way to neutral or acidic marshy grassland, dominated by purple moor-grass, Yorkshire-fog and false oat-grass. In some places, they grade through brackish marsh of sea club-rush and sea rush into saltmarsh.

Birds
The area supports internationally important numbers of wintering pintail, knot and redshank, and nationally important numbers of wintering shelduck, red-breasted merganser, oystercatcher, ringed plover, curlew, sanderling and dunlin, and breeding little tern.

The estuary is a wetland of international importance by virtue of regularly supporting in winter over 20,000 waterfowl. In the five-winter period 1984/85 to 1988/89 the average peak count was 26,780 birds, comprising 21,880 waders and 4900 wildfowl. Totals for individual species include 780 **shelduck** (1% of British), 1200 **pintail** (2% of NW European, 5% of British), 180 **red-breasted merganser** (2% of British), 6200 **oystercatcher** (2% of British), 250 **ringed plover** (1% of British), 3800 **knot** (1% of EAF, 2% of British), 390 **sanderling** (3% of British), 5500 **dunlin** (1% of British), 1900 **curlew** (2% of British) and 1400 **redshank** (1% of EAF, 2% of British). Notable also are wintering wigeon, teal, grey plover and turnstone.

In summer the estuary holds up to 31 breeding pairs of **little tern** (1% of British). Notable also are breeding Sandwich tern, common tern, and arctic tern.

Conservation issues
Waterfowl that winter on estuaries are vulnerable to land-claim and other developments, such as the construction of barrages that would disturb or damage the existing ecology of these sites. Other human influences such as recreational disturbance, commercial exploitation of shellfish and worms, and oil and industrial pollution, are also potentially damaging to the conservation interest of estuaries.

Specific proposals for a generating barrage exist, and if constructed, this would result in a loss of low-water feeding grounds for birds, the disruption of normal tidal regimes and a corresponding effect on saltmarsh vegetation and wader roost sites, the alteration of sedimentation patterns resulting from changes in current velocities, and changes in salinity and water quality.

Other issues include development of adjacent derelict industrial areas, increasing recreational pressure, management of saltmarshes and cord-grass encroachment, urban development, and pollution from adjacent industry. Wildfowling can cause disturbance to roosting wildfowl and waders on the saltmarsh at high tide.

Morecambe Bay

SPA/Ram Code	IBA Europe number
508A	135

County/Region	District(s)	OS sheet(s)	Grid Reference(s)	Map 11
Cumbria	Barrow-in-Furness, South Lakeland	96, 97, 102	SD 3565	
Lancashire	Lancaster City, Wyre			

Area (ha)	NNR	SPA		Ramsar	
39,800	No	Designated	N	Designated	N
		Candidate	Y	Candidate	Y

A very large system of intertidal mud- and sandflats, with associated saltmarshes, shingle beaches and other coastal habitats, of outstanding importance for passage and over-wintering waterfowl, and for breeding waterfowl, gulls and terns.

Site description

'Morecambe Bay' refers to Morecambe Bay itself, and the Lune estuary, and comprises one of the largest estuarine areas in the UK. Five main river channels (the Leven, Kent, Keer, Lune and Wyre) drain through the intertidal flats of sand and silt. Mussel beds and banks of shingle are present, and locally there are stony outcrops. The whole system is dynamic, with shifting channels, and phases of erosion and accretion affecting the estuarine deposits and the surrounding saltmarshes. The flats contain an abundant invertebrate fauna which supports many of the species of birds using the bay. In the Piel Channel Flats, near Barrow, there are small areas of eelgrass, which is unknown elsewhere in north-west England.

The capacity of the bay to support large numbers of birds derives from the rich food resources available in the tidal flats and adjacent freshwater wetlands, and the fringing saltmarshes and shingle banks, which provide secure roosts at high tide.

Pioneer saltmarsh with glasswort and common cord-grass gives way at intermediate levels to marsh dominated by common saltmarsh-grass, but the majority of saltmarshes are high level types and are grazed, mainly by sheep. Some marshes are also cut for turf. These grazed saltings are typically rather species-poor. There is greater diversity along creeks and channels, especially in ungrazed areas, of which there are small patches around the bay and a larger area on the Isle of Walney.

At the top of the saltmarsh, there is frequently a zone of sea rush or sea couch. Brackish water marshes with species such as sea club-rush, common reed and grey club-rush are present locally. Transitions to freshwater marsh also occur. At Middleton Marsh, sand leek and sea radish, both nationally scarce species, grow on sandy areas bordering the marsh.

The saltmarshes and transitional habitats support interesting invertebrate fauna. A number of nationally scarce species have been found, particularly among the beetles, associated with strandline vegetation, exposed mud and brackish pools as well as the saltmarsh itself.

At several localities around the bay, but especially on South Walney and Foulney Islands, vegetated shingle beaches with their distinctive flora are found.

There are also some sand dunes on South Walney; marram and sand couch dominate, but more fixed swards including those in hollows have greater plant species diversity. Some scarce species, including sea spurge and dune fescue, are found in these dunes.

Birds
The area is of significance in supporting wintering waterfowl (internationally important numbers of 12 species and nationally important numbers of an additional 9 species), passage waders (internationally important numbers of 2 species) and breeding birds (internationally important numbers of one species; nationally important numbers of 6 species).

The site is a wetland of international importance by virtue of regularly supporting in winter over 20,000 waterfowl. In the five-year period 1984/85 to 1988/89 the average peak count was 180,775 birds, comprising 23,725 wildfowl and 157,050 waders. After the Wash, Morecambe Bay holds greater numbers of wintering wildfowl than any other estuary in Great Britain. Totals for individual species include 170 **great-crested grebe** (2% of British), 525 **cormorant** (3% of British), 8500 **pink-footed geese** (8% of the world total), 3700 **shelduck** (1% of NW European, 5% of British), 3200 **wigeon** (1% of British), 1600 **teal** (2% of British), 2300 **pintail** (3% of NW European, 9% British), 4800 **eider** (10% of British), 360 **goldeneye** (2% of British), 220 **red-breasted merganser** (2% of British), 56,800 **oystercatcher** (6% of EAF, 20% of British), 605 **ringed plover** (1% of EAF, 3% of British), 1900 **golden plover** (1% of British), 2000 **grey plover** (1% of EAF, 9% of British), 17,000 **lapwing** (2% of British), 26,300 **knot** (8% of EAF, 12% of British), 190 **sanderling** (1% of British), 43,000 **dunlin** (3% of EAF, 10% of British), 140 **black-tailed godwit** (3% of British), 3500 **bar-tailed godwit** (3% of EAF, 6% of British), 10,400 **curlew** (3% of EAF, 11% of British), 7200 **redshank** (7% of EAF, 10% of British) and 2000 **turnstone** (3% of EAF, 4% of British).

In addition, during spring and autumn passage migration periods, the bay supports internationally important numbers of **ringed plover** (1600 birds, 3% of EAF) and **sanderling** (3600 birds, 3% of EAF). Whimbrel occur in notable numbers.

In summer the bay holds 720 pairs of **Sandwich terns** (5% of British, 1.5 of W European), 285 pairs of **common terns** (2% of British) and 29 pairs of **little terns** (1% of British). Smaller numbers of arctic terns also breed. Also present are 950 pairs of **eider** (5% of British), 10,000 pairs of **lesser black-backed gulls** (12% of British) and 10,000 pairs of **herring gulls** (7% of British).

Conservation issues
Waterfowl that winter on estuaries are vulnerable to land-claim and other developments that would disturb or damage the existing ecology of these sites. Other human influences such as recreational disturbance, commercial exploitation of shellfish and worms, and oil and industrial pollution, are also potentially damaging to the conservation interest of estuaries.

Recreational pressures on the site include increasing windsurfing activity adjacent to wader roosts and microlight aircraft using the foreshore for landing as well as plans for hovercraft trips which could cause disturbance to roosting or feeding waterbirds, and a plan for a marina at Morecambe. Although Morecambe Bay barrage is not an imminent threat, the proposals to construct a barrage across the River Wyre could have implications for the hydrology of the area.

Extensive sea defence works are proposed, the design of which needs to take full account of their potential impact on the ecological character of the site.

Further reading
Cumbria Naturalists Union and Cumbria Bird Club *Birds in Cumbria. County Natural History Reports* 1981-90.
Walney Bird Observatory Logs/Reports 1981-90.
Robinson, N A and Pringle, A W (eds.) 1987 *Morecambe Bay: An Assessment of Present Ecological Knowledge.* Centre for North-West Regional Studies in conjunction with Morecambe Bay Study Group.
Wilson, J 1988 *Birds of Morecambe Bay.* Cicerone, Morecambe.

Leighton Moss

SPA/Ram Code	IBA Europe number
509A	137

County/Region	District(s)	OS sheet(s)	Grid Reference(s)	Map 11
Lancashire	Lancaster	97	SD 483749	

Area (ha)	NNR	SPA	Ramsar
125	No	Designated Y	Designated Y
		Candidate N/A	Candidate N/A

A large reedbed with shallow pools and associated fens and carrs, important for breeding reedbed birds and wintering wildfowl.

Site description

Leighton Moss, situated between Silverdale and Warton on the edge of Morecambe Bay, contains the largest reedbed in north-west England. Originally a peat moss, the area was drained and cultivated before flooding and taking on its present character. Since 1964, it has been managed by the RSPB to maintain and diversify the wetland habitats.

The base-rich water, which flows into the marsh from the surrounding limestone hills, contributes to an overall richness in the vegetation and associated fauna. As well as the large reedbeds, there are extensive areas of open water, large areas of tussock sedge, and transitional communities through fen to woodland.

Mammals present include otters, at one of their few Lancashire breeding localities, a red deer population based within the reedbeds, and red squirrels in the woods.

Rare invertebrates include beetles, moths, hoverflies, caddisflies and water fleas. Many of these species are regionally and nationally rare, as they are associated with rare fenland habitat. Twenty-six species of butterfly have been recorded.

Birds

The area supports nationally important numbers of breeding bittern, marsh harrier, bearded tit, pochard and shoveler, and wintering teal and shoveler.

Breeding marshland birds present in 1990 include 4 booming male **bitterns** (20% of British), 15 pairs of **shoveler** (1% of British), 8 pairs of **pochard** (2% of British), 1-2 pairs of **marsh harrier** (1% of British) and 20-30 pairs of **bearded tit** (3% of British). Notable also are c. 25 pairs of water rail.

Average peak counts of wintering wildfowl in the five-year period 1985/86 to 1989/90 include 1100 **teal** (1% of British) and 190 **shoveler** (2% of British).

Conservation issues

A proposal exists to deepen and de-water Middlebarrow quarry adjacent to the site. This could affect water levels at Leighton Moss and may give rise to problems with water quality. The popularity of this site requires the successful management of 16,000 visitors per year.

Further reading
Wilson, J 1990 *Leighton Moss and Morecambe Bay. The First Twenty Five Years.* RSPB, Sandy.

Ribble and Alt Estuaries

SPA/Ram Code	IBA Europe number
510A	139

County/Region	District(s)	OS sheet(s)	Grid Reference(s)	Map 11
Lancashire	Fylde, Preston,	102, 108	SD 375240 (Ribble)	
	South Ribble,		SD 285030 (Alt)	
	West			
	Lancashire			
Merseyside	Sefton			

Area (ha)	NNR	SPA		Ramsar	
15,934	Parts	Designated	Y	Designated	Y
		Candidate	Y	Candidate	Y

A large area of mud and sand flats, backed by saltmarsh and sand dunes, of international importance for passage and wintering wildfowl and waders.

Site description

The area extends from the Ribble estuary in the north to Crosby in the south, where it includes the mouth of the River Alt. In addition to the mud- and sandflats, there is much saltmarsh, particularly in the Ribble estuary, and behind the open shore there are the sand dunes of Birkdale, Ainsdale, Formby and Altcar.

The intertidal flats are rich in invertebrates on which the waders and many of the wildfowl feed. The highest densities of feeding birds are in the muddier substrates of the two river mouths, but the sandier shores are also used, and the saltmarshes and foreshore throughout are used as high tide roosts. Roosts in the Alt estuary attract birds from as far as the more disturbed Dee roost sites (Mitchell *et al* 1988).

The extensive saltmarshes in the Ribble estuary are mainly species-poor, composed of common saltmarsh-grass and red fescue with a pioneer zone of common cord-grass at the outer edge. There is also a small area of saltmarsh at the mouth of the Alt. At Crossens and Marshside marshes, near Southport, there is some unimproved brackish grazing marsh, an uncommon habitat in north-west England.

The sand dune complex stretching from Southport to the Alt estuary supports a diverse flora, and forms the prime example of a calcareous dune-system in north-west England, even though some areas have been lost through development, woodland creation or modified for golf course use. A classic dune succession is present, from embryo dunes with sparse plant cover through marram-dominated yellow dunes, to more fixed types characterised by red fescue and sand sedge, or creeping willow and false oat-grass. Some dune pastures have developed on formerly cultivated land.

The dune slacks are typically dominated by creeping willow, or, where rabbit grazing or trampling is heavier, a mixed and species-rich community of grasses, sedges, and highly characteristic species such as marsh pennywort. Wetter areas and pools have emergent aquatic plants such as yellow iris, reed canary-grass and bulrush, and fully aquatic species. The pools are the breeding sites for the nationally rare natterjack toad.

The dunes are rich in plant species typical of the calcareous conditions, and include some that are scarce both regionally and nationally. The fauna, too, is highly diverse and contains numerous species that are scarce on a local or national basis, and includes sand lizard.

Birds

The area supports internationally important numbers of wintering Bewick's swan, whooper swan, pink-footed goose, shelduck, wigeon, teal, pintail, oystercatcher, grey plover, knot, sanderling, dunlin, black-tailed godwit, bar-tailed godwit and redshank, and nationally important numbers of wintering golden plover, lapwing and curlew, and breeding common tern.

The area is a wetland of international importance by virtue of regularly supporting in excess of 20,000 waterfowl. In the five-winter period 1985/86 to 1989/90 the average peak count was 218,915 waterfowl, comprising 161,500 waders and 57,415 wildfowl. Totals for individual species include 540 **Bewick's swans** (3% of NW European, 8% of British), 380 **whooper swans** (2% of world total, 6% of British), 16,000 **pink-footed geese** (15% of the world total), 4200 **shelduck** (2% of NW European, 6% of British), 33,800 **wigeon** (5% of NW European, 14% of British), 5800 **teal** (1% of NW European, 6% of British), 700 **pintail** (1% of NW European, 3% of British), 14,000 **oystercatcher** (2% of EAF, 5% of British), 5300 **golden plover** (3% of British), 3600 **grey plover** (2% of EAF, 17% of British), 16,500 **lapwing** (2% of British), 76,700 **knot** (22% of EAF, 34% of British), 2500 **sanderling** (2% of EAF, 18% of British), 15,000 **dunlin** (1% of EAF, 3% of British), 1400 **black-tailed godwit** (2% of EAF, 3% of British), 17,500 **bar-tailed godwit** (2% of EAF, 3% of British), 1100 **curlew** (1% of British) and 2000 **redshank** (2% of EAF, 3% of British).

Nationally important numbers of breeding **common tern** (565 pairs 1989, 4% of British) occur at this site and large numbers of **black-headed gulls** (16,000 pairs 1989) also breed. Notable also are passage ruff.

Conservation issues

Waterfowl that winter on estuaries are vulnerable to land-claim and other developments, such as the construction of barrages that would disturb or damage the existing ecology of these sites. Other human influences such as recreational disturbance, commercial exploitation of shellfish and worms, and oil and industrial pollution, are also potentially damaging to the conservation interest of estuaries.

Controls are necessary to ensure that any increase in sand winning would not affect the hydrology of the estuaries, and that vehicle movements do not cause disturbance. Proposals exist to create a landfill site at Hesketh Out Marsh. This would be the first such development adjacent to the Ribble and has worrying implications in terms of contamination and disturbance. Proposals affecting the Ribble Estuary include hover-craft services across the estuary and clay pigeon shooting adjacent to the estuary. Horse riding, dog walking and pedestrian access to the estuary at key locations at critical times of the year can cause disturbance to waders and wildfowl. There are proposals for the development of marinas on the Ribble from time to time. Recent changes to the grazing regime at Crossens and Marshside marshes (ie retention of cattle on the marshes for longer periods of time, or no grazing at all) have led to a decrease in usage by wintering pink-footed geese.

Further reading

Kirby, J S, Cross, S, Taylor, J E and Wolfenden, I H 1988 The distribution and abundance of waders wintering on the Alt Estuary, Merseyside, England. *Wader Study Group Bulletin*, 54: 23-28.

Mitchell, J R, Moser, M E and Kirby, J S 1988 Declines in midwinter counts of waders roosting on the Dee estuary. *Bird Study* 35 (3): 191-198.

Martin Mere

SPA/Ram Code	IBA Europe number
511A	140

County/Region	District(s)	OS sheet(s)	Grid Reference(s)	Map 11
Lancashire	West Lancashire	108	SD 420146	

Area (ha)	NNR	SPA	Ramsar
119	No	Designated Y Candidate N/A	Designated Y Candidate N/A

A wetland complex supporting internationally important numbers of wintering swans, geese and ducks.

Site description

This low-lying wetland complex comprises open water, marsh, and damp acid hay meadows overlying deep peat, with some regionally scarce plants; notably tubular water-dropwort, whorled caraway, golden dock, fine-leaved water-dropwort, large-flowered hemp-nettle and tall ramping-fumitory. Up to 300 moth species have been recorded, including some rare species. A large variety of fungi and a healthy mammal population are also present.

Birds

The area supports internationally important numbers of wintering Bewick's swan, whooper swan, pink-footed geese, wigeon, teal and pintail and nationally important numbers of wintering ruff.

The site is a wetland of international importance by virtue of regularly supporting over 20,000 waterfowl. In the five-winter period 1985/86 to 1989/90 the average peak was 23,990 birds. Totals for individual species include 650 **Bewick's swan** (4% of NW European, 9% of British), 400 **whooper swan** (2% of world total, 7% of British), 16,750 **pink-footed geese** (15% of world total), 16,250 **wigeon** (2% of NW European, 7% of British), 5500 **teal** (1% of NW European, 6% of British), 1730 **pintail** (2% of NW European, 7% of British) and 170 ruff.

Notable also are wintering mallard and lapwing, and breeding shelduck, gadwall, shoveler, lapwing, snipe, redshank, barn owl, tree sparrow and corn bunting. Martin Mere at times acts as a feeding and roost site for almost the entire Bewick's and whooper swan population of SW Lancashire, and for at least two-thirds of the pink-footed goose population of SW Lancashire and the Ribble.

Conservation issues

A proposal to construct a golf driving range adjacent to Martin Mere has been averted. Turf removal occurs on abutting land and there is intensive shooting close to the reserve boundaries.

Mersey Estuary

SPA/Ram Code	IBA Europe number
513A	158

County/Region	District(s)	OS sheet(s)	Grid Reference(s)	Map 11
Merseyside	Wirral,	108, 117	SJ 440800	
	Liverpool			
Cheshire	Ellesmere Port			
	and Neston,			
	Halton, Vale			
	Royal			

Area (ha)	NNR	SPA		Ramsar	
6702	No	Designated	N	Designated	N
		Candidate	Y	Candidate	Y

An estuary with large areas of intertidal mudflats and saltmarshes, of international importance for passage and wintering wildfowl and waders.

Site description
The site includes the extensive intertidal areas of the Mersey estuary, and some nearby pools at Frodsham.

The intertidal flats, with their abundant invertebrate life, and the saltmarshes are important feeding areas for the waterfowl that use the estuary. At high tide, important roost sites include the saltings, and also adjoining land, notably at Hale Marsh.

The saltmarshes have pioneer stands of glasswort, but common saltmarsh-grass is dominant over most areas. Grazing is widespread, but at Stanlow Banks, where grazing is absent, plant species diversity is higher, including abundant sea aster and spear-leaved orache, and also frequent sea plantain, annual sea-blite, and other typical saltmarsh plants. The saltmarsh is undergoing erosion to the south of the main river channel, as the river shifts its course southwards. As a result of this, saltmarsh is accreting on the northern shore at Oglet Bay. In places, the saltmarsh grades into brackish marsh dominated by common reed. Sandy areas support a characteristic range of species.

Some sections of the north side of the estuary are composed of boulder clay cliffs, which periodically slump onto the shore. A number of unusual plants grow on these cliffs, including yellow-wort and bristly ox-tongue, at the northern limits of their distributions.

Birds
The site supports internationally important numbers of wintering shelduck, wigeon, teal, pintail, dunlin and redshank, and nationally important numbers of wintering great crested grebe, grey plover and curlew.

The site is a wetland of international importance by virtue of regularly supporting over 20,000 waterfowl. In the five-winter period 1985/86 to 1989/90 the average peak was 56,415 birds, comprising 26,995 waders and 29,420 wildfowl. Totals for individual species include 115 **great crested grebe** (2% of British), 3000 **shelduck** (1% of NW European, 4% of British), 7700 **wigeon** (1% of NW European, 3% of British), 9500 **teal** (2% of NW European, 9% of British), 7100 **pintail** (10% of NW European, 28% of British), 290 **grey plover** (1% of British), 1200 **curlew** (1% of British), 18,500 **dunlin** (1% of EAF, 4% of British) and 3300 **redshank** (3% of EAF, 4% of British). Notable also are passage ringed plover and wintering black-tailed godwit.

Conservation issues

Waterfowl that winter on estuaries are vulnerable to land-claim and other developments, such as the construction of barrages that would disturb or damage the existing ecology of these sites. Other human influences such as recreational disturbance, commercial exploitation of shellfish and worms, and oil and industrial pollution, are also potentially damaging to the conservation interest of estuaries.

A proposal exists for a Mersey Barrage to harness tidal energy to generate power. Such a scheme would result in a reduction in the tidal range of the Mersey and would affect the extent of saltmarsh and mudflats upstream.

The construction of a second runway for Liverpool airport is proposed on land to be claimed from the estuary. This will have major implications for the hydrological, sedimentation and biological systems within the estuary. The lack of coordination between this proposal and the Mersey Barrage proposal is also a major cause for concern. A proposed new road crossing to service the airport could lead to the loss of parts of nearby grazing marshes.

The Mersey estuary is heavily industrialised and is regularly subject to pollution incidents. The vagaries of wind strength and direction, tidal level, type of oil discharged and time of year when the spillage occurs highlight the need for improved contingency planning.

Bowland Fells

SPA/Ram Code 515A	IBA Europe number 138

County/Region	District(s)	OS sheet(s)	Grid Reference(s)	Map 11
Lancashire	Lancaster, Ribble Valley, Wyre	97, 98, 102, 103	SD 620570	

Area (ha) 15,759	NNR No	SPA Designated N Candidate Y	Ramsar Designated N Candidate N

An extensive upland area of moorland and blanket mire, with typical upland breeding birds including birds of prey, and a large colony of lesser black-backed gulls.

Site description
The Forest of Bowland forms a western outlier to the Pennines, to the east of Lancaster. Although not especially high, with summits mostly in the range 450-550 m, the land is generally over 250 m and with an upland character. The underlying rock is predominantly millstone grit, which gives rise to the acidic vegetation covering the hills. The area is drained by fast-flowing streams.

The more gentle slopes, and level ground on ridges, have blanket mire dominated by heather and hare's-tail cottongrass. Locally, heather is replaced by bilberry, and in some places degradation has proceeded further, to cottongrass dominated stands, and active peat erosion. *Sphagnum* mosses are sparse owing to past burning practices, but other typical bog plants are present, including bog-rosemary, cranberry, crowberry and cloudberry.

Heather moorland is found on steeper slopes and is mostly burnt in small patches, for the benefit of red grouse. Bilberry is generally present with the heather, and with wavy hair-grass can become dominant where sheep grazing is heavy. Heavier grazing produces species-poor acidic grassland dominated by mat-grass.

Uncommon plants survive on unburnt and ungrazed areas, for example, on crags and in flushes and springs. Scarcer plant species include fir clubmoss, Wilson's filmy-fern and hay-scented buckler-fern. Lesser twayblade, broad-leaved cottongrass and the nationally scarce, pale forget-me-not occur.

On lower ground, bracken forms extensive stands, with bilberry found in more open areas. Scrubby oak cover exists in the valleys and on some steep slopes.

Birds
The area supports internationally important numbers of breeding lesser black-backed gull, and nationally important numbers of breeding hen harrier and merlin.

Recent counts of breeding birds include up to 9 pairs of **hen harrier**s (1% of British), 31 pairs of **merlin**s (5% of British) and 7600 pairs of **lesser black-backed gull**s (4% of Western and Central European, 9% of British). Notable also are breeding peregrine, oystercatcher, golden plover, lapwing, snipe, curlew, redshank, common sandpiper and short-eared owl.

Conservation issues

Birds that depend on moorland areas are vulnerable to widescale habitat change, especially afforestation and agricultural intensification. The breeding raptors in this area, especially hen harriers, continue to suffer from a high level of illegal persecution.

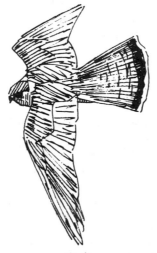

Merlin

Thorne and Hatfield Moors

SPA/Ram Code	IBA Europe number
517A	141

County/Region	District(s)	OS sheet(s)	Grid Reference(s)	Maps 12, 13
South Yorkshire	Doncaster	112	SE 730160 (Thorne)	
Humberside	Boothferry		SE 705060 (Hatfield)	

Area (ha)	NNR	SPA		Ramsar	
1000-9999	Part	Designated	N	Designated	N
		Candidate	Y	Candidate	Y

Two areas of cut-over lowland raised mire, with associated scrub and wetland habitats, important for a range of breeding birds, especially nightjar.

Site description

These two moors, lying to the east and north-east of Doncaster, are the largest remaining areas of lowland peat in England, although much peat exploitation has already taken place. Large parts of both sites are currently cleared of vegetation and drained for large-scale peat milling. The land lies close to sea level, but the peat, which is of variable depth, up to perhaps 4 m, was laid down in the basin of an inland lake.

Commercial peat cutting operations began in the late 19th century with traditional hand cutting techniques being used extensively up until the mid 1960s. Most of the moors' flora and fauna survived this period because hand cutting produced a mosaic of dry and wet areas which allowed ample time for recolonisation before cutting again, although it destroyed the original raised mire's hydrological system.

The mire communities are dominated by hare's-tail and common cotton-grasses, cross-leaved heath, soft-rush and *Sphagnum* mosses, and include a variety of scarcer bog plants such as bog rosemary and cranberry. Drier heath is dominated by heather, bracken and purple moor-grass. Birch scrub, dense in places, occurs throughout much of the two areas.

The numerous ditches and drains have varied aquatic vegetation, especially to the south of Hatfield Moor, with 12 pondweed species having been recorded. Other species of interest include arrowhead, greater bladderwort, and short-leaved water-starwort.

The invertebrate interest of the moors is considerable, and 2,500 species have been recorded. Several are nationally or regionally rare, including three species occurring at their only station in the UK, namely the ground beetle *Bembidion humerale*, the pill-beetle *Curimopsis nigrita* and *Phaonia jaroschewski*, a rare fly.

Birds

Thorne and Hatfield each support nationally important numbers of breeding **nightjar**: in 1990 a total of 50-60 churring males was recorded (3% of British). Notable also are breeding teal, snipe, curlew, long-eared owl, nightingale, whinchat, tree pipit and twite. Hobbies are regularly recorded in summer. During the winter hen harriers, merlins, short-eared owls and stonechats occur.

Conservation issues

Planning permission for peat extraction covering both moors was granted in the early 1950s. Commercial peat extraction has continued to intensify in the 1980s with several kilometres of new drains being cut and over 200 ha stripped of vegetation between 1988 and 1989, particularly on Hatfield Moor.

Remaining vegetated areas on both moors are under threat from further drainage work and vegetation clearance in advance of peat extraction. There is concern over changes in water-levels on the moors and also the surrounding area.

Habitat creation experiments are being carried out by the peat extraction company.

The NNR safeguards a part of Thorne Moor but even this area may be affected by cutting and drainage in the surrounding area.

Further reading

Skidmore, P, Limbert, M and Eversham, B C 1987 *The Insects of Thorne Moors*. Sorby Natural History Society, Sheffield.

Shap Fells

SPA/Ram Code	IBA Europe number
520A	136

County/Region	District(s)	OS sheet(s)	Grid Reference(s)	Map 11
Cumbria	Eden	90, 91	NY 5509	

Area (ha)	NNR	SPA		Ramsar	
10,000+	No	Designated	N	Designated	N
		Candidate	Y	Candidate	N

Hill country with heather moorland and blanket bog, supporting a diverse assemblage of upland breeding birds including raptors and waders.

Site description
This extensive upland area in the eastern Lake District is divided into two by the A6 trunk road. The underlying rocks are granites, silurian grits and slates, which give a predominantly acidic character to the vegetation, but there are some beds of more calcareous silts and mudstones.

Blanket bog is the most widespread vegetation type. Typically, heather and hare's-tail cotton-grass are co-dominant over *Sphagnum* mosses, with associated species such as cross-leaved heath, bilberry and crowberry, and in some places cloudberry. Where over-grazing or poor burning practices have occurred, the vegetation has become degraded and is dominated by cotton-grass or deergrass, with associated heath rush. Locally, bilberry replaces heather on degraded peat haggs.

In the eastern part of Birkbeck Fells, east of the A6, there are some areas of upland raised mire, in which *Sphagnum* mosses grow with heather species, cotton-grasses, cranberry, bog asphodel and round-leaved sundew.

Heather moorland occurs most extensively in the north of Birkbeck Fells and around rocky outcrops on Shap Fells. Burning and grazing pressure have often encouraged the invasion of grasses, or, on wetter ground, cotton-grass and heath rush. In areas of reduced pressure, heather is dominant with associated bilberry on drier ground or cross-leaved heath and *Sphagnum* mosses where wetter conditions prevail.

Several different acidic grassland types occur, some of which are moderately species-rich. These include purple moor-grass and rush-dominated swards, found along the north-facing valleyside of Wet Sleddale.

Flushes, ranging from strongly acidic to moderately basic, are found throughout the area. The acidic communities include rush-dominated and sedge-dominated soligenous mires, and also some bog-myrtle – purple moor-grass mires which are not common in the Lake District. The basic flushes tend to be more species-rich, but are highly varied in size and composition. Sedge-brown moss mires are widespread but small features, occurring on rather open stony ground; these contain various small sedges and mosses such as *Ctenidium molluscum* and *Campylium stellatum*, together with associated herbs including common butterwort and marsh arrowgrass.

Birds

The site supports a large and diverse upland breeding bird assemblage. Breeding waders, especially golden plover, lapwing, dunlin, snipe and curlew, nest at relatively high densities. Birds of prey which breed on the site include merlin, peregrine and short-eared owl. Other characteristic upland breeding birds present include raven, twite and red grouse, the last of which is managed for sport.

Conservation issues

Birds that depend on moorland areas are vulnerable to widescale habitat change, especially afforestation and agricultural intensification. Poor moorland management through overgrazing by sheep and excessive heather burning pose the greatest threat to the continued interest of this site. Recreational disturbance is a potential problem during the breeding season.

Further reading

Lake District National Park. Field Surveys of the Lake District National Park 1977 to present.

Lake District National Park. 1988, Section 3 Conservation Map. Mountain, Moor and Heath. Consultation Report.

NCC 1987. Changes in the Cumbrian Countryside. Research and Survey in Nature Conservation. Paper No. 6

North of England Montane Sites

SPA/Ram Code	IBA Europe number
523A	N/A

County/Region	District(s)	OS Sheet(s)	Grid Reference(s)	Map 11
Cumbria	Allerdale, Eden	89, 90	NY3031	

Area (ha)	NNR	SPA		Ramsar	
10,000	No	Designated	N	Designated	N
		Candidate	Y	Candidate	N

A montane area with an important assemblage of upland breeding birds.

Site description

This site comprises a group of mountain massifs. They support a range of upland vegetation types with particularly extensive tracts of montane and submontane dwarf shrub heath communities. Other habitats of special interest are high-level tarns, montane moss heath and juniper scrub.

Birds

This site is important for its rich assemblage of montane bird species. These include waders, such as snipe, golden plover and dotterel; raptors, such as peregrine and merlin, together with raven, ring ousel, red grouse and twite.

Conservation issues

The birds that use this site are vulnerable to human disturbance from increased public access, particularly from hill-walkers, to the high tops, and to habitat degradation through high livestock levels.

Lindisfarne

	SPA/Ram Code	IBA Europe number
	601A	142

County/Region	District(s)	OS sheet(s)	Grid Reference(s)	Map 9
Northumberland	Berwick-upon-Tweed	75	NU 100430	

Area (ha)	NNR	SPA		Ramsar	
3966	Part	Designated	N	Designated	Y
		Candidate	Y	Candidate	Y

Coastal habitats, including rocky shore, sand dunes, saltmarshes and mudflats, which attract large numbers of wintering waterfowl, including the majority of the Spitzbergen population of brent geese; important tern colonies are also present.

Site description

The area comprises about 20 km of coastline, stretching from near Berwick-upon-Tweed south to Budle Bay, and including Holy Island and the extensive intertidal flats of Holy Island Sands and Budle Bay.

A wide range of marine habitats is present, including intertidal flats, saltmarsh, rocky shore and sand dunes. The extensive intertidal flats of sand and silt contain abundant invertebrates, and also support beds of eelgrass; important as food sources for the wintering birds. The rocky shores have a rich algal flora, and locally eelgrass grows in mid-shore pools, an unusual habitat for the species. There is a large area of saltmarsh, especially around Holy Island Sands. The lower marsh is dominated by the introduced common cord-grass, but at higher levels common saltmarsh-grass and thrift are the main species.

Extensive sand dunes are found on the eastern and northern parts of Holy Island, and on the mainland at Ross Links, between Holy Island and Budle Bay. The foredunes are dominated by marram, with older dunes supporting rather acidic communities including dune heath. Dominated by creeping willow and cross-leaved heath, the dune slacks tend to be more species-rich and are notable for the variety of scarce plants present. Occasional exposures of shingle amongst the dunes support unusual lichen communities.

The invertebrate fauna of the dunes is diverse, and includes a number of specialists of this habitat. These include, for example, the sand dart, shore wainscot and Portland moths.

Birds

The area supports internationally important numbers of wintering greylag goose, light-bellied brent goose, wigeon, ringed plover, bar-tailed godwit and redshank, and nationally important numbers of wintering whooper swan, shelduck, eider, common scoter, red-breasted merganser, golden plover, grey plover, sanderling and dunlin and breeding roseate, common and little terns.

The site is a wetland of international importance by virtue of regularly supporting over 20,000 waterfowl. In the five-winter period 1983/84 to 1987/88 the average peak was

61,000 birds. Totals for individual species include 95 **whooper swans** (2% British), 3520 **greylag geese** (4% of the world total), 2310 **light-bellied brent geese** (58% of the world total, 77% of the numbers wintering in Britain; with numbers dependent on the severity of the weather in Danish wintering areas), 930 **shelduck** (1% British), 17,700 **wigeon** (2% of NW European, 7% of British), 2900 **eider** (6% of British), 590 **common scoter** (2% of British), 100 **red-breasted merganser** (1% of British), 2350 **golden plovers** (1% of British), 790 **ringed plover** (2% of EAF, 3% of British), 1120 **grey plover** (5% of British), 140 **sanderling** (1% of British), 9940 **dunlin** (2% of British), 7430 **bar-tailed godwit** (6% EAF, 12% of British), 3260 **redshank** (3% of EAF, 4% of British) and 17 greenshank.

In summer the area supports nationally important numbers of **roseate tern** (4 pairs 1990, 5% of British), **common tern** (103 pairs 1990, 1% of British) and **little tern** (42 pairs 1989, 2% of British), although the last mentioned species did not breed in 1990.

In late summer, large numbers of red-breasted mergansers moult close to Lindisfarne (peak of 248 in 1988).

Conservation issues
Waterfowl that winter on estuaries are vulnerable to land-claim and other developments that would disturb or damage the existing ecology of these sites. Other human influences, such as recreational disturbance, commercial exploitation of shellfish and worms, and oil and industrial pollution, are also potentially damaging to the conservation interest of estuaries.

Specific issues at this site include disturbance from bait-digging (currently controlled on part of the site by NCC byelaws), expansion of coastal caravan sites and an increase in residential planning applications. The impacts of controlled wildfowling (allowed over part of the area), wind surfing and micro-light aircraft are being carefully monitored. There are problems from major visitor pressure (up to 750,000 visitors to Holy Island per annum), cord-grass invasion of the intertidal zone and a decline in eelgrass.

Further reading
Northumberland and Tyneside Bird Club. *Birds in Northumbria. Annual Bird Reports 1980-89.*

Farne Islands

SPA/Ram Code	IBA Europe number
602A	143

County/Region	District(s)	OS sheet(s)	Grid Reference(s)	Map 9
Northumberland	Berwick-upon-Tweed	75	NU 230370	

Area (ha)	NNR	SPA		Ramsar	
97	No	Designated	Y	Designated	N
		Candidate	N	Candidate	N

A group of rocky islands, with large numbers of breeding seabirds especially terns and auks.

Site description

This group of islands and stacks lies between 2 km and 6 km off the Northumberland coast at Bamburgh. They form the easternmost outcropping of the Great Whin Sill of quartz dolerite. Although some islands retain cappings of boulder clay or peaty deposits, vegetation is limited to pioneer communities, severely affected by the maritime conditions and the large numbers of seabirds.

In addition to the ornithological interest, the islands are notable for the largest North Sea colonies of breeding grey seals (4000-5000 individuals present). These are concentrated on the outer islands, particularly North and South Wamses and Northern Hares. The surrounding waters are of very high marine conservation importance.

Birds

The area supports internationally important numbers of breeding shag, Sandwich tern, roseate tern and arctic tern, and nationally important numbers of breeding cormorant, eider, lesser black-backed gull, kittiwake, common tern, guillemot and puffin.

A census of breeding seabirds (1989 unless stated) found 305 pairs of **cormorants** (4% of British), 1690 pairs of **shags** (1% of Western European, 5% of British), 1450 pairs of **eider** (7% of British), 1380 pairs of **lesser black-backed gulls** (2% of British), 6150 pairs of **kittiwakes** (1% of British), 2846 pairs of **Sandwich terns** (1990, 6% of Western European, 19% of British), 12 pairs of **roseate terns** (14% of British), 267 pairs of **common terns** (1990, 2% of British), 3228 pairs of **arctic terns** (1990, 1% of Western and Central European, 4% of British), 12975 pairs of **guillemots** (2% of British) and 26,330 pairs of **puffins** (8% of British).

Conservation issues

Seabirds are sensitive to changes in the quality of the marine environment, especially to changes in fish stocks and to oil pollution. Casualties from oiling and monofilament nets are difficult to quantify; most impact is likely to be away from the breeding colonies.

The National Trust controls the numbers of visitors (currently 35,000 per annum) to the islands. Some islands are kept free of visitors whilst access to others is limited. The increasing puffin population is causing increased soil erosion, and there is also vegetation erosion from seals and visitors.

Further reading

Hawkey, P *Birds on the Farne Islands. Annual Ornithological Reports 1981-89.* Natural History Society of Northumbria and National Trust.

Sandwich tern

Coquet Island

SPA/Ram Code	IBA Europe number
603A	145

County/Region	District(s)	OS sheet(s)	Grid Reference(s)	Map 9
Northumberland	Alnwick	81	NU 294047	

Area (ha)	NNR	SPA	Ramsar
7	No	Designated Y Candidate N/A	Designated N Candidate N

A small island, with very large colonies of breeding seabirds, notably terns.

Site description

Coquet Island is a small flat-topped island about 1 km off the Northumberland coast at Amble. The plateau measures only about 7 ha, and is surrounded by low sandstone cliffs and a broad rock platform at tide level, which is partly the result of former quarrying.

The peaty soil of the plateau supports grassland dominated by Yorkshire-fog and fescues, which is kept close-cropped by rabbits. The turf is not especially rich, and while grazing-resistant plants such as common ragwort and dock species are frequent, maritime plants such as thrift and sea campion have disappeared. Where nutrient input from the seabird colonies is greatest, there are dense stands of nettles; these provide valuable cover for nesting terns.

Birds

The area supports internationally important numbers of breeding Sandwich tern and roseate tern, and nationally important numbers of breeding eider, black-headed gull, common tern and puffin.

A breeding season survey in 1990 found 395 pairs of **eider** (2% of British), 3850 pairs of **black-headed gulls** (1.5% of British), 1200 pairs of **Sandwich terns** (3% of Western European, 8% of British), 23 pairs of **roseate terns** (1% of EC, 27% of British), 650 pairs of **common terns** (5% of British) and 6460 pairs of **puffins** (2% of British).

Notable also is breeding arctic tern.

Conservation issues

Seabirds are sensitive to changes in the quality of the marine environment, especially to changes in fish stocks and to oil pollution. Ground-nesting seabirds on islands are vulnerable to the introduction of predatory mammals.

Denudation of much of the island's vegetation caused by dry weather conditions and increased soil erosion by the rapidly growing puffin population, in addition to pressure from rabbits, has led to a decrease in the amount of cover available and therefore increased predation of fledgling roseate and other tern species. There exists the potential for disturbance from future recreational development in Amble, and the impact upon eider ducklings from developments in the Coquet estuary.

Further reading

Birds in Northumbria. Annual County Bird Report 1980–1989. Northumberland and Tyneside Bird Club.

Holburn Lake and Moss

SPA/Ram Code	IBA Europe number
604A	146

County/Region	District(s)	OS sheet(s)	Grid Reference(s)	Map 9
Northumberland	Berwick-upon-Tweed	75	NU 051365	

Area (ha)	NNR	SPA	Ramsar
22	No	Designated Y Candidate N/A	Designated Y Candidate N/A

A lake surrounded by mire and swamp, of importance especially for roosting greylag geese in winter.

Site description

Holburn Moss is a fairly small mire, about 5 km inland from the Northumberland coast. *Sphagnum* mosses dominate the vegetation together with heather, cross-leaved heath and common cottongrass. The lake was created during the 1930s, when the outflow was dammed. The island in the centre now has a dense stand of reedmace, while along the eastern shore there is a floating bog consisting of several species of *Sphagnum*.

To the west, drier slopes are covered by bracken and gorse, with locally heather and bell heather.

Birds

The area supports internationally important numbers of wintering **greylag goose**. In the five-winter period 1985/86 to 1989/90 the average peak count was 1840 birds, representing 2% of the world population of Icelandic greylags.

Conservation issues

Roosting geese are vulnerable to human disturbance. The site is vulnerable to heather burning on adjacent slopes (in 1990 an uncontrolled fire damaged 60% of the mire), drying out of the moss due to past drainage and encroachment of conifers from nearby forestry plantations.

The site provides an additional safe roost for wildfowl disturbed from Fenham Flats, on the coast. Unpermitted recreational disturbance, by birdwatchers, is a problem, as access to the site is strictly limited. Occasional shoots adjacent to the Moss can cause disturbance, but the Moss itself is not subject to shooting pressure.

Further reading

Birds in Northumbria. Annual County Report 1987-1989. Northumberland and Tyneside Bird Club.

Teesmouth and Cleveland Coast

SPA/Ram Code	IBA Europe number
606A	151

County/Region	District(s)	OS sheet(s)	Grid Reference(s)	Map 12
Cleveland	Hartlepool, Langbaurgh, Stockton-on-Tees	93, 94	NZ 5326	

Area (ha)	NNR	SPA		Ramsar	
1000-9999	No	Designated	N	Designated	N
		Candidate	Y	Candidate	Y

An estuary with associated saltmarsh and damp grassland, together with open rocky and sandy coast, important for wintering waterfowl.

Site description

The Tees estuary has been greatly reduced in area by land-claim, but a substantial expanse of invertebrate-rich intertidal mud remains at Seal Sands. Some of the claimed land has retained bird interest, where there are shallow lagoons with brackish marginal vegetation or serving as roost sites for birds at high tide.

On the west side of the estuary, Greatham Creek and Cowpen Marsh form a large area of saltmarsh and grazing marsh, and there are smaller areas of these habitats elsewhere around the estuary, and along the open shore. The saltmarsh is dominated by common saltmarsh-grass with much sea aster, but there is considerable diversity of communities and species. Some nationally scarce species occur within the saltmarsh and associated habitats.

The grazing marshes consist of semi-improved grassland, originally derived from saltmarsh, together with brackish fleets and ditches.

Sand dunes are found on either side of the mouth of the Tees and, while dominated by marram, are very varied. The fore-dune includes large stands of lyme-grass as well as sand couch, sea rocket and other pioneer species. More stabilised dunes and dune grassland contain a large number of species, including some scarce species. The slacks hold large populations of orchids and there is some scrub, dominated by sea-buckthorn. The dunes are also notable for their rich invertebrate communities, which include several rare beetles and spiders.

Sandy beaches, interspersed with rocky platforms and promontories make up the foreshore of the open coast and attract different species of waders from the mudflats of the estuary.

Birds

The area supports nationally important numbers of wintering shelduck, teal, shoveler, knot, sanderling, purple sandpiper, redshank and turnstone, and of breeding little tern.

In the five-winter period 1985/86 to 1989/90 the average peak counts were 1380 **shelduck** (2% of British), 1230 **teal** (1% of British), 105 **shoveler** (1% of British), 4200+ **knot** (1% of EAF, 2% of British), 430 **sanderling** (3% of British), 345 **purple sandpiper** (2% of British), 980 **redshank** (1% of British), 20 ruff and 450+ **turnstone** (1% of British). Notable also are wintering wigeon, grey plover, dunlin, bar-tailed godwit and curlew.

Nationally important numbers of little tern breed at the site (32 pairs 1990, 1% of British).

Ringed plovers (average peak 347, maximum 464) and Sandwich terns occur in large numbers on passage.

Conservation issues
Waterfowl that winter on estuaries are vulnerable to land-claim and other developments, such as the construction of barrages that would disturb or damage the existing ecology of these sites. Other human influences such as recreational disturbance, commercial exploitation of shellfish and worms, and oil and industrial pollution, are also potentially damaging to the conservation interest of estuaries. A large area of intertidal flats at Teesmouth has been lost to land-claim for industrial development in recent decades. There is also damage to sensitive sand dune habitats, particularly from trail bikes and off-road vehicles, and recreational pressures on breeding little terns.

Further reading
Evans, P R, Herdson, D M, Knights, P J and Pienkowski, M W 1979 Short-term effects of reclamation of part of Seal Sands, Teesmouth, on wintering waders and shelduck. *Oecologia* 41: 183-206.

Evans, P R 1978-79 Reclamation of inter-tidal land: some effects on shelduck and wader populations in the Tees estuary. *Verhandlung Ornithologische Gesellschaft Bayern* 23: 147-168.

Derwent Ings

SPA/Ram Code	IBA Europe number
609A	154

County/Region	District(s)	OS sheet(s)	Grid Reference(s)	Maps 12, 13
Humberside	Boothferry, East Yorkshire	105, 106	SE 7042	
North Yorkshire	Selby			

Area (ha)	NNR	SPA	Ramsar
783	No	Designated Y Candidate N/A	Designated Y Candidate N/A

Alluvial grasslands with some swamps, which attract large numbers of wildfowl in winter, and also have important populations of breeding wetland birds.

Site description
The lower Derwent Valley consists of a series of neutral alluvial flood meadows, fens, swamps, valley mire, alder woodland and freshwater habitats lying adjacent to the river Derwent, Pocklington Canal and Thornton Beck. The lower Derwent Valley represents one of the largest and most important examples of agriculturally unimproved, species-rich, alluvial flood meadow habitat remaining in the UK.

The character and species composition of the grassland, fen and swamp communities is largely controlled by topography, differences in the extent of winter flooding, and by the type of agricultural management.

In the wettest areas the vegetation is dominated by stands of reed sweet-grass, reed canary-grass, bladder-sedge and slender-tufted sedge. Where flooding is less severe, a different suite of sedge and grass species are present, with a diverse herb community also present.

Small areas of grassland are present above the flood level and include species which are more characteristic of long-established neutral or calcareous grassland.

The river, canal and dyke system supports a rich diversity of plant species, including several nationally scarce species.

The outstanding assemblage of invertebrates found at the site includes up to 16 species of damselflies and dragonflies, along with important assemblages of freshwater molluscs, wetland beetles and fenland flies.

The Derwent is noted for its diversity of fish species, several of which occur at the edge of their UK range, for example, bleak, ruffe and burbot. The site is one of the few lowland river systems in lowland Britain which still supports a population of otters.

Birds
The area supports nationally important numbers of breeding wigeon, gadwall, garganey, shoveler and pochard, and wintering Bewick's swan, wigeon and teal.

The Derwent Ings support an extremely diverse breeding bird community, with over 100 species known to have bred at the site in recent years. They are of major importance for their lowland breeding wader assemblage, which includes (1989 survey figures) lapwing (245 pairs), snipe (209 drumming birds), curlew (52 pairs) and redshank (124 pairs), together with small numbers of oystercatcher, little ringed plover, ruff and woodcock. Ringed plover, black-tailed godwit and common sandpiper breed sporadically.

Breeding wildfowl (post 1980 figures) include **wigeon** (9 pairs, 2% of British), **gadwall** (16 pairs, 3% of British), **garganey** (8 pairs, 16% of British), **shoveler** (100 pairs, 8% of British), **pochard** (12 pairs, 3% of British) and many other wetland species.

Large numbers of ruff (up to 256) and whimbrel (136) occur on spring passage.

Wildfowl also occur in large numbers in winter. In the five-winter period 1985/86 to 1989/90 the average peak counts were 80 **Bewick's swans** (1% of British), 6850 **wigeon** (3% of British) and 3300 **teal** (3% of British). Notable also are wintering whooper swan, European white-fronted goose, shoveler, mallard, pochard and smew. Wintering waders include lapwing, golden plover, dunlin, ruff, curlew and redshank.

Conservation issues
In the late 1970s, pump-drainage scheme proposals and pressure for agricultural intensification threatened part of the Ings, but following much heated debate the conservation case won through. The area is now safeguarded by EN and Yorkshire Wildlife Trust in cooperation with the local farming community. This has been achieved through the establishment of the National Nature Reserve, and also by management agreements (under the Wildlife and Countryside Act 1981). Positive conservation management here has not only protected the existing outstanding wildlife interest, but substantially improved its value as evidenced, for example, by steadily increasing populations of breeding waders (contrary to the national trend) and wintering wildfowl.

Further reading
O'Brien, M G and Smith, K W (in press) Changes in the status of waders breeding on wet lowland grassland in England and Wales between 1982 and 1989. *Bird Study*
Smith, K W 1983 The status and distribution of waders breeding on wet lowland grasslands in England and Wales. *Bird Study* 30: 177-192.
York Ornithological Club Annual Reports.

Flamborough Head and Bempton Cliffs

SPA/Ram Code	IBA Europe number
610A	155

County/Region	District(s)	OS sheet(s)	Grid Reference(s)	Maps 12, 13
Humberside	East Yorkshire	101	TA 258705	
North Yorkshire	Scarborough			

Area (ha)	NNR	SPA		Ramsar	
340	No	Designated	N	Designated	N
		Candidate	Y	Candidate	N

High chalk cliffs with large seabird colonies.

Site description
Flamborough Head projects into the North Sea from the Yorkshire coast, rising to 135 m on the Bempton Cliffs, and exposing a wide section of chalk strata; the chalk is capped by clays, which are themselves more extensively exposed at Speeton.

The cliff-top vegetation comprises maritime species such as thrift and sea plantain, growing alongside species more typical of chalk grassland, for example, kidney vetch.

Birds
The area supports internationally important numbers of breeding kittiwake, and nationally important numbers of breeding guillemot, razorbill and puffin.

A census for the Seabird Colony Register in 1987 found 85,400 pairs of **kittiwakes** (4% of Western European, 18% of British), 32,600 individual **guillemots** (3% of British), 7700 individual **razorbills** (5% of British) and 7000 individual **puffins** (1% of British). Notable also are breeding fulmar, gannet (the largest British mainland colony), shag and herring gull.

The headland is famous as a bird migration watchpoint, especially for observing seabird movement and spring and autumn passerine migration across the North Sea.

Conservation issues
Seabirds are sensitive to changes in the quality of the marine environment, especially to changes in fish stocks and to oil pollution.

Significant threats in recent years have come from off-shore related developments including licensing of oil and gas exploration to within 1 km of the cliff face. This could pose risks to the breeding seabird populations not only from accidental oil pollution but also disturbance from associated shipping and helicopter movements.

The aggregate industries have made preliminary investigations seeking permission to extract gravel from the sea-bed around Flamborough Head and in Filey Bay. These off-shore gravel deposits are important spawning grounds for fish and damage to them could pose a serious threat to the marine ecosystem and thus affect the birds' food sources.

The breeding birds are susceptible to disturbance from rock-climbers, hang-gliders and helicopters, the latter including pleasure rides and military training exercises. Sea anglers fishing from the cliff-top lose and discard line and hooks which occasionally cause mortality to seabirds, particularly gannets and kittiwakes, which become ensnared.

The whole of the Flamborough headland is designated Heritage Coast and this together with the management of the RSPB Bempton Cliffs reserve contributes significantly towards avoiding potential problems for the breeding seabirds. The seabird colonies are a major visitor attraction with at least 60,000 visitors annually to the RSPB reserve and many more to the headland as a whole. Fenced, safe viewpoints and interpretative material are provided on the RSPB reserve where there is a visitor centre and the Heritage Coast also has a visitor centre at South Landing.

Further reading
RSPB Bempton Cliffs Nature Reserve Annual Reports.

Gannet

Humber Flats, Marshes and Coast

SPA/Ram Code	IBA Europe number
611A	157

County/Region	District(s)	OS sheet(s)	Grid Reference(s)	Maps 12, 13
Humberside	Beverley, Boothferry, Cleethorpes, Glanford, Great Grimsby, Holderness, Kingston-upon-Hull	106, 107, 112, 113, 122	TA 2010	
Lincolnshire	East Lindsey			

Area (ha)	NNR	SPA		Ramsar	
16,374	Yes	Designated	N	Designated	N
		Candidate	Y	Candidate	Y

Extensive mud- and sandflats and associated saltmarshes, sand dunes and marshes, of importance for wintering waterfowl and waders, and also attracting notable breeding populations of birds.

Site description

The Humber Estuary drains a catchment of some 24,240 square km and forms the largest single input of freshwater from Britain into the North Sea. It also has the second highest tidal range in Britain (7.2 m). The estuary broadens from the confluence of the rivers Ouse and Trent, the two main rivers which flow into it, and then stretches over 50 km to Spurn Point. The huge areas of invertebrate-rich intertidal flats (approximately a third of the estuary, comprising the majority of the IBA, is exposed at low water) become increasingly sandy towards the east. There are extensive areas of reedbed in the inner estuary at Blacktoft Sands, Broomfleet and the Barton and Barrow Claypits, and areas of mature and developing saltmarshes backed by grazing marsh in the middle and outer estuary. On the North Lincolnshire coast the saltmarsh is backed by low sand dunes with marshy slacks and brackish pools.

Pioneer species on the mudflats include stands of glassworts and common cord-grass and eelgrasses, an important food for brent geese, grow on the flats in some areas. Saltmarshes fringe the mudflats. Middle level marsh is dominated by common saltmarsh-grass. In the upper parts of the estuary, the reduced salinity allows sea club-rush and common reed to become the primary colonisers of the mudflats.

Spurn Point is an elongated shingle spit, capped by sand dunes. The dunes are dominated by marram, but in places there is dense growth of sea-buckthorn, which is noted for attracting migrant birds. A bird observatory here has undertaken important studies on bird migration.

More extensive dunes are found along the Lincolnshire coast between Cleethorpes and Mablethorpe. Based on calcareous sand, these are rich in invertebrate and plant species.

Dune slacks also support a wide range of species, including southern and early marsh-orchids. Here, scrub has developed in the absence of grazing, and is composed of sea-buckthorn, hawthorn, elder and wild privet.

A number of brackish and freshwater wetlands occur around the estuary, ranging from natural dune slack pools to clay pits, borrow pits and ditches. There are also some freshwater fens supporting a range of sedges and herbs. These habitats support a breeding population of natterjack toads and a wide range of dragonfly species.

Sand and shingle banks on the Lincolnshire coast hold the southernmost breeding colony of grey seals on the east coast of Britain.

Birds

The area supports nationally or internationally important numbers of 3 breeding species and 21 wintering species.

The site is a wetland of international importance by virtue of regularly supporting over 20,000 waterfowl. In the five-winter period 1984/85 to 1988/89 the average peak was 104,760 birds, comprising 84,985 waders and 19,775 wildfowl. Totals for individual species include 2200 **dark-bellied brent geese** (1% of the world total, 2% of British), 4000 **shelduck** (2% of NW European, 5% of British), 3000 **wigeon** (1% of British), 2000 **teal** (2% of British), 6400 **mallard** (1% of British), 680 **pochard** (1% of British), 100 **scaup** (2% of British), in excess of 5100 **oystercatcher** (2% of British), 400 **ringed plover** (2% of British), in excess of 14,200 **golden plover** (1% of EAF, 7% of British), in excess of 1400 **grey plover** (1% of EAF, 7% of British), 13,200 **lapwing** (1% of British), 28,900 **knot** (8% of EAF, 13% of British), 470 **sanderling** (3% of British), 25,900 **dunlin** (2% of EAF, 6% of British), 40 ruff, 1400 **bar-tailed godwit** (1% of EAF, 2% of British), 4100 **curlew** (1% of EAF, 5% of British), 4300 **redshank** (4% of EAF, 6% of British) and 430 **turnstone** (1% of British).

Also present in winter are 20+ **hen harriers** (3% of British).

In addition the site supports internationally important numbers of **ringed plover** during the spring and autumn passage periods (up to 1500 birds, 3% EAF), and internationally important numbers of **sanderling** during the spring passage period (1000+ birds, 1% EAF).

Breeding species include nationally important numbers of **pochard** (25 pairs, 7% of British), **little tern** (118 pairs 1990, 5% of British) and **bearded tit** (100 pairs, 17% of British), and current or recent breeding by marsh harrier and short-eared owl.

Conservation issues

Waterfowl that winter on estuaries are vulnerable to land-claim and other developments that would disturb or damage the existing ecology of these sites. Other human influences such as recreational disturbance, commercial exploitation of shellfish and worms, and oil and industrial pollution, are also potentially damaging to the conservation interest of estuaries.

The estuary is subject to much industrial development along certain stretches of its banks, and is a busy commercial waterway with several deep water ports and a number of additional minor wharfs.

Shipping accidents have caused spillages of oil and other chemicals. Waste-tipping and land-claim for industrial development have led to loss of mudflats in the fairly recent past, but such losses have now ceased due to vigorous defence of the estuary by the voluntary and statutory conservation organisations. In recent years there have been several proposals for small-scale wharf developments and marina developments involving the loss of mudflats. A tidal barrage for electricity production has been proposed and is in the early stages of feasibility study.

Pollution is a major concern since many of the industries discharge their effluents (some containing various toxic wastes) into the estuary. For some installations measures are planned to clean up effluent discharges to bring them in line with EC Directives; this has involved new pipelines (or extensions) across the mudflats and new processing plant. Other new industrial installations are planned, including gas-fired power station, and a straw-pulp processing mill.

Further reading

Goodall, A 1988a Birds of the Humber. In: *The Humber Ecosystem. Proceedings of a conference in support of European year of the Environment*, Ed. A M C Edwards. Humber Estuary Committee.

Goodall, A 1988b Life in the Humber (D) Birds. In: *A Dynamic Estuary: Man, Nature and the Humber*, ed. N V Jones. Hull University Press, Hull.

Norman, R 1989 *The Birds of Cleethorpes Shore*.

Northumberland Coast

SPA/Ram Code	IBA Europe number
613A	144

County/Region	District(s)	OS sheet(s)	Grid Reference(s)	Map 9
Northumberland	Alnwick, Berwick-upon-Tweed, Blyth Valley, Castle Morpeth, Wansbeck	75, 81, 88	NU 0053	
Tyne and Wear	North Tyneside			

Area (ha)	NNR	SPA		Ramsar	
1000-9999	No	Designated	N	Designated	N
		Candidate	Y	Candidate	Y

A long stretch of coastline, with a variety of habitat types, supporting important numbers of wintering waders, and breeding little terns.

Site description

This site includes much of the coastline between the Scottish border and the Tyne estuary. The coast consists of sandy bays separated by rocky headlands with wavecut platforms, backed by dunes and soft and hard cliffs, with cliff-top agricultural land. Other important habitats include pasture land, small estuaries and man-made roosting sites. The inshore waters are important as sea duck feeding areas.

Birds

The area supports internationally important numbers of wintering purple sandpiper and turnstone, and nationally important numbers of wintering ringed plover, golden plover, sanderling and breeding little terns.

In the five-winter period 1983/84 to 1987/88 the average peak counts were 340 **ringed plover** (1.5% of British), 4000 **golden plover** (2% of British), 240 **sanderling** (2% of British), 690 **purple sandpiper** (1% of EAF, 4% of British) and 1340 **turnstone** (2% of EAF, 3% of British).

Notable also are wintering eider, long-tailed duck, common scoter and goldeneye, and over 600 moulting **mute swans** (3% of British).

The Northumberland Coast supports nationally important numbers of breeding **little tern** (41 pairs 1990, 2% of British) and smaller numbers of arctic tern. Large numbers of Sandwich and roseate tern occur in autumn.

Conservation issues

Birds that depend on these coastal habitats are vulnerable to land-claim, oil pollution and human disturbance.

Stretches of this coastline are vulnerable to the expansion of caravan sites, holiday homes and other building developments. Recreational activities, notably jet skiing, water skiing and wind surfing are causing local disturbance problems, especially in the Tweed. Sand excavation from the dunes at Druridge Bay is a locally serious problem with adverse coastal erosion implications.

Further reading

Birds in Northumbria. Annual County Bird Reports 1980–1989. Northumberland and Tyneside Bird Club.

Northumberland Coast Management Plan 1989. Northumberland County Council Draft Issues Report.

North Yorkshire Moors

SPA/Ram Code	IBA Europe number
616A	152

County/Region	District(s)	OS sheet(s)	Grid Reference(s)	Maps 12, 13
Cleveland	Langbaurgh on Tees	93, 94, 100, 101	NZ 7293	
North Yorkshire	Hambleton, Ryedale, Scarborough			

Area (ha)	NNR	SPA		Ramsar	
10,000+	Part	Designated	N	Designated	N
		Candidate	Y	Candidate	N

The North Yorkshire Moors IBA was formerly known as Spaunton, Wheeldale, Egton and Glaisdale Moors IBA.

A large upland area important for a variety of breeding upland species particularly raptors and waders.

Site description
The moor and heath which covers the North Yorkshire Moors includes the largest continuous tract of open heather moorland in England and Wales. The topography of the moors is very important. Long fingers of moor and heath run down to farmland or abut woodland edge (both deciduous and coniferous woodland) which provides diversity for hunting raptors.

Some 15% of the total moorland area has developed on deep peat deposits, while the bulk of the rest of the moorland is dominated by *Ericaceous* species on shallow free-draining peaty soils. Much of it is managed for grouse. Common heather dominates the higher ground, covering some 55-60% of the total moorland area. Better drained banks, and areas with some scrub encroachment have *Vaccinium* dominated heath.

Boggy flushes and valley mires are dominated by rushes, and can support diverse plant and insect communities of considerable conservation importance.

About 5% of the total moorland area is blanket bog, with a peat depth of up to 2.5 m, reaching a maximum depth of up to 5 m in the valley heads.

A further 5% of the moorland area supports acidic grassland. This is dominated by mat grass in the drier areas and by purple moor grass in the wetter ones.

Up to 30% of the area of moorland is dominated by bracken. This includes many of the edge areas of the North Yorkshire Moors, although bracken also occurs in combination with acidic dry heath or acidic grassland. The National Park Authority, MAFF and NCC are actively involved in grant aiding bracken control and the reinstatement of heath vegetation.

Birds
The Moors support nationally important numbers of **merlin** with about 8% of the British population present. Dotterel traditionally use this area as a staging site on passage.

Notable also are breeding red grouse, golden plover, lapwing, snipe, curlew, redshank, short-eared owl and ring ousel.

Conservation issues
Birds that depend on moorland areas are vulnerable to widescale habitat change, especially afforestation and agricultural intensification.

Conversion of moorland, particularly to agriculture and forestry was a major threat up until the mid 1980s. The introduction of a Moorland Management Programme by the North York Moors National Park Committee, coupled with active grant aid programmes from NYMNP, MAFF and EN, has helped to reduce this conversion. This programme includes a farm conservation scheme to assist farmers in protecting and enhancing landscape and wildlife interest.

Essential survey and monitoring of ground nesting birds needs to be expanded and management prescriptions compiled to take advantage of such work.

Continuing persecution of raptors, particularly hen harriers and peregrines, is limiting the natural occupancy of these species. Uncontrolled fires, either deliberate or accidental, can pose a threat to ground nesting species.

Further reading
Mather, J R 1986 *The Birds of Yorkshire*. Croom Helm, Beckenham.

Hornsea Mere

SPA/Ram Code	IBA Europe number
617A	156

County/Region	District(s)	OS sheet(s)	Grid Reference(s)	Maps 12, 13
Humberside	Holderness	107	TA 190470	

Area (ha)	NNR	SPA		Ramsar	
230	No	Designated	N	Designated	N
		Candidate	Y	Candidate	N

A shallow eutrophic lake, with reedbeds, fen and carr, with a wide range of breeding and wintering wetland birds.

Site description

Hornsea Mere lies immediately inland of Hornsea on the Humberside coast. The lake is only about 1-2 m deep, and its shallowness has encouraged the development of extensive swamps of common reed, reedmace and common club-rush. These are best developed at the west end of the mere, where they grade into carr woodland of alder and willow. There are also fen communities, which are rich in plant species.

The open water plant communities are dominated by Canadian waterweed, fennel pondweed, spiked water-milfoil, rigid hornwort and yellow water-lily, but, as a result of eutrophication, dense algal blooms occur.

The reedbeds, swamp communities and wet woodland support a diverse invertebrate fauna.

Birds

The area supports internationally important numbers of wintering **gadwall**. In the five-winter period 1985/86 to 1989/90 the average peak count was 155 birds, representing 1% of the NW European wintering population and 2.5% of British. Notable also are wintering greylag goose, mallard, shoveler, pochard, tufted duck, goldeneye and coot.

The site supports a rich assemblage of breeding wetland species including great crested grebe, mute swan, mallard, tufted duck, water rail, sedge warbler and reed warbler. Little gulls (>200) occur in late summer during the post-breeding period.

Conservation issues

Birds that use this site are vulnerable to changes in water quality due to agricultural run-off from adjacent land and incoming water source.

Yorkshire Dale Moorlands

SPA/Ram Code	IBA Europe number
621A	153

County/Region	District(s)	OS sheet(s)	Grid Reference(s)	Maps 11, 12
Cumbria	Eden, South Lakeland	91, 92, 98, 99	SD 8789	
North Yorkshire	Craven, Harrogate, Richmondshire			

Area (ha)	NNR	SPA		Ramsar	
10,000+	No	Designated	N	Designated	N
		Candidate	Y	Candidate	N

Yorkshire Dale Moors IBA was formerly known as Abbotside, Askrigg and Mallerstang Commons IBA.

Moorland and associated grasslands, with high densities of breeding waders and other upland birds.

Site description
This upland area includes a rich variety of habitat types. The major types are neutral, acidic, calcareous and marshy grasslands, bracken, acidic dry heath, wet heath, wet and dry bogs and flushes.

Extensive blanket bog, dominated by hare's tail cotton grass and deergrass, occurs on summit plateaux and some slopes, ranging in height from 400–700 m; where the peat is wetter, a rich bog vegetation is found. Wet flush areas within areas of blanket bog and acidic grassland give rise to mires, characterised by sedges, rushes and *Sphagnum* species.

Heather-dominated heath, managed for red grouse, is extensive, particularly where grazing pressure is less intense. The areas of limestone plateau have a herb-rich calcareous grassland, with nationally scarce species found here. The moorland edges and valleys have agriculturally improved grasslands, and extensive stands of bracken.

Birds
These moors support nationally important numbers of breeding merlin, peregrine, golden plover and dunlin.

Estimates of breeding population sizes are c. 7% of the British population of **merlins**, 2% of British population of **peregrines**, a minimum of 2000 pairs of **golden plover** (9% of British) and 100+ pairs of **dunlin** (1% of total population of temperate *schinzii* race). Notable also are breeding red grouse, black grouse, lapwing, snipe and curlew.

Conservation issues
Birds that depend on moorland areas are vulnerable to widescale habitat change, especially afforestation and agricultural intensification.

Essential survey and monitoring work remains to be carried out for certain key species at this site, for example comprehensive surveys of golden plover, dunlin and curlew have not been attempted.

As in other upland sites, over-grazing, moor-gripping/drainage, abandonment of heather burning, over stocking, conversion from hay/pastures to silage and improved grass leys are all having an impact on ground nesting birds.

An increase in recreational activities includes increased usage of off the road vehicles and long distance walks and bridleways.

There is continuing direct persecution of raptors, particularly hen harrier, buzzard and peregrine by poisoning, trapping, shooting and theft. Consequently these species probably do not occupy their natural range, and other raptors cannot re-establish.

Further reading

Drewitt, A and Stewart, A 1989 *Phase 1 Habitat Survey of Yorks Dale National Park, North Yorks Section*.

Kelly, P G and Perry, K A 1990 *Wildlife habitat in Cumbria*. NCC Research and Survey in Nature Conservation Series. No. 30.

Radcliffe, D A 1976 Observations on the breeding of golden plover in Great Britain. *Bird Study* 23: 63–116.

North Pennine Moors

SPA/Ram Code	IBA Europe number
627A	147, 148, 149, 150

County/Region	District(s)	OS sheet(s)	Grid Reference(s)	Map 11
Cumbria	Carlisle, Eden	86, 87, 91, 92	NY 7146	
Durham	Derwentside,			
	Teesdale,			
	Wear Valley			
Northumberland	Tynedale			

Area (ha)	NNR	SPA		Ramsar	
10,000+	Part	Designated	Y	Designated	N
		Candidate	Y	Candidate	Y

The area incorporates the following IBAs as listed in the IBA Europe book: Bowes Moor (SPA/Ram 605A), Upper Teesdale and Moor House (SPA/Ram 607A), Bollihope and Middleton Commons (SPA/Ram 619A) and Muggleswick, Stanhope and Wolsingham Commons (SPA/Ram 620A).

A large upland area of heather and grass moorland and associated habitats, important for breeding raptors, waders and other upland birds.

Site description
The area straddles the Cumbrian, Durham and Northumberland borders, rising to nearly 900 m above sea level. The underlying rock is composed largely of Carboniferous sedimentary rocks along with a major intrusion of igneous rock (the Whin Sill). A range of habitat types are present within the area. These include blanket bog, valley bog, heath, bracken, acid, neutral and calcareous grasslands, marshes and flushes and woodland.

Blanket bog dominates the wetter western moors, where it may attain a depth of up to 10 m, and covers all but the steepest slopes. Heather and hare's-tail cottongrass are the dominant plant species, often with a characteristic layer of *Sphagnum* mosses. In places peat erosion gives rise to expanses of bare peat. More species-rich valley bogs are better developed on the shallower peats in the east of the area, notably at Pow Hill.

A range of heath types dominated by heather and crowberry occur on drier ground, and are managed as grouse moor. Where heavy grazing occurs, heather and dwarf shrubs are replaced by acid grassland supporting a limited range of plant species. In places invasion of heath and grassland by bracken have taken place, most notably in the east of the area. The area is renowned for its species-rich limestone grassland which includes a blue moor-grass–limestone bedstraw grassland as the characteristic type, along with a series of distinct grassland types found only in the North Pennines. These support a wide range of nationally rare plant species. Neutral grasslands are found on areas of alluvium on lower valley slopes and valley floors. Much of this grassland type is now improved, although herb–rich hay meadows remain, particularly in the upper part of the dales.

Woodland within the area is principally confined to steep-sided ravines, river gorges and rocky fell sides. Ash and wych elm are the dominant species on base-rich soils giving way to oak on more acid soils with stands of juniper scrub occurring at scattered localities. A rich lichen assemblage is associated with a number of the woodlands within the site. A wide range of flush and fen vegetation occurs within the site, most often associated with limestone or calcareous drift. These wetlands support a wide range of nationally rare plant species.

An assemblage of nationally rare species of invertebrates of northern distribution occurs in the North Pennines. Mammals present include otter and populations of the scarce Brandt's and whiskered bats.

Birds
These moors support nationally important numbers of breeding merlin, black grouse, golden plover, dunlin, snipe and curlew.

Provisional and conservative estimates of population sizes for breeding birds include c. 12% of the British population of **merlins** (at their highest British densities in some areas), 1900 individual **black grouse** (c. 6% of British), 2250 pairs of **golden plover** (10% of British), **dunlin** (minimum 80 pairs, 1% of total population of temperate *schinzii* race), 500 pairs of **snipe** (2% of British), 1000 pairs of **curlew** (3% of British) and **redshank** (minimum 250 pairs, 1% of British).

Notable also are breeding peregrine, short-eared owl, nightjar, raven and twite.

Conservation issues
Birds that depend on moorland areas are vulnerable to widescale habitat change, especially afforestation and agricultural intensification.

Past and present agricultural support schemes, particularly the Hill Livestock Compensatory Allowance, the Annual Ewe Premium and the 'Variable Premium' have served to increase stock numbers, particularly sheep, with resultant over-grazing of unenclosed semi-natural vegetation. In addition, there has been a reduction in the numbers of farmers, particularly those using traditional shepherding methods, and a switch to feeding at 'fothering' points. This concentrates stock and trampling kills off heather plants.

In some areas lack of keepering has led to a poor mosaic of heather, with an abandonment of the burning cycles.

Field 'improvements' and field treatments (especially drainage, conversion to improved grass and associated increased stocking rates) have had, and continue to have, an impact on ground nesting birds and their productivity.

Recreational activities and mineral extraction permissions need to be carefully monitored to ensure that they do not conflict with nature conservation interest.

Continuing persecution of breeding birds, particularly hen harriers, peregrines and ravens, is a long-term problem within this site, which also militates against any recolonisation by, for example, buzzards.

ESA prescriptions do not take account of ornithological interest, and stocking rates are not controlled. Harrowing and rolling in pastures and rolling in hay meadows present problems for wader productivity. Essential survey and monitoring of ground nesting birds needs to be expanded and management prescriptions compiled to take advantage of such work. Heather allotments not contained in ESA 'whole farm systems' need to be incorporated for effective conservation, for example, in-bye, allotment land and moor.

Further reading

Durham Bird Club/Northumberland and Tyneside Bird Club Annual Reports and Black Grouse Lek Surveys 1986–89 inclusive.

Garson, P J and Starling, A E 1990 Explaining the present distribution of black grouse in NE England. In Lumeij, T J and Hoogeveen, Y R (eds.). *The Future of Wild Galliformes in Netherlands*. Gegerens Koninklijke Bibliotheek, The Hague.

Reed, T M 1985 Grouse Moors and Wading Birds. *Game Conservancy Annual Review*.

Peak District Moors

SPA/Ram Code	IBA Europe number
702A	159

County/Region	District(s)	OS sheet(s)	Grid Reference(s)	Map 11
Cheshire	Macclesfield	118, 119	SK 0265	
Derbyshire	High Peak, North East Derbyshire, The Derbyshire Dales			
Greater Manchester	Stockport, Tameside			
South Yorkshire	Barnsley, Sheffield			
Staffordshire	Staffordshire Moorlands			
West Yorkshire	Kirklees			

Area (ha)	NNR	SPA		Ramsar	
10,000+	No	Designated	N	Designated	N
		Candidate	Y	Candidate	N

An upland area supporting a high density of breeding waders and other upland species.

Site description

An area of open moorland, mire and blanket bog dominated by dwarf shrubs with adjacent unenclosed pasture and grassland. This is the southernmost English station of a habitat type typical of northern British uplands. A number of plants and animals occur here at the south-eastern extremity of their British range. Other habitats include moorland flushes, wet in-bye land, fast-flowing rivers and streams, and reservoirs.

Birds

The area supports a nationally significant assemblage of upland breeding birds.

Breeding species include 27 pairs of **merlins** (4.5% of British), 725 pairs of **golden plover** (3% of British), 140 pairs of **dunlin** (1% of the total temperate *schinzii* race), 590 pairs of **curlew** (2% of British), 125 pairs of **ring ousels** (1% of British) and 355 pairs of **twite** (2% of British). A survey of a small part of the site (Leek Moors SSSI, Staffordshire) in 1985 found 385 pairs of **snipe** (>1% of British). Notable also are breeding peregrine, red grouse, fieldfare, short-eared owl and a declining population of black grouse. Hen harriers winter at the site.

Conservation issues

Birds that depend on moorland areas are vulnerable to widescale habitat change, especially afforestation and agricultural intensification. Another major issue is increased recreational pressure, which has had a demonstrable effect on breeding golden plover and common sandpiper.

Further reading

Anderson, P 1990 Moorland Recreation and Wildlife in the Peak District. Peak Park Joint Planning Board.

Brown, A F and Shepherd, K B (1990, unpubl.). Breeding birds of the South Pennine Moors. NCC CSD Report No. 1188.

Holland, P K, Robson, J E and Yalden, D W 1982 The Status and Distribution of the Common Sandpiper (*Actitis hypoleucos*) in the Peak District. *The Naturalist* 107: 77-87.

Lovenburg, G A, Waterhouse, M and Yalden, D W 1978 The Status of Black Grouse in the Peak District. *The Naturalist* 103: 3-14.

Yalden, D W 1974 The status of Golden Plover (*Pluvialis apricaria*) and Dunlin (*Calidris alpina*) in the Peak District. *The Naturalist* No. 930: 81-91.

Yalden, D W 1979 An Estimate of the Number of Red Grouse in the Peak District. *The Naturalist* 104: 5-8.

Yalden, D W 1986 The Further Decline of the Black Grouse in the Peak District 1975-1985. *The Naturalist* 111: 3-8.

Snipe

Walmore Common

SPA/Ram Code	IBA Europe number
705A	160

County/Region	District(s)	OS sheet(s)	Grid Reference(s)	Maps 16,
Gloucestershire	Forest of Dean	162	SO 745150	17, 18

Area (ha)	NNR	SPA	Ramsar
58	No	Designated Y Candidate N/A	Designated Y Candidate N/A

An area of damp grassland and ditches, important for wintering Bewick's swans.

Site description
The Common comprises mainly clayey soils, which overlay the only significant area of peatland in Gloucestershire. It lies in the Severn Vale, about 10 km south-west of Gloucester, in an area subject to winter flooding.

The site comprises both unimproved and improved grassland, with fields separated by ditches or rhynes. The improved grassland is species-poor, composed mainly of perennial rye-grass, creeping bent and timothy. The grazed, unimproved pastures are tussocky and dominated by tufted hair-grass, marsh foxtail and creeping bent, but with a wider range of other plants, such as soft-rush, lesser spearwort and silverweed.

The ditches throughout the area contain a wide range of aquatic and marginal plants, including abundant floating sweet-grass, sedge species, flowering-rush, tubular water-dropwort and several pondweeds.

Birds
This site supports internationally important numbers of wintering **Bewick's swan**, with 170 birds regularly present (1% of NW European, 2% of British) and a maximum of 265 recorded in January 1991.

Conservation issues
The possibility of drainage of adjacent land for agricultural purposes continues to pose a threat to regular winter flooding of the site. Continued sensitive hydrological management will be required in order to maintain the swan interest.

The Wash

SPA/Ram Code	IBA Europe number
802A	164

County/Region	District(s)	OS sheet(s)	Grid Reference(s)	Maps 13, 14
Lincolnshire	Boston, East Lindsey, South Holland	122, 131, 132	TF 550400	
Norfolk	West Norfolk			

Area (ha)	NNR	SPA	Ramsar
63,135+	Part	Designated Y Candidate N/A	Designated Y Candidate N/A

An extensive intertidal embayment supporting large concentrations of passage and wintering waders and wildfowl, and providing an important breeding area for several species of waterfowl.

Site description

The Wash is one of the most important areas of estuarine mudflats, sandbanks and saltmarsh in the United Kingdom. Included at the eastern end of the site are low chalk cliffs at Hunstanton.

The intertidal flats have a rich invertebrate fauna and colonising beds of glasswort, which are important food sources for the large numbers of wildfowl and waders present. Cord-grass is also colonising. Large areas of sea aster dominated lower marsh and middle marsh are present, with a wide range of other species found on the middle marsh. The absence of much mature upper marsh and associated transition zones is due to a history of reclamation for high grade agricultural land, and gives rise to a less diverse plant community than might otherwise be expected.

Gravel extraction on the east side of the Wash has left a series of flooded pits at Snettisham. These now act as an important high tide roost area. Another important high tide roost is located on two trial banks at Terrington, built for an experimental water storage scheme. One has subsequently developed into a breeding area for gulls and terns.

Lying at the northern end of the Lincolnshire Wash, Gibraltar Point is a southward extension of the Lincolnshire coastline, noted for its coastal geomorphology, particularly sand dune systems. The dune and saltmarsh communities found here provide good examples of plant succession. Other habitats found here include a cattle-grazed freshwater marsh and reed-fringed open water, the latter areas supporting the uncommon brackish water-crowfoot. The rich invertebrate community includes 12 nationally rare species.

The sheltered nature of the Wash creates suitable breeding conditions for shellfish, principally mussels, cockles and shrimps, and has given rise to a highly productive shellfish industry. The shallow waters of the Wash act as an ideal nursery ground for flatfish, particularly plaice, dab and sole.

The largest breeding colony of common seals in Europe (>6000 individuals) pup on the offshore sandbanks, along with a smaller population of grey seals.

Birds

The site supports internationally important numbers of 13 species of wintering waterfowl; and nationally important numbers of 7 species of wintering waterfowl and 1 species of passerine. It also supports a large assemblage of breeding waterfowl.

The Wash is a wetland of international importance by virtue of regularly supporting over 20,000 waterfowl. In the five-winter period 1985/86 to 1989/90 the average peak count for total waterfowl was 283,415, comprising 215,870 waders and 67,545 wildfowl. Totals for individual species were 226 **cormorants** (1% of British), 70 **Bewick's swans** (1% of British), 7100 **pink-footed geese** (6.5% of the world total), 22,600 **dark-bellied brent geese** (13% of the world total), 19,300 **shelduck** (8% of NW European, 26% of British), 3900 **wigeon** (2% of British), 130 **gadwall** (1% of NW European, 2% of British), 4900 **mallard** (1% of British), 4900 **pintail** (7% of NW European, 20% of British), 35,100 **oystercatcher** (4% of EAF, 13% of British), 7300 **grey plover** (4% of EAF, 34% of British), 95,900 **knot** (28% of EAF, 43% of British), 530 **sanderling** (4% of British), 49,400 **dunlin** (3.5% of EAF, 11% of British), 305 **black-tailed godwit** (6% of British), 10,550 **bar-tailed godwit** (9% of EAF, 17% of British), 3860 **curlew** (1% of EAF, 4% of British), 4900 **redshank** (4.5% of EAF, 6.5% of British) and 1150 **turnstone** (2% of EAF, 2.5% of British). Notable also are wintering long-tailed duck, common scoter, goldeneye, avocet, ringed plover, golden plover, lapwing and ruff.

The saltmarshes support very large numbers of wintering **twite** (estimate of 17,000 in February 1986, 17% of British and comprising possibly the entire Pennines breeding population).

The Wash is of great importance as a staging area during passage periods for many waterfowl species, especially ringed plover, sanderling, ruff, whimbrel, spotted redshank, greenshank and common sandpiper.

The Wash is also an important breeding area for shelduck, oystercatcher and avocet. It supports an exceptionally high density of breeding **redshank** (estimate for Wash saltmarshes of 1087-1852 pairs, minimum 3% of British). **Black-headed gulls** (total 2869 pairs 1989, 1% of British), **common terns** (231 pairs 1989, 2% of British) and little terns (11 pairs 1989) also breed, together with fulmars and, occasionally, short-eared owls.

Conservation issues

Waterfowl that winter on estuaries are vulnerable to land-claim and other developments, such as the construction of barrages that would disturb or damage the existing ecology of these sites. Other human influences such as recreational disturbance, commercial exploitation of shellfish and worms, and oil and industrial pollution, are also potentially damaging to the conservation interest of estuaries.

Over the centuries, large areas of the Wash have been claimed for agriculture, but no further areas have been lost in this way since 1979.

Pressure comes from a variety of sources, including disposal of dredgings and proposals for port and industrial expansion (including new power stations and steel works). Port expansion at Sutton Bridge, and the likelihood of further pressure for developments at Boston, and possibly Fosdyke, have implications for increasing risks of shipping accidents, associated pollution and disposal of dredgings.

The water quality of the Wash, although much cleaner than many more heavily industrialised estuaries, is still significantly affected by inputs of sewage and trade effluent from the four rivers that flow into it. As a result, environmental health authorities have imposed closure orders on shellfish taken from the Wash, requiring them to be cleansed or steam-cooked before sale.

The Wash is a major shell fishery. Until recently, traditional fishing methods have dominated, but increased use of mechanical methods, including suction dredging for cockles, may pose significant threats to the invertebrate populations of the mudflats. There is also increasing emphasis on more intensive cultivation of shellfish (both native and alien species), rather than reliance upon a 'wild' fishery. Bait digging of lugworms has also been practised on a commercial scale in certain parts of the Wash, leading to depletion of stocks and causing disturbance to feeding birds and other invertebrate populations in the mud.

Parts of the Wash are used as military firing ranges, but the disturbance so caused to feeding and roosting flocks of birds is not fully understood. The range fires in summer cause damage to saltmarsh vegetation. Since 1989 the range has been used by army units for machine-gun practice; this is being closely monitored.

Further reading
Davies, M 1988 The Importance of Britain's Twites. *RSPB Conserv. Rev* 2: 91–94. RSPB, Sandy.
Doody, P and Barnett, B 1987 *Research and Survey in Nature Conservation No. 7. The Wash and its environment*. Nature Conservancy Council, Peterborough.
The Norfolk and Norwich Naturalists' Society. *Norfolk Bird and Mammal Report 1988*. Jarrold and Sons, Norwich.

Nene Washes

SPA/Ram Code	IBA Europe number
803A	162

County/Region	District(s)	OS sheet(s)	Grid Reference(s)	Map 13
Cambridgeshire	Peterborough, Fenland	142	TL 200977 to TL 395029	

Area (ha)	NNR	SPA		Ramsar	
1310	No	Designated	N	Designated	N
		Candidate	Y	Candidate	Y

Washland habitat used for seasonal storage of flood waters, important for wintering wildfowl and breeding ducks and waders.

Site description

The cycle of winter storage of flood waters and traditional summer cattle grazing at this site give rise to a mosaic of rough grassland and wet pasture, with a diverse ditch flora. This includes locally uncommon specialities such as frogbit, water-violet and flowering-rush, and the nationally scarce fringed water-lily. Areas of arable cropping within the site boundary provide some winter feeding sites for wildfowl. The site plays an additional role in accommodating wildfowl displaced by deep flooding on the nearby Ouse Washes.

Birds

The area supports internationally important numbers of wintering Bewick's swan and gadwall, and nationally important numbers of wintering European white-fronted goose, teal, wigeon, pintail, shoveler, and breeding gadwall, garganey, shoveler and black-tailed godwit.

In the five-winter period 1985/86 to 1989/90 the average peak counts were 780 **Bewick's swans** (4.5% of NW European, 11% of British), 75 European **white-fronted geese** (1% of British), 4950 **wigeon** (2% of British), 130 **gadwall** (1% of NW European, 2% of British), 1100 **teal** (1% of British), 675 **pintail** (3% of British) and 120 **shoveler** (1% of British). Notable also are wintering mute swan, pochard and smew. The variety of raptor species wintering on the Washes includes hen harrier, merlin, peregrine and short-eared owl.

Breeding wildfowl include **gadwall** (25 pairs, 5% of British), **garganey** (5 pairs, 10% of British) and **shoveler** (46 pairs, 4% of British). **Black-tailed godwits** also breed (10 pairs in 1990, 19% of British) and occur annually on passage. Other breeding waders include lapwing, snipe and redshank.

Conservation issues

Wildfowling occurs on all sections of the Washes including the RSPB reserve and can cause considerable disturbance to feeding and roosting wildfowl. Changes to the flooding pattern of the Washes, for example, due to river improvements upstream of Peterborough, could be significantly detrimental to breeding bird communities.

Ouse Washes

	SPA/Ram Code	IBA Europe number
	804A	163

County/Region	District(s)	OS sheet(s)	Grid Reference(s)	Maps 13,
Cambridgeshire	East Cambridgeshire	143	TL 393747 to TL 471987	14, 19, 20
Norfolk	West Norfolk			

Area (ha)	NNR	SPA	Ramsar
2403	No	Designated N Candidate Y	Designated Y Candidate N/A

An extensive area of washland habitat subject to regular winter flooding, important for wintering and breeding ducks and waders.

Site description

The Ouse Washes lie between the Old and New Bedford rivers and act as a flood water storage system during the winter months, subjecting the unimproved neutral grassland to regular winter flooding. The sward provides grazing and hay during the summer months, and is characterised by grass and reed species such as reed sweet-grass, reed canary-grass and marsh foxtail, and herb species including amphibious bistort, water-pepper and tubular water-dropwort.

A diverse aquatic flora is found in the adjacent dykes and rivers; pondweeds and duckweeds (four species) are particularly well represented.

The Old Bedford River and River Delph provide good examples of base-rich, slow-moving lowland rivers and are floristically rich; notable species include arrowhead, long-stalked pondweed, perfoliate pondweed and river water-dropwort.

Birds

The area supports internationally important numbers of wintering whooper swan, Bewick's swan, wigeon, gadwall, pintail and shoveler and nationally important numbers of wintering cormorant, mute swan, mallard, pochard, tufted duck and coot, as well as breeding lapwing, ruff, snipe, black-tailed godwit and redshank.

The Ouse Washes is a wetland of international importance by virtue of regularly supporting over 20,000 waterfowl. In the five-winter period 1985/86 to 1989/90 the average peak count for total waterfowl was 64,110 birds. Totals for individual species were 293 **cormorants** (2% of British), 500 **mute swans** (3% of British), 4900 **Bewick's swans** (29% of NW European, 70% of British), 545 **whooper swans** (3% of the world total, 9% of British), 40,100 **wigeon** (5% of NW European, 16% of British), 300 **gadwall** (2% of NW European, 5% of British), 3650 **teal** (4% of British), 5470 **mallard** (1% of British), 1450 **pintail** (2% of NW European, 6% of British), 720 **shoveler** (2% of NW European, 8% of British), 2270 **pochard** (4.5% of British), 920 **tufted duck** (1.5% of British) and 2450 **coot** (1% of British). Notable also are wintering European white-fronted goose and smew.

The site is of major importance for an assemblage of ducks and waders breeding on lowland wet grassland. It is the most important breeding area in Britain for **black-tailed godwit**, with an average of over 26 pairs between 1982-87 (44% of British). In recent years, up to 535 (max. 2008, March 1990) birds have been seen at the site on spring migration to other breeding areas. An important breeding population of ruff occurs at the Washes. In addition to these two species, other notable breeding waders include **lapwing** (320 pairs, 9% of the lowland grassland total for England and Wales), **snipe** (500 pairs, 25% of the lowland grassland total for England and Wales) and **redshank** (200 pairs, 9% of lowland grassland total of England and Wales).

The Ouse Washes also hold an important and diverse assemblage of breeding wildfowl, notably shelduck, **gadwall** (minimum 111 pairs 1989, 20% of British), teal, **mallard** (minimum 850 pairs 1989, 2% of British), **pintail** (minimum 1 pair 1989, 2.5% of British), **garganey** (minimum 14 pairs 1989, 28% of British), **shoveler** (minimum 155 pairs 1989, 12% of British), pochard, tufted duck (30-50 pairs), moorhen (120-600+ pairs) and coot (50-450 pairs). Conditions of spring flooding and summer water-tables dictate the precise numbers of breeding birds in any given year.

Conservation issues

Much of the conservation importance of the Ouse Washes is due to its continued use as functional washland, with extensive winter flooding and traditional forms of agricultural management, including grazing and mowing of permanent grassland and rotational ditch clearance. The hydrological regime is also of critical importance to the use of the site by breeding waterfowl. In recent years, summer flooding (April-May) has adversely affected both breeding birds and the traditional washland management regime. This problem is now being addressed by the National Rivers Authority.

Rutland Water

SPA/Ram Code	IBA Europe number
805A	161

County/Region	District(s)	OS sheet(s)	Grid Reference(s)	Map 13
Leicestershire	Rutland	141	SK 928070	

Area (ha)	NNR	SPA	Ramsar
1540	No	Designated Y	Designated Y
		Candidate N/A	Candidate N/A

The largest reservoir (1260 ha) in the United Kingdom, important for wintering and passage wildfowl.

Site description

This man-made major wetland area comprises extensive sheets of open water with a mosaic of wetland and lakeside habitats, characterised by a succession from open water to semi-natural mature woodland. Terrestrial and marsh habitats of wildlife interest occur mainly at the western end of the reservoir, and include lagoons, reedswamp, marsh, old meadows, scrub and woodland. Stands of common reed and bulrush have been planted in shallow water at the edges of lagoons, with pondweed species, Canadian waterweed and spiked water-milfoil found in the deeper water; drainage dykes hold a typical range of aquatic plants, including mare's-tail. The areas of grassland include poorly-drained old ridge and furrow pastures supporting marsh-marigold and cuckoo flower. Small mixed deciduous woods have been widely planted, the woodland close to the former Burley fish-ponds being dominated by willow and poplar species.

Birds

Rutland Water is a wetland of international importance by virtue of regularly supporting over 20,000 waterfowl. In the five-winter period 1985/86 to 1989/90 the average peak was 21,054 wildfowl. Rutland supports internationally important numbers of wintering shoveler and autumn populations of gadwall, being the main site in the UK for the latter species. Nationally important numbers of wintering great crested grebe, mute swan, wigeon, teal, tufted duck, goldeneye, goosander and coot occur here.

In the five-winter period 1985/86 to 1989/90 the average peak counts were 520 **great crested grebes** (5% of British), 200 **mute swans** (1% of British), 4380 **wigeon** (2% of British), 1320 **gadwall** (11% of NW European, 22% of British), 1340 **teal** (1% of British), 450 **shoveler** (1% of NW European, 5% of British), 3230 **tufted duck** (5% of British), 285 **goldeneye** (2% of British), 60 **goosander** (1% of British) and 4600 **coot** (2% of British).

Notable also are wintering little grebe, mallard, pochard, smew and ruddy duck.

Conservation issues

From Rutland Water's creation, the implementation of a planned zonation policy for wildlife and recreation usage has benefited the birds using the reservoir. These zones allow varying degrees of disturbance, and include specially constructed lagoons which act as disturbance-free refuges. Nine miles of shoreline set at the west end of the reservoir, incorporating these lagoons, are managed as a nature reserve by Leicestershire and Rutland Trust for Nature Conservation. Additionally, parts of the shoreline and surrounding land are managed for nature conservation to provide grazing areas for wildfowl. Despite the success of the zonation plan, pressure for increased recreational use of the reservoir and its surroundings nonetheless needs continued monitoring to avoid conflict with conservation interests.

The owners, Anglian Water plc, fund management of the Nature Reserve but are also keen to maintain, and where possible, increase recreational uses. Pressure to protect the value of the reservoir for such recreational uses has led Anglian Water to take measures to control late summer blue-green algal blooms, which have occurred in recent years, and are potentially hazardous to people, dogs and sheep. Treatment involves heavy dosing of the water with ferric sulphate to 'lock-up' the excess aluminium phosphate derived from agricultural run-off and sewage. The impact of this on the reservoir's invertebrate populations and the consequent effects on birdlife is unknown; this is being monitored by English Nature and Anglian Water.

Further reading
Appleton, T P 1982 Rutland Water Nature Reserve: concept, design and management. *Hydrobiologia* 88: 211–221.
Leicestershire and Rutland Trust for Nature Conservation. *Birds of Rutland Water annual reports*.

North Norfolk Coast

SPA/Ram Code	IBA Europe number
903A	165

County/Region	District(s)	OS sheet(s)	Grid Reference(s)	Maps 13, 14
Norfolk	North Norfolk, West Norfolk	132, 133	TF 690443 to TG 095440	

Area (ha)	NNR	SPA	Ramsar
7701	Parts	Designated Y Candidate N/A	Designated Y Candidate N/A

A 40 km stretch of coast incorporating intertidal sands and muds, saltmarshes, shingle banks, sand dunes, brackish lagoons, reedbeds and grazing marshes, important for migratory birds, wintering waterfowl and breeding species.

Site description

This site extends for 40 km from Hunstanton in the west to Salthouse in the east. Extensive intertidal sand and mud is found along the entire coast. Some of the best examples of saltmarsh in Europe have accreted behind sand bars, eg at Scolt Head, or in sheltered positions along the coast, eg at Stiffkey. The differences in age and height of the saltmarsh give rise to a diverse saltmarsh flora.

Extensive deposits of shingle are found at Blakeney Point and Scolt Head. This provides an important breeding habitat for terns. Stands of the uncommon shrubby sea-blite occur along Blakeney Point and provide important cover for migrant birds.

Both natural and artificial brackish lagoons occur along this stretch of coast; the former at Holme and in the Cley-Salthouse area, and the latter at Titchwell and Cley. The rich invertebrate fauna found in these lagoons is an important food source for waders and wildfowl. Extensive reedbeds supporting breeding wetland species occur at Brancaster, Cley and Titchwell.

Dune systems, supporting a diverse flora, are found on Scolt Head Island and Blakeney Point, and at Holme and Holkham. The greatest number of species are found on the stabilised 'grey' dunes, where red fescue often co-dominates with marram. Self-seeding Corsican pine, originally planted to stabilise the dunes, is well established at Holkham, and an area of secondary mixed woodland and scrub has developed on the landward side of the pines, and provides valuable cover for migratory passerine birds.

Maritime pasture is present at Cley and extensive areas of grazing marsh are present along the coast. The grazing marsh at Holkham has a network of clear water dykes holding a rich diversity of aquatic plant species.

Natterjack toads breed in shallow pools in the dune slacks and otters hunt in the area.

Birds

The area supports internationally important numbers of breeding Sandwich tern and little tern, and wintering pink-footed goose, dark-bellied brent goose; together with nationally important numbers of breeding oystercatcher, avocet, ringed plover, black-headed gull and bearded tit, and wintering European white-fronted goose, shelduck, pintail, oystercatcher, grey plover and redshank.

The site is a wetland of international importance by virtue of regularly supporting over 20,000 waterfowl. In the five winter period 1984/85 to 1988/89 the average peak was 43,160 birds, comprising 15,350 waders and 27,810 wildfowl. Totals for individual species include 7400 **pink-footed geese** (7% of the world total), 295 European **white-fronted geese** (5% of British), 10,340 **dark-bellied brent geese** (6% of the world total), 2600 **shelduck** (1% of NW European, 3% of British), 450 **pintail** (2% of British), 4400 **oystercatcher** (2% of British), 500 **grey plover** (2% of British) and 800 **redshank** (1% of British). Notable also is wintering turnstone.

The North Norfolk Coast is also important for a wide range of passage waders.

Breeding species along the coast include **bittern** (3 booming males, 15% of British), **marsh harrier** (8 nests in 1990, 11% of British), **oystercatcher** (360 pairs in 1989, 1% of British), **avocet** (110 pairs 1989, 29% of British), **ringed plover** (240 pairs in 1989, 2% of British), **black-headed gull** (4100 pairs, 1.5% of British), **Sandwich tern** (3000 pairs in 1990, 7% of Western European, 20% of British), **common tern** (640 pairs, 5% of British), **little tern** (425 pairs in 1988, 3% of Western European, 17% of British) and **bearded tit** (100 pairs, 17% of British). Notable also are breeding gadwall, shoveler, barn owl and kingfisher.

Conservation issues

Waterfowl that winter on estuaries are vulnerable to land-claim and other developments that would disturb or damage the existing ecology of these sites. Other human influences such as recreational disturbance, commercial exploitation of shellfish and worms, and oil and industrial pollution, are also potentially damaging to the conservation interest of estuaries.

The North Norfolk Coast attracts an increasing number of visitors each year causing disturbance and trampling damage in some areas. Offshore aggregate winning may pose a threat to the ecology of the coastal system. There have been tentative proposals for marinas in the area.

Further reading

Norfolk and Norwich Naturalists' Society. *Norfolk Bird and Mammal Report 1988*. Jarrold and Sons, Norwich.

Norfolk Naturalists Trust (1976). *Nature in Norfolk: a heritage in trust*. Jarrold and Sons, Norwich.

Minsmere – Walberswick

SPA/Ram Code	IBA Europe number
910A	171

County/Region: Suffolk	District(s) Suffolk Coastal, Waveney	OS sheet(s) 156	Grid Reference(s) TM 465735	Maps 14, 20

Area (ha) 2004	NNR Parts	SPA Designated N Candidate Y	Ramsar Designated Y Candidate Y

A composite site comprising two large marshes, the tidal Blyth estuary, and lowland heathland and woodland, important for a rich diversity of breeding, wintering and passage species.

Site description

Minsmere is noted for a complex range of habitats, particularly reedbeds and lowland heathland. The development of the site was aided by the flooding of grazing marshes as a war-time defence measure in 1940. This allowed for the establishment of extensive reedbeds, dominated by common reed, and a network of shallow pools and deep water channels which provide important cover for breeding marshland birds. The marshes have a rich insect fauna, notably moths. The 18 ha of islands and shallow lagoons ('The Scrape') which have been created at Minsmere are renowned for breeding avocets and other waders, and provide a feeding and roosting area for both waders and wildfowl.

The seaward side of the site comprises a shingle beach backed by a narrow strip of 'yellow' dune and dune grassland extending southwards from Minsmere, and a series of shallow brackish lagoons and saltmarsh behind the shingle beach between Walberswick and Dunwich. Shingle species that are found here include sea pea, sea campion, sea-kale, grey hair-grass and yellow horned-poppy.

Inland, a continuous 400-ha tract of heather-dominated lowland heath is interspersed with bracken and dry acidic grassland, forming part of the Suffolk Sandlings heath complex.

Woodland and scrub ranges from naturally regenerating alder, sallow and birch on wet ground and Scots pine on former heathland, to plantations of mature oak and Scots pine, with some sycamore and sweet chestnut.

Walberswick National Nature Reserve covers 607 ha on the coast south of Southwold. It includes Westwood Marshes, which extend inland for 4 km, and form one of the largest continuous areas of freshwater reedbeds in the country. Invading scrub of sallow, alder and birch is controlled to protect the reedbeds.

The Blyth estuary lies just to the north of Walberswick Marshes, and is banked along its lower reaches, opening out into a shallow basin some 2.5 km inland.

Birds

The area supports nationally important numbers of wintering European white-fronted goose and hen harrier, and breeding bittern, marsh harrier, avocet, little tern and nightjar.

Wintering species include 130 European white-fronted geese (2% of British) and up to 15 roosting hen harriers (2% of British). Notable also is wintering Bewick's swan.

Minsmere-Walberswick has an outstanding diversity of breeding birds, supporting approximately 100 breeding species (1990 figures unless stated), including 5 booming male **bitterns** (25% of British), 24 pairs of **gadwall** (4% of British), 73 pairs of **teal** (1% of British), 23 pairs of **shoveler** (2% of British), 15 breeding female **marsh harriers** (20% of British), 47 pairs of **avocet** (12% of British), 32 pairs of **little tern** 1990 (1.5% of British), 24 pairs of **nightjars** (1% of British) and c. 50 pairs of **bearded tit** (8% of British). Notable also are breeding garganey, redshank, black-headed gull, common tern, Cetti's warbler and Savi's warbler.

Conservation issues

There is a continued need to maintain and improve existing habitat for breeding species, for example, heathland, fen and coastal lagoons. The Minsmere-Dunwich area especially is used as a showpiece for complex conservation and visitor management. Breeding tern colonies on the foreshore are vulnerable to disturbance, while the extensive reedbeds are vulnerable to scrub encroachment. Salt water inundation of the freshwater marsh, exacerbated by sea level rise, poses management problems.

Marsh harrier

Orfordness – Havergate

SPA/Ram Code	IBA Europe number
911A	172

County/Region	District(s)	OS sheet(s)	Grid Reference(s)	Maps 14, 20
Suffolk	Suffolk Coastal	156, 169	TM 400472	

Area (ha)	NNR	SPA		Ramsar	
c. 2800	Part	Designated	Y	Designated	N
		Candidate	Y	Candidate	Y

An estuary complex of the Rivers Alde, Butley, and Ore, a large island (Havergate), and saline lagoons, important for wintering wildfowl and waders, and breeding birds.

Site description

This coastal strip stretches from Aldeburgh to Bawdsey and includes mudflats, saltmarsh, vegetated shingle and coastal lagoons. Orfordness, a large shingle spit, deflects the channel of the River Alde from its former mouth near Aldeburgh to a course lying parallel to the shore and extending down the coast to Shingle Street. From east of Orford to the river mouth, this channel is known as the River Ore. The Orfordness/ Shingle Street landform is unique within Great Britain in combining a shingle spit with a cuspate foreland.

Behind the shingle spit lies a broad belt of grazing marshes, much of which has been converted to arable land. This belt of land protects the river from casual human disturbance. The remote Lantern and King's marshes lie on the inner edge of the spit between the river and the sea. On Havergate and Orfordness, former grazing marsh forms a neutral grassland sward, dominated by sea couch grass. A small area of reedbed occurs at the head of the Butley River.

Havergate Island is owned and managed by the RSPB; the six shallow lagoons on the island have been created to encourage breeding avocets. Mudflats of mixed clay, silt and shingle border the Ore and Butley Rivers and Havergate Island. Saltmarsh occurs along the river edges and around lagoons and borrowpits throughout the site. Sea-purslane and common sea-lavender are the dominant species with other notable saltmarsh species also occurring. The lagoons and borrowpits on Shingle Street, Havergate Island and the King's and Lantern Marshes on Orfordness contain the rare spiral and beaked tasselweeds.

The second largest and best preserved area of vegetated shingle in Britain is found at Orfordness and supports a highly specialised flora. Sea pea and sea-kale are abundant here, and extensive patches of sea campion and English and biting stonecrops are found on more stable ground. Lichen communities are well developed.

Birds

The area supports internationally important numbers of breeding lesser black-backed gull, and nationally important numbers of wintering Bewick's swan, European white-fronted goose, shelduck, wigeon and avocet, and breeding avocet, herring gull and little tern.

In the five-winter period 1985/86 to 1989/90 the average peak counts were 90 **Bewick's swans** (1% of British), 190 European **white-fronted geese** (3% of British), 800+ **shelduck** (1% of British), 5000+ **wigeon** (2% of British) and 300 **avocets** (30% of British). Notable also are wintering mute swan, dark-bellied brent goose, pintail, shoveler, grey plover and black-tailed godwit.

Breeding species include **avocets,** largest breeding colony in Britain (61 pairs in 1990, 15% of British), **lesser black-backed gull** (7500 pairs in 1988, 4% of Western and Central European, 9% of British), **herring gull** (2500 pairs in 1988, 2% of British) and **little tern** (55 pairs in 1990, 2% of British). Notable also are breeding black-headed gull, Sandwich tern, common tern and barn and short-eared owls.

Conservation issues
Increased use of the estuary for recreation, for example jet-skiing would lead to disturbance of breeding and wintering birds. Sea level rise threatens saltwater inundation and possible loss of coastal lagoons, depending on future decisions on sea defences. The use of four-wheel drive vehicles on Orfordness threatens breeding birds and the fragile shingle ecosystem. The coastal lagoons require management to maximise avocet breeding success.

Further reading
Beardall, C H, Dryden, R C and Holzer, T J 1988. *The Suffolk Estuaries.* Suffolk Wildlife Trust, Saxmundham.

Fuller, R M and Randall, R E 1988. The Orford shingles, Suffolk, UK. Classic conflicts in coastline management. *Biol Conserv.* 46: 95-114.

Stour and Orwell Estuary

SPA/Ram Code	IBA Europe number
912A	173

County/Region	District(s)	OS sheet(s)	Grid Reference(s)	Maps 14, 20
Essex	Tendring	169	TM 170415 to	
Suffolk	Babergh,		TM 260343 (Orwell	
	Ipswich,		Estuary), TM 180330	
	Suffolk Coastal		(Stour Estuary)	

Area (ha)	NNR	SPA		Ramsar	
3379	No	Designated	N	Designated	N
		Candidate	Y	Candidate	Y

Two estuaries with extensive mudflats and saltmarsh, supporting important numbers of wintering waders and wildfowl.

Site description

The Stour Estuary straddles the eastern part of the Essex/Suffolk border and comprises five main bays, Seafield, Holbrook and Erwarton on the north, and Jacques and Copperas on the south. These encompass most of the invertebrate-rich intertidal flats. The Orwell is a relatively long and narrow estuary, supporting a sandy and fairly calcareous saltmarsh with a wide range of plant communities.

The extensive mudflats of both estuaries are colonised by glasswort species, dwarf eelgrass, eelgrass, cord-grass and *Enteromorpha* algae. Sea aster is common on the lower marshes, whilst on higher levels common saltmarsh grass, sea-purslane and common sea-lavender dominate. Most of the saltmarsh is fringed by sea couch, common reed and sea club-rush. Along the Stour estuary, the vegetation ranges from oak-dominated wooded cliffs, through scrub to grassy seawalls and reed-fringed borrow dykes.

The site also includes an area of low-lying grazing marsh at Shotley Marshes on the south shore of the Orwell.

Birds

The area supports internationally important numbers of wintering dark-bellied brent goose, ringed plover, grey plover, dunlin, black-tailed godwit and redshank, and nationally important numbers of wintering mute swan, shelduck, pintail, wigeon, curlew and turnstone.

The site is a wetland of international importance by virtue of regularly supporting over 20,000 waterfowl. In the five winter period 1985/86 to 1989/90 the average peak counts for individual species were 300+ **mute swans** (2% of British), 1700+ **dark-bellied brent geese** (1% of the world total, 2% of British), 2000+ **shelduck** (3% of British), 300+ **pintail** (1% of British), 2500+ **wigeon** (1% of British), 500+ **ringed plover** (1% of EAF, 2% of British), 1700+ **grey plover** (1% of EAF, 8% of British), 16,000+ **dunlin** (1% of EAF, 4% of British), 1300+ **black-tailed godwit** (2% of EAF, 26% of

British), 1300+ **curlew** (1% of British), 2000+ **redshank** (1% of EAF, 3% of British) and 600+ **turnstone** (1% of British).

Notable also are wintering mallard, goldeneye, oystercatcher and knot.

Conservation issues

Waterfowl that winter on estuaries are vulnerable to land-claim and other developments that would disturb or damage the existing ecology of these sites. Other human influences such as recreational disturbance, commercial exploitation of shellfish and worms, and oil and industrial pollution, are also potentially damaging to the conservation interest of these estuaries.

Large areas of intertidal flats at Fagbury on the Orwell are being progressively reclaimed to facilitate expansion of the container port of Felixstowe. Dredging of the estuaries, for the ports of Ipswich, Felixstowe and Harwich appears to cause some erosion of mudflats and saltmarsh. Sewage pollution is of concern in the upper Orwell estuary.

Recreational development is a serious problem at this site. Boating use of both estuaries is expanding and especially heavy on the Orwell, with marina proposals threatening the destruction of feeding areas for birds. Consequent disturbance needs to be carefully monitored.

Further reading

Beardall, C H, Dryden, R C, Holzer, T J 1988 *The Suffolk Estuaries*. Suffolk Wildlife Trust.

Hamford Water

SPA/Ram Code	IBA Europe number
913A	174

County/Region	District(s)	OS sheet(s)	Grid Reference(s)	Maps 14, 20
Essex	Tendring	169	TM 235255	

Area (ha)	NNR	SPA		Ramsar	
2143	Part	Designated	N	Designated	N
		Candidate	Y	Candidate	Y

A large shallow estuarine basin important for wintering waders and wildfowl and breeding little terns.

Site description

Hamford Water is a large, shallow estuarine basin comprising tidal creeks and islands, intertidal mud- and sandflats, and saltmarshes. It is a tidal inlet, the mouth of which lies three miles to the south of Harwich. The open areas of water may shelter tens of thousands of wildfowl, particularly in severe weather. Saltmarsh accounts for one third of the site and supports an abundance of invertebrates and a rich flora. Several species of saltmarsh plant which occur here are uncommon in the UK, notably rock and lax-flowered sea-lavender on the higher saltmarsh, whilst on the mudflats, small cord-grass, narrow-leaved eelgrass and dwarf eelgrass are found.

Dune-topped shingle spits extend from Dovercourt to Crabknowe Spit and from Walton to Stone Point. In addition to a characteristic sand dune community, species such as sea-kale, sea-holly and sea sandwort are found here.

Improved grass fields at Horsey Island provide an important feeding and wintering site for dark-bellied brent geese. The scrub and grassland area at the Naze forms the most easterly point in Essex, and serves as a landfall for migrant birds.

Birds

The area supports internationally important numbers of wintering dark-bellied brent goose, black-tailed godwit and redshank, and nationally important numbers of wintering shelduck, teal, avocet and grey plover, and breeding little tern.

In the five-winter period 1985/86 to 1989/90 the average peak counts were 5400 **dark-bellied brent geese** (3% of the world total, 6% of British), 1200 **shelduck** (2% of British), 1800 **teal** (2% of British), 50 **avocet** (5% of British), 640 **grey plover** (3% of British), 1000 **black-tailed godwit** (1% of EAF, 20% of British), 1200 **redshank** (1% of EAF, 2% of British). Twite occur in winter in nationally important numbers. Notable also are wintering ringed plover, sanderling, dunlin and curlew.

During the autumn, amongst the other species which occur here, spotted redshank and greenshank use the site on passage.

In summer the site supports breeding **little terns** (an average of 35 pairs was present during the five-year period 1986-90, 1% of British). Notable also are breeding **black-headed gull** (3910 pairs 1989, 1.5% of British) and common tern.

Conservation issues

Waterfowl that winter on estuaries are vulnerable to land-claim and other developments. Other human influences such as recreational disturbance, commercial exploitation of shellfish and worms, and pollution, are also potentially damaging to the conservation interest of estuaries.

Expansion of caravan sites could result in increased disturbance to breeding little terns. Proposals for marina expansion are a continuing threat which could result in the loss of intertidal habitats and increased disturbance to estuarine birds. Saltmarsh erosion from rising sea level and other factors is of particular concern.

Further reading

Durdin, C J 1990 The Tendring Estuaries. RSPB report for Tendring District Council. The Essex Birdwatching Society. Essex Bird Report 1989.

Abberton Reservoir

SPA/Ram Code	IBA Europe number
914A	175

County/Region	District(s)	OS sheet(s)	Grid Reference(s)	Maps 14, 20
Essex	Colchester	168	TL 970180	

Area (ha)	NNR	SPA	Ramsar
716	No	Designated Y	Designated Y
		Candidate N/A	Candidate N/A

Man-made storage reservoir with adjacent grassland and arable land, important as a moulting and wintering site for wildfowl.

Site description

Abberton Reservoir was created between 1939 and 1941 by the flooding of a long shallow valley, and is the largest freshwater body in Essex with a water area of 490 ha. Storage water is pumped mainly from the River Stour, 14 km to the north of the reservoir. Lying less than 8 km from the coast, Abberton is used as a roost by the local estuarine population of wildfowl, and is extremely important as an autumn arrival point for birds. Abberton's attractiveness for wildfowl is a result of its open aspect, the predominant shallowness of the water (mean depth <5 m), the abundance of plant and animal life and the long shoreline. The reservoir is divided into three parts by road causeways; the two small upper pools have natural banks with the larger eastern pool being concrete-faced. Since 1954, the most successful duck ringing station in the country has operated at the western pools (between 1949 and 1982, 74,291 ducks were ringed in the cage traps).

An inaccessible area of willow and reed swamp occupies the south-western arm of the reservoir. This has allowed for the development of an invertebrate fauna, and provides cover for breeding birds.

Adjacent improved pasture is extensively used by wigeon, and the unimproved grassland provides a winter feeding area for golden plover, lapwing and curlew.

Birds

The area supports internationally important numbers of wintering wigeon, gadwall, shoveler and nationally important numbers of wintering great crested grebe, mute swan, teal, pochard, tufted duck, goldeneye and coot, as well as breeding cormorants.

The site is a wetland of international importance by virtue of regularly supporting over 20,000 waterfowl. In the five-winter period 1985/86 to 1989/90 the average peak was 33,985 wildfowl. Totals for individual species include 180 **great crested grebe** (2% of British), 500 **mute swan** (3% of British), 8400 **wigeon** (1% of NW European, 3% of British), 480 **gadwall** (4% of NW European, 8% of British), 2200 **teal** (2% of British), 480 **shoveler** (1% of NW European, 5% of British), 2400 **pochard** (5% of British), 3500 **tufted duck** (6% of British), 560 **goldeneye** (3% of British) and 11,500 **coot** (10% of British).

In autumn the site regularly supports moulting concentrations of 450 **mute swan** (3% of British wintering population). Notable also are moulting gadwall, shoveler, pochard and tufted duck.

In summer the site holds a large breeding colony of **cormorants** (200 pairs, 3% of the British breeding population). This colony is unusual in Great Britain because the birds are nesting in trees instead of the usual cliff ledges or rocky islets.

Conservation issues

The suitability of this site for wintering waterfowl is dependent upon the water management regime and the lack of disturbance over the majority of the reservoir.

Benfleet and Southend Marshes

SPA/Ram Code	IBA Europe number
917A	179

County/Region	District(s)	OS sheet(s)	Grid Reference(s)	Maps 14,
Essex	Castle Point, Southend-on-Sea	178	TQ 854847	19, 20

Area (ha)	NNR	SPA		Ramsar	
2100	Part	Designated	N	Designated	N
		Candidate	Y	Candidate	Y

An extensive area of saltmarshes, mudflats, scrub and grassland, important for wintering geese and waders.

Site description

Adjacent to Canvey Island, this site extends eastwards along the foreshore to Southend, and comprises extensive areas of mudflats and saltmarshes. The colonisation of the mudflats by eelgrasses and dense patches of *Enteromorpha*, and a rich invertebrate estuarine fauna provide an important food source for wintering birds.

Both the sea-wall and the saltmarsh have distinct plant communities. A high marsh flora of sea-purslane, common sea-lavender and sea arrowgrass is replaced on the lower marsh and along the creek edges by a wide range of glasswort species, including perennial glasswort.

The north-western corner of the site comprises south-facing downland slopes representing the line of former river cliffs along the Benfleet Creek. The sand-capped London Clay soils give rise to neutral-acidic grassland and scrub.

The reclaimed alluvial grassland at the foot of the cliff-line is grazed by horses and cattle. The grassland and ditch communities are diverse. Sea club-rush, reed-sweet grass and mare's-tail dominate the dykes. Great crested newts occur in the ponds and dykes. Terrestrial invertebrates are well represented at the site, and include white-letter hairstreak and marbled white butterflies, Roesel's bush-cricket, great green bush-cricket and scarce emerald damselfly.

Birds

The area supports internationally important numbers of wintering dark-bellied brent goose, grey plover and knot, and nationally important numbers of wintering ringed plover and dunlin.

The site is a wetland of international importance by virtue of regularly supporting over 20,000 waterfowl. In the five-winter period 1985/86 to 1989/90 the average peak was 30,450 birds, comprising 22,850 waders and 7600 wildfowl. Totals for individual species include 7200+ **dark-bellied brent geese** (4% of the world total, 8% of British), 435 **ringed plover** (2% of British), 2500 **grey plover** (1% of EAF, 12% of British), 8400

knot (2% of EAF, 4% of British) and 11,100 **dunlin** (3% of British). Notable also are wintering oystercatcher, curlew, redshank and turnstone.

Conservation issues

Waterfowl that winter on this site are vulnerable to land-claim and other developments that would disturb or damage the existing ecology of these sites. Other human influences such as recreational disturbance, commercial exploitation of shellfish and worms, and sewage and industrial pollution, are also potentially damaging to the conservation interest of this area.

This site is vulnerable to development pressures; marina/housing proposals have been made in recent years. There has been a substantial loss of grazing marshes as a result of conversion to arable land and landfill.

Further reading

Durdin, C J and Land, R A 1990 The Castle Point Coast. RSPB report for Castle Point District Council.
The Thames Estuary Conservation Group 1982 *The Thames Estuary*.

Breckland Heaths

SPA/Ram Code	IBA Europe number
920A	170

County/Region	District(s)	OS sheet(s)	Grid Reference(s)	Maps 14, 20
Norfolk	Breckland	143, 144, 155	TL 7886	
Suffolk	Forest Heath,			
	St.			
	Edmundsbury			

Area (ha)	NNR	SPA		Ramsar	
1000-9999	Parts	Designated	N	Designated	N
		Candidate	Y	Candidate	N

An important complex of grass, heather and lichen heath sites, supporting the UK's largest concentration of breeding stone-curlews, and other open heath bird species.

Site description

The ecological unit includes the following areas: Foxhole Heath, Weather and Horn Heaths, Stanford Training Area, Weeting Heath, Barnham Heath, Berners Heath, Cavenham/Icklingham Heaths, Deadman's Grave, Lakenheath Warren, Little Heath (Barnham), Thetford Heaths, Wangford Warren and Carr, Bridgham and Brettenham Heaths, and Eriswell Low Warren.

The range of habitats throughout the site is very diverse, dominated by dry grassland and heathland, with coniferous and deciduous woodland, and including meres, inland dune systems, alluvial fen, fen meadows and wet carr.

Grazed grasslands and heaths reflect the soil type and history of Breckland, based upon sporadic cultivation of areas, followed by periods of neglect.

This general region known as Breckland displays a flora unique within Britain, characterised by a number of continental climate species typical of low rainfall areas, notably field wormwood, Spanish catchfly, perennial knawel, bur medick, Breckland wild thyme, wild grape hyacinth and Breckland, spiked, fingered and spring speedwells. The grasslands range from variants of chalk grassland to acid grasslands and lichen heath.

Extensive areas of wetland include open water, reed dominated fenland and mixed fen, dominated variously by reed, reed sweet-grass and greater pond-sedge, and including typical wetland herbaceous species. Open water areas consist of small pools, pingos, fluctuating meres, for example, Fowl Mere and man made lakes.

Woodland includes oak and sweet chestnut in older deciduous plantations, and there are blocks of coniferous plantation.

The site as a whole supports a varied invertebrate fauna, including scarce species of spider, beetles, bugs, and dragon and damselflies, typical of wetland and heath-grassland communities.

Birds
The area supports nationally important numbers of breeding stone-curlew.

Breckland is the main UK breeding stronghold for **stone-curlew** (84 pairs in 1990, 58% of British). Birds within this population make use of both heathland and arable land. Other breeding species of note include ringed plover, curlew, woodlark, nightjar and an isolated breeding population of wheatear.

Wintering species include hen harrier and short-eared owl.

Conservation issues
The Breckland heaths were formerly much more extensive. Some were lost to scrub and conifer encroachment from adjacent forestry land owing to progressive reduction in grazing intensity. Heath-nesting stone-curlews also suffer from predation (some by egg-collectors), while arable nesting stone-curlews are at risk from damage from agricultural operations. All the important Breckland species have declined rapidly during this century, even on nature reserves, due to habitat loss and changes in land management. Rabbit and sheep grazing is essential in maintaining the open habitat favoured by the breeding bird population. The Breckland ESA, which was established in 1988, only partially addresses these problems.

Further reading
Dolman, P and Sutherland, W J 1991 Historical clues to conservation. *New Scientist* 1751: 40–43.
Green, R E 1988 Stone-curlew conservation. *RSPB Conserv. Rev* 2: 30–33.
Petch, C P and Swann, E L 1968 *The Flora of Norfolk*. Jarrold and Sons, Norwich.
Trist, P J O 1979 *An ecological flora of the Breckland*. E P Publishing, Wakefield.

Stone-curlew

Mid-Essex Coast

SPA/Ram Code	IBA Europe number
924A	176, 177, 178

County/Region	District(s)	OS sheet(s)	Grid Reference(s)	Maps 14,
Essex	Chelmsford, Colchester, Maldon, Rochford, Southend-on-Sea, Tendring	167, 168, 178	TM 0715	19, 20

Area (ha)	NNR	SPA		Ramsar	
29,807	Part	Designated	N	Designated	N
		Candidate	Y	Candidate	Y

This site includes the former sites Blackwater, Colne and Dengie (915A), Foulness and Maplin Sands (916A) and River Crouch Marshes (919A) listed in the European IBA, in addition to Sandbeach Meadows.

An extensive complex of estuaries, intertidal mudflats, saltmarshes and grazing marshes, important for passage and wintering waders and wildfowl and breeding birds.

Site description

The Mid-Essex Coast includes one of the three largest continuous sand-silt flats in Britain (Foulness and Maplin Sands) and the largest saltmarsh in Essex (Dengie). The estuarine complex comprises the largest of the main estuaries on the Essex coast north of the Thames (the Blackwater), the five tidal arms and the main river channel of the Colne Estuary, and the narrower estuary of the River Crouch and associated marshes.

Foreshore colonisation of the saltmarshes is by algal species, for example *Enteromorpha* and eelgrass species, including one of the largest surviving continuous areas of dwarf eelgrass in Europe at Foulness and Maplin Sands. These provide an important winter food source for dark-bellied brent geese. The abundant invertebrate fauna is dominated by the mollusc *Hydrobia ulvae* in fine silt and mud conditions, with a change in species where the substrate becomes sandier.

The saltmarshes exhibit a characteristic flora. Glasswort, annual sea-blite and sea aster are found on the lower marsh, with sea-purslane and saltmarsh grass co-dominant over large areas of higher saltmarsh, particularly at Dengie.

Shell, sand and shingle spits are present in the Colne and Blackwater estuaries and at Dengie, with the most extensive shell beach accumulations in Britain occurring off Foulness Point. These are important for nesting terns, and support a sparse shingle flora. Colne Point and parts of the Blackwater hold extensive stands of shrubby sea-blite. One of the few dune systems in Essex is found at Colne Point.

Herb-rich neutral grassland in the form of grazing marshes is found behind the sea-walls and supports a diverse range of plant species. The former saltmarsh creeks and ditches are fringed with stands of sea club-rush, common reed and lesser reedmace. Ray Island on the Blackwater and Woodham Fen are among very few sites on the Essex coast which still show the natural transition between mudflat and coastal grassland without the interruption of a sea wall.

A rich invertebrate fauna includes several rare species of water beetle and outstanding assemblages of dragonflies including the ruddy darter, hairy dragonfly and scarce emerald damselfly. Rough grassland along much of this coast is frequented by the nationally uncommon Roesel's bush-cricket, the Essex skipper butterfly and several uncommon moth species, with great green bush-cricket in more scrubby areas

Birds
The area supports internationally important numbers of dark-bellied brent goose, shelduck and 10 species of wader, and nationally important numbers of a further ten species of wildfowl and 3 species of wader.

The Mid-Essex Coast is a wetland of international importance by virtue of regularly supporting over 20,000 waterfowl. In the five-winter period 1985/86 to 1989/90 the average peak total was 144,400 birds, comprising 37,400 wildfowl and 107,000 waders. These figures represent a summation of the species totals of species occurring at nationally and internationally important levels, as given below. The Mid-Essex Coast supports internationally important numbers of wintering **dark-bellied brent goose** (22,800, 13% of the world total, 25% of British), **shelduck** (3790, 1.5% of NW European, 5% of British), **oystercatcher** (12,570, 1% of EAF, 4.5% of British), **ringed plover** (990, 2% of EAF, 4% of British), **grey plover** (4660, 3% of EAF, 22% of British), **knot** (20,760, 6% of EAF, 9% of British), **dunlin** (38,450, 3% of EAF, 9% of British), **black-tailed godwit** (740, 1% of EAF, 15% of British), **bar-tailed godwit** (3930, 4% of EAF, 6.5% of British), **redshank** (4140, 3% of EAF, 5.5% of British), **curlew** (4250, 1% of EAF, 5% of British) and **turnstone** (920, 1% of EAF, 2% of British) and nationally important numbers of **great crested grebe, mute swan** (460, 2.5% of British), **wigeon** (4430, 2% of British), **gadwall** (105, 2% of British), **teal** (3790, 4% of British), **pintail** (390, 1.5% of British), **shoveler** (220, 2.5% of British), **pochard** (540, 1% of British), **goldeneye** (560, 4% of British), **red-breasted merganser** (110, 1% of British), **golden plover** (5150, 2.5% of British), **lapwing** (10,140, 1% of British), **sanderling** (270, 2% of British), and ruff (30). Notable also are wintering great crested grebe, cormorant, hen harrier, merlin, snipe, short-eared owl and twite.

Passage waders of note include curlew sandpiper, whimbrel, spotted redshank, greenshank and green sandpiper.

Breeding species include **Sandwich tern** at Foulness (350 pairs in 1990, 2% of British), **common tern** at Foulness (c. 180 pairs in 1990, 1.5% of British) and **little tern** at Foulness and Colne Point (40 pairs in 1990, 2% of British). Notable also are breeding shelduck, garganey, shoveler, oystercatcher, ringed plover, redshank, short-eared owl, black-headed gull and yellow wagtail.

Conservation issues
Waterfowl that winter on estuaries are vulnerable to land-claim and other developments, such as the construction of barrages that would disturb or damage the existing ecology of these sites. Other human influences such as recreational disturbance, commercial

exploitation of shellfish and worms, and sewage and industrial pollution, are also potentially damaging to the conservation interest of estuaries.

The Mid-Essex Coast has suffered from the conversion of grazing marsh to arable land; >64% of grazing marsh has been lost on the Crouch, Roach and Foulness between 1933 and 1980. An increase in recreational activities, for example jet skiing around Mersea Island, power-boating, parascending (on the Crouch) and low-flying light aircraft has resulted in increased disturbance to birds and in some cases exacerbates saltmarsh erosion. Parts of the site are especially vulnerable to saltmarsh loss through erosion, for example Tollesbury Saltings, River Blackwater saltmarsh and Brandy Hole Creek, River Crouch. A range of development proposals have been put forward in recent years, notably the 3rd London airport proposed for Maplin Sands in the early 1970s, chalet/caravan development, marina and housing developments, and the Colne Barrier at Wivenhoe (accepted, with proposals for careful monitoring of impact). A proposal for a new airport in the mid-Thames could have knock-on effects on Maplin Sands, such as changes in tidal and sedimentation patterns, and potential for associated developments.

Further reading

Durdin, C J 1990 The Tendring Estuaries. RSPB report for Tendring District Council.
Durdin, C J and Land, R A 1990 The Rochford Estuaries and Coastlands. RSPB report for Rochford District Council.
Land, R A and Durdin, C J 1991 The Maldon Estuaries and Coast. RSPB report for Maldon District Council.
NCC Estuaries Review Summary.
Prater, A J 1981 *Estuary Birds of Britain and Ireland*. T and A D Poyser, Calton.

Norfolk Broads

SPA/Ram Code	IBA Europe number
925A	166, 167, 168, 169

County/Region	District(s)	OS sheet(s)	Grid Reference(s)	Map 14
Norfolk	Broadland, Great Yarmouth, North Norfolk, South Norfolk	134	TG 3621	

Area (ha)	NNR	SPA		Ramsar	
1000-9999	Parts	Designated	N	Designated	Y
		Candidate	Y	Candidate	Y

This site includes the former IBA sites Yare Broads and Marshes (906A), Bure Broads and Marshes (907A), Upper Thurne Broads and Marshes (908A) and Ant Broads and Marshes (921A) as listed in the European IBA book, along with the intertidal Breydon Water.

A composite site comprising reed-fringed shallow lakes and other open water, fen habitats, carr woodland and grazing marshes, important for breeding and wintering birds.

Site description
The Norfolk Broads are a series of flooded medieval peat-diggings. They lie within the floodplains of five principal river valley systems, known locally as Broadland. Together with associated fen and grazing marsh habitat it is one of the finest marshland complexes in the United Kingdom. The best areas of Broadland are included within the Norfolk Broads IBA. The subsequent management of the vegetation for reed, sedge and marsh hay, coupled with variations in hydrology and substrate supports an extremely diverse range of plant communities.

Open water is most extensive in the Upper Thurne valley, comprising four large shallow lakes (Hickling Broad, Heigham Sound, Horsey Mere and Martham Broad) along with smaller water bodies. In common with large areas of Broadland, water quality has declined significantly in recent years as a result of nutrient enrichment from the river system. This has resulted in the near elimination of the former diverse assemblages of water plants.

At isolated broads and in drainage ditches, a typically diverse aquatic flora would include frogbit, water soldier, water-violet and pondweed species. However eutrophic conditions are more commonly found and support white and yellow water-lilies.

Open water is usually fringed by common reed or reed sweet-grass and a fen swamp community is found on firmer ground. There is a high floristic diversity within the Norfolk Broads fen swamps. Less common species include cowbane, marsh pea, marsh sow-thistle and milk-parsley.

There is scrub invasion throughout the Norfolk Broads where management no longer occurs. Mixed scrub comprises common sallow, guelder-rose, alder buckthorn, wild privet and locally bog-myrtle. Notable expanses of alder carr are found along the Ant (particularly in the vicinity of Barton Broad), Bure and Yare rivers. A diverse ground flora occurs and includes straggling lianas of hop, characteristic of this carr vegetation.

The five principal Broadland rivers reach the sea at Breydon Water. Breydon is important as a roosting area and disturbance refuge for waders and wildfowl and provides feeding grounds for wildfowl. The only areas of intertidal mudflats on the east Norfolk coast are found here, small areas of saltmarsh occur at the lower end of the estuary, being replaced by extensive stands of common reed in the upper reaches.

Other noteworthy habitat types found in Broadland are fen meadows, notably along the Yare valley, and extensive grazing marshes particularly along the Upper Thurne Valley. The latter are important for wintering and breeding birds, and the associated network of dykes and drainage ditches are an important refuge for some of the less common wetland plant species.

The Norfolk Broads hold a notable invertebrate fauna, including relict fen species. A large population of the British race of swallowtail butterfly is found throughout the site. The long established reed-dominated communities support populations of rare moths, including the reed leopard, flame wainscot, Fenn's wainscot and small dotted footman (the only British site). Rare spiders, weevils, flies and beetles are also present. A wide variety of dragonflies are associated with the broads and dykes, amongst which are the uncommon variable damselfly, hairy dragonfly and Norfolk hawker, the last known in Britain from only a few Broadland localities.

Birds
The area supports internationally important numbers of wintering Bewick's swan, wigeon, gadwall and shoveler, and nationally important numbers of 7 species of wintering and 10 species of breeding wetland birds.

Breeding species include up to 4 booming male **bitterns** (20% of British), 19 pairs of **marsh harrier** (25% of British), 220 pairs of **common terns** (2% of British), up to 60 pairs of **gadwall** (11% of British), 60 pairs of **shoveler** (5% of British), 2 pairs of **garganey** (4% of British), 40 pairs of **pochard** (11% of British), 30 pairs of **Cetti's warbler** (16% of British), 6 pairs of **Savi's warbler** (30% of British) and 130 pairs of **bearded tit** (22% of British). Notable also are breeding snipe, redshank and kingfisher.

In the five-winter period 1984/85 to 1988/89 the following peak mean counts were recorded: 300 **mute swans** (2% of British), 550 **Bewick's swans** (3% of NW European, 8% British), 80 **whooper swans** (1% of British), 360 **bean geese** (81% of British), 140 European **white-fronted geese** (2% of British), 10,300 **wigeon** (1% of NW European, 4% of British), 360 **gadwall** (3% of NW European, 6% of British), 1400 **teal** (1% of British), 420 **shoveler** (1% of NW European, 5% of British), 610 **pochard** (1% of British), up to 20 **hen harriers** (3% of British) and up to 140 **Lapland buntings** (23% of British). Notable also is wintering ruff.

Conservation issues
The Broads have suffered ecological degradation as a result of enrichment by phosphates and nitrates from sewage and agricultural run-off. This has caused major losses in

botanical and invertebrate communities with some impact on breeding birds. Attempts to rectify the deterioration of water quality, with some success, have included isolation of some broads from the river system and mud-pumping to remove nutrient-enriched sediment, for example, at Strumpshaw Fen and Cockshoot Broad. This has led to recolonisation by aquatic plants. Phosphate-stripping at some sewage treatment works has so far only brought about modest improvements.

Much grazing marsh has been converted to arable or been part-drained. Although this trend has been reversed since 1987 when the Broads Environmentally Sensitive Area was established, much effort to raise water levels is still required. Some fen sites are suffering from scrub invasion as a result of a lack of traditional management. Rising sea level with consequent salt water inundation may alter the botanical nature of much of Broadland. A longstanding issue in the Broads has been the potential damage by boats, especially from wash and disturbance. There have been proposals for additional marinas in the area.

Deben Estuary

SPA/Ram Code	IBA Europe number
926A	N/A

County/Region	District(s)	OS sheet(s)	Grid Reference(s)	Maps 14, 20
Suffolk	Suffolk Coastal	156, 169	TM 295504 – 330378	

Area (ha)	NNR	SPA		Ramsar	
976	No	Designated	N	Designated	N
		Candidate	Y	Candidate	Y

A sheltered estuary comprising extensive intertidal mudflats important for wintering wildfowl and waders.

Site description

This narrow estuary extends south-eastwards from the town of Woodbridge for a distance of over 12 km, reaching the sea just to the north of the town of Felixstowe. The estuary mouth is the narrowest section of the estuary, and is protected by the presence of shifting sand banks. Such protection has allowed the development of intertidal mudflats and the associated invertebrate fauna which act as a food supply for wintering waders and wildfowl. A diverse range of saltmarsh communities has developed, which in total accounts for approximately 40% of Suffolk's area of saltmarsh, and provides breeding grounds for waders, notably redshank. Lower marsh is dominated by sea aster, annual sea-blite, glasswort, sea pea and sea-purslane and is mainly found at the head of the estuary, with more typical mid-marsh communities occurring towards the lower end and extensive swards of common cord-grass also occur. Upper marsh is less frequent but still occurs in several areas.

Other habitats within the site include extensive stands of sea couch showing a natural transition to blackthorn scrub at the northern-most end of the estuary. Swamp communities narrowly fringe the estuary in places, occasionally forming larger stands. In general these are dominated by common reed, but with stands of sea club-rush and greater pond sedge sometimes present.

Birds

The area supports internationally important numbers of wintering and passage redshank, and nationally important numbers of wintering dark-bellied brent goose, shelduck and black-tailed godwit.

In the five-winter period 1985/86 to 1989/90 the average peak counts were 1490 **dark-bellied brent geese** (2% of British), 1080 **shelduck** (1% of British), 150 **black-tailed godwit** (3% of British) and 1740 **redshank** (2% of EAF, 2% of British). Notable also are wintering mute swan, wigeon, pintail, grey plover, dunlin and curlew.

Marsh harriers (4 nests 1990, 5% of British) nest in reedbeds adjacent to the estuary, and hunt over the whole area.

Conservation issues
Waterfowl that winter on estuaries are vulnerable to land-claim, the intensification of the commercial exploitation of shellfish, and sewage and industrial pollution. Recreation, especially sailing, water skiing and jet skiing, is significant, and threatens to intensify.

Further reading
Beardall, C H, Dryden, R C and Holzer, T J 1988 *The Suffolk Estuaries*. Suffolk Wildlife Trust.

Great Yarmouth North Denes

SPA/Ram Code	IBA Europe number
927A	N/A

County/Region	District(s)	OS sheet(s)	Grid Reference(s)	Map 14
Norfolk	Great Yarmouth	134	TG 5309	

Area (ha)	NNR	SPA		Ramsar	
1-999	No	Designated	N	Designated	N
		Candidate	Y	Candidate	N

Shingle beach and low dune system holding nationally important numbers of little terns.

Site description

The North Denes dune system at Great Yarmouth North Beach is an actively accreting low sand dune system, with a wide shingle beach. The dunes are stabilised by marram and there are extensive areas of grey hair grass.

Birds

The site is nationally important for breeding **little terns** with 201 pairs 1990 (2% of W European, 8% of British).

Conservation issues

The little tern colony is vulnerable to disturbance by dogs and people and to predation. Development of this area for the tourist trade may be of longer term concern.

Further reading

The Norfolk and Norwich Naturalists' Society. *Norfolk Bird and Mammal Report 1986*. Jarrold and Sons, Norwich.

The Norfolk and Norwich Naturalists' Society. *Norfolk Bird and Mammal Report 1988*. Jarrold and Sons, Norwich.

Somerset Levels and Moors

SPA/Ram Code	IBA Europe number
1003A	185

County/Region	District(s)	OS sheet(s)	Grid Reference(s)	Map 16
Somerset	Mendip, Sedgemoor, South Somerset, Taunton Deane, Yeovil	193	ST 4033	

Area (ha) 6528+	NNR Part	SPA Designated N Candidate Y	Ramsar Designated N Candidate Y

One of the largest and richest areas of traditionally managed wet grassland and fen habitats in lowland UK, supporting important populations of breeding and wintering waterfowl and other wetland birds.

Site description

The Levels and Moors have formed in the valleys of five rivers which drain a large area of north Somerset. The whole area is low lying, and the naturally poor drainage has encouraged a build up of peat, especially in inland parts of the system. Nearer the coast and in the upper river valleys, the soils are derived more from alluvial deposits.

A variety of grassland habitats exists, ranging from agriculturally improved and intensively managed land to traditionally grazed damp grasslands; wildlife interest is now centred on the latter and small remnants of raised mires and other similar habitats.

Many of the grasslands are dominated by meadow fescue, perennial rye-grass and other widespread grasses. Many fields in wetter locations have more diverse vegetation, with generally larger amounts of rushes and sedges and a suite of characteristic species including meadowsweet, ragged-robin, tubular water-dropwort and marsh ragwort. The most species-rich fields have a mire-like community typified by carnation sedge, meadow thistle, and marsh-orchids.

In some areas, fields are used for the cultivation of osiers in withy beds, and although some beds have been abandoned, many are still cut on the traditional annual rotation.

In some peaty areas, such as on Catcott and Shapwick Heaths, there are wet heathy grasslands, dominated by purple moor-grass, common bent, with much bog-myrtle, cross-leaved heath, and, in the wettest parts, *Sphagnum* mosses. Ashcott Heath has the last active raised mire on the Somerset Levels and Moors, with *Sphagnum* moss carpet and wet heath, including plants such as bog asphodel, round-leaved sundew and bogbean. Scrub and woodland development, of alder, willow, birch and oak, has occurred in some of these heathy areas. These acidic communities are notable for the number of uncommon plants which occur in them, including the nationally rare marsh pea, milk-parsley and marsh fern.

The ditches or rhynes which separate fields throughout the Levels and Moors are of outstanding botanical interest. Emergent, floating and submerged aquatic species are well represented: typical constituents of these three groups are sea club-rush and reed sweet-grass, duckweeds and frogbit, and rigid hornwort and various pondweeds. Species-richness is often high, and several nationally uncommon plants are present, including fen, flat-stalked and hairlike pondweeds and greater water-parsnip.

The diverse plant communities support a correspondingly rich invertebrate fauna, and the aquatic groups are particularly well represented with many Red Data Book and nationally rare species present.

Among vertebrates, species such as grass snake and common frog are widespread, and this is one of few areas in lowland England where otters have retained a presence.

Birds
The Somerset Levels and Moors support internationally important numbers of Bewick's swan and lapwing, and passage whimbrel, together with nationally important numbers of breeding mute swan, marsh harrier and black-tailed godwit and wintering mute swan, wigeon, teal, golden plover and snipe.

The site supports a nationally important assemblage of breeding waders associated with wet grassland, especially lapwing, snipe, redshank and curlew. The breeding wader population is one of the five largest on lowland wet grassland in England and Wales. Individual breeding species that occur in nationally important numbers include **mute swan** (70 pairs, 2% of British), **marsh harrier** (1 pair, 1% of British) and **black-tailed godwit** (7 pairs, 13% of British). Notable also are nightjar, kingfisher, yellow wagtail, whinchat and sedge warbler.

The site is classed as a wetland of international importance by regularly supporting in winter over 20,000 waterfowl. During five winters in the period 1976/77 to 1989/90 the average peak count was 42,790 birds, comprising 7960 wildfowl and 34,830 waders. Average peaks for individual species included 320 **mute swans** (2% of British), 210 **Bewick's swans** (1% of the NW European population, 3% of British), 4740 **wigeon** (2% of British), 2690 **teal** (3% of British), over 1530 **golden plover** (c.1% of British), 30,700 **lapwing** (1.5% of EAF, 3% of British), 3220+ snipe and 27 ruff.

In addition, during spring passage, the site supports internationally important numbers of **whimbrel** (c. 1100 birds, 2% of the EAF population of the nominate race).

Conservation issues
Traditionally, the area has been used for hay cropping and summer cattle grazing, with some small scale peat cutting. However in recent years, a series of major land-drainage projects aimed at reducing flood risks, along with reduced water levels through manipulation of water management regimes have caused a decline in breeding, passage and wintering waders and wintering waterfowl. Until recently land drainage benefits have been prioritised for agriculture rather than nature conservation. This decline will only be reversed with more sensitive management of the water levels throughout the year over the site as a whole.

Further reading

Ferns, P N, Green, G H and Round, P D 1979 Significance of the Somerset and Gwent Levels in Britain as feeding areas for migrant Whimbrels. *Biol. Conserv.* 16: 7-22.

Green, R E and Robins, M (in prep) The decline of the ornithological importance of the Somerset Moors, England, and changes in the management of water levels.

Lapwing

Chew Valley Lake

SPA/Ram Code	IBA Europe number
1004A	186

County/Region	District(s)	OS sheet(s)	Grid Reference(s)	Maps 16, 17
Avon	Wansdyke	172	ST 570600	

Area (ha)	NNR	SPA	Ramsar
565	No	Designated Y Candidate N/A	Designated N Candidate N

A large artificial reservoir, attracting important numbers of wintering waterfowl, and also of interest for passage and breeding wetland birds.

Site description

Chew Valley Lake is one of the largest freshwater bodies in south-west England. The large expanse of very shallow open water has peripheral areas of reedbed, carr, woodland and grassland. Open water plant communities are rather sparse, and composed principally of fennel and lesser pondweeds, opposite-leaved pondweed and water crowfoot.

Habitats on the lake shore include traditionally managed pasture and hay meadows. Characteristic plants of the neutral soils are pepper-saxifrage, burnet-saxifrage and devil's-bit scabious. There are also some more calcareous soils, where fairy flax, dwarf thistle and salad burnet are found.

Birds

The site supports nationally important numbers of breeding and wintering great crested grebe and wintering gadwall, teal, shoveler, pochard and goosander.

In the five-winter period 1985/86 to 1989/90 the average peak counts were 470 **great crested grebes** (6% of British), 115 **gadwall** (2% of British), 1050 **teal** (1% of British), 390 **shoveler** (4% of British), 1040 **pochard** (2% of British) and 90 **goosander** (2% of British). Notable also are wintering little grebe, bittern, tufted duck, goldeneye, smew and ruddy duck.

Breeding species include **great crested grebe** (30-50 pairs, 1% of British), heron, shelduck, gadwall, garganey, pochard, tufted duck, kingfisher, and sedge and reed warblers.

There is a notable passage of black terns and *Acrocephalus* warblers.

Conservation issues

A conflict between fishing and wildlife interests has highlighted the need to retain and enhance zoning. Other extensive recreational use of the lake includes sailing, nature trail use, bird ringing station, picnic sites and information centres. The birds that use this site are vulnerable to any changes in abstraction regimes.

Further reading
Avon Ornithological Group. *Avon County Bird Report.*
Chew Valley Ringing Station Annual Reports.

Taw and Torridge Estuary

SPA/Ram Code	IBA Europe number
1005A	184

County/Region	District(s)	OS sheet(s)	Grid Reference(s)	Map 15
Devon	North Devon, Torridge	180	SS 470310	

Area (ha)	NNR	SPA		Ramsar	
1337	No	Designated	N	Designated	N
		Candidate	Y	Candidate	N

Converging estuaries with mud- and sandflats and saltmarshes, attracting a diverse assemblage of wintering wildfowl and waders.

Site description

This estuarine complex has two major arms, the rivers Taw and Torridge, extending inland as far as Barnstaple and Bideford respectively, and entering the sea between the dune systems of Northam and Braunton Burrows.

The intertidal areas are predominantly sand or sandy-mud. There is a varied invertebrate fauna, and rocky outcrops add to this variety by providing suitable substrates for algal growth and mussel beds.

The lower saltmarshes are dominated by glassworts, cord-grass and common saltmarsh-grass. Middle level marsh tends to be more species-rich, and has such characteristic species as sea aster and annual sea-blite, while the upper limit is marked by stands of red fescue and sea rush. Common reed and sea wormwood also occur locally at the upper edge of the marsh, and on harder substrates rock sea-lavender and the nationally rare sea stock can be found.

Birds

These estuaries support nationally important numbers of wintering curlew.

In the five-winter period 1985/86 to 1989/90 average peak counts included 20 greenshank and 1400 **curlew** (2% of British). Notable also are regular large numbers of wintering wigeon, teal, ringed plover, golden plover and grey plover. Average peaks for each of these species approach the 1% British level. Other wintering species include little egret, spoonbill, hen harrier, merlin, peregrine, green sandpiper and common sandpiper.

Conservation issues

This estuary is largely unspoilt, but development proposals for marinas and a holiday village may threaten intertidal areas and also increase the demand for leisure and recreational activities within the estuary. New and expanding activities suggest the need for controls and a management scheme to resolve conflicting demands for intertidal areas and open water.

There is gravel extraction from Crow Neck foreshore.

Isles of Scilly Coastal Habitats

SPA/Ram Code	IBA Europe number
1006A	180

County/Region	District(s)	OS sheet(s)	Grid Reference(s)	Map 15
Isles of Scilly	N/A	203	SV 900120	

Area (ha)	NNR	SPA		Ramsar	
1-999	No	Designated N		Designated N	
		Candidate Y		Candidate N	

A collection of islands with a varied coastline, including large numbers of rocky islets, rocky shores, sand and shingle beaches, mudflats and lagoons, of prime importance for breeding seabirds and some wintering wader species.

Site description

The Isles of Scilly comprise over 200 low-lying granite islands and rocks, lying 28 miles to the south-west of Land's End. The combination of this isolated south-westerly location, extreme maritime influence and shallow soils on granite bedrock has resulted in the development of an island complex of international nature conservation importance. The natural vegetation has been modified by strong winds and salt spray, restricting the growth of trees and scrub, but forming distinctive waved heath dominated by heather, bell heather and western gorse and headlands covered in thrift. The flora is important for a number of rare species that are normally found around the Mediterranean and Western Europe, but which occur in Britain only on Scilly. These species include dwarf pansy, orange bird's-foot, least adder's-tongue and small adder's-tongue. The purity of the air has allowed a rich lichen flora (250 species recorded) to develop. Clear waters between the islands support a rich maritime flora and fauna and grey seals breed around the rocky shores. Areas of natural and semi-natural habitat include cliff, uncultivated coastal margins, wetlands, heathlands, permanent pasture and sand dunes.

Birds

This area supports internationally important numbers of breeding lesser black-backed and great black-backed gulls and wintering turnstone, together with nationally important numbers of breeding storm petrel, shag, roseate tern and common tern, and wintering ringed plover and sanderling.

Recent estimates of breeding seabird numbers from the Seabird Colony Register include **storm petrel** (1000+ pairs, c. 2% of British), **shag** (1160 pairs, 3% of British), **lesser black-backed gull** (3800 pairs, 2% of Western and Central European population, 5% of British), **great black-backed gull** (1030 pairs, 1% of Western European, 6% of British), **roseate tern** (6 pairs, 7% of British), **common tern** (170 pairs, 1.5% of British). Notable also are breeding Manx shearwater, cormorant, Sandwich tern, guillemot, razorbill, and puffin.

Wintering waders were surveyed in detail in 1984/85 and included **ringed plover** (310 birds, 1% of British), **sanderling** (330 birds, 2% of British) and **turnstone** (940 birds, 1% of EAF, 2% of British).

Conservation issues

Seabirds are sensitive to changes in the quality of the marine environment, especially to changes in fish stocks and to oil pollution. Ground-nesting seabirds on offshore islands are vulnerable to the introduction of predatory mammals.

There is concern about the effects of synthetic gill nets (used by local and mainland fishermen) on feeding seabirds. There are indications that the puffin population has recently declined, and there is a need for access restrictions to some islands during the breeding season. Visitor pressure from birdwatchers is very heavy in the autumn.

Further reading

Kirby, J S 1990 Numbers, distribution and habitat preferences of waders wintering on the Isles of Scilly. *Wader Study Group Bulletin*, 57: 47-52.
Breeding seabirds, Isles of Scilly. NCC Report 1983.
Breeding seabirds, Isles of Scilly. NCC Report 1987.

Exe Estuary

SPA/Ram Code	IBA Europe number
1008A	183

County/Region	District(s)	OS sheet(s)	Grid Reference(s)	Map 16
Devon	East Devon, Exeter, Teignbridge	192	SX 980845	

Area (ha)	NNR	SPA		Ramsar	
2182	No	Designated	N	Designated	N
		Candidate	Y	Candidate	Y

An estuary with broad intertidal flats and grazing marshes important for passage and wintering wildfowl and waders.

Site description

The Exe Estuary contains a complex of habitats which together provide an important wintering and passage area for waterfowl, as well as supporting important populations of breeding birds. It extends over 10 km south from Exeter to the open sea at Dawlish Warren.

The site contains a full sequence of intertidal habitats, which are important for invertebrate fauna: tidal flats, saltmarsh, reedbeds, sand dunes and enclosed grazing marsh are all well represented.

The upper end of the estuary and the adjoining Exeter canal have large stands of reed and sea club-rush. Towards the mouth of the estuary patches of cord-grass saltmarsh have developed and there are estuarine beds of eelgrass in places. Grazing marshes claimed from the intertidal part of the upper estuary consist of fields separated by ditches which hold a varied aquatic community. The estuary is sheltered by Dawlish Warren, a sand spit across the mouth of the estuary, which supports a variety of plant and animal communities representative of south-west Britain.

The mud- and sandflats support growths of eelgrass and *Enteromorpha* algae, and contain an abundance of invertebrates including extensive mussel beds. These provide rich feeding areas for the wintering waders and wildfowl. Dawlish Warren provides a roosting area for many species, especially oystercatchers, brent geese and bar-tailed godwits, while the intertidal areas around it provide a feeding area. At the head of the estuary, the Exminster and Bowling Green Marshes provide important high tide feeding and roosting sites for waders and wildfowl, and breeding habitat for redshank and lapwing.

By virtue of its south-westerly location in Britain the Exe Estuary assumes proportionally much greater importance for waterfowl during periods of severe winter weather when birds are forced to move away from frozen wetlands elsewhere.

Birds

The Exe Estuary supports internationally important numbers of wintering dark-bellied brent goose, together with nationally important numbers of wintering Slavonian grebe, oystercatcher, avocet, grey plover, dunlin and black-tailed godwit, and passage ringed plover and greenshank.

In the five-winter period 1985/86 to 1989/90 the average peak counts were 2650 **dark-bellied brent geese** (2% of the world population, 3% of British), 20 **Slavonian grebes** (5% of British), 3980 **oystercatcher** (1% of British), 200 **avocets** (20% of British), 350 **grey plover** (2% of British), 5300 **dunlin** (1% of British) and 580 **black-tailed godwit** (12% of British). Notable also are large regular wintering populations of wigeon, red-breasted merganser, bar-tailed godwit, curlew and redshank.

In addition, the site supports, during migration, up to 440 **ringed plover** (1% of the British passage population) and 50 greenshank, as well as notable numbers of whimbrel and turnstone. Notable also are passage populations of Sandwich, common and little terns.

Conservation issues
There are few threats directly resulting from built development around the estuary. At present, water quality restricts the shell fishing industry and limits its activity to one area. Future expansion following cleaner water could have an adverse impact on the birds. The growth of the industry requires a framework to ensure it does not cause significant damage to the birdlife from disturbance and land-claim. Such a management approach is also required to avoid conflict between and from the growing number of recreational users of the site. The estuary requires management to place potentially damaging activities away from the sensitive areas. The expansion of the number of users of the estuary for recreation is likely to continue.

Further reading
Prater, A J 1981 *Estuary Birds in Britain and Ireland*. T and A D Poyser, Calton.

Chesil Beach and The Fleet

SPA/Ram Code	IBA Europe number
1009A	187

County/Region	District(s)	OS sheet(s)	Grid Reference(s)	Maps 16, 18
Dorset	West Dorset, Weymouth and Portland	194	SY 6081	

Area (ha)	NNR	SPA	Ramsar
990	No	Designated Y Candidate N/A	Designated Y Candidate N/A

A long, linear shingle beach, enclosing a brackish lagoon, with large breeding populations of mute swan, ringed plover and terns, and attracting many waterfowl in winter.

Site description

Chesil Beach is one of the largest shingle structures in Britain. It is a storm beach, only 150-200 m wide, which runs for 28 km from Burton Bradstock in the west, to the Isle of Portland in the east. The beach encloses the Fleet, which is the largest tidal lagoon in Britain. Both the beach and the lagoon are highly unusual features, and support similarly scarce plant and animal communities.

The landward side of Chesil Beach is vegetated with characteristic shingle flora, including sea-kale, yellow horned poppy, sea pea and shrubby sea-blite. Sea-holly, Portland spurge and the nationally rare little-robin also are present.

The Fleet is shallow, generally less than 2 m deep, with variations in salinity from marine at Portland Harbour to almost freshwater at the western end. There is abundant aquatic vegetation, with a wide range of algae. Important communities of vascular plants of brackish conditions include both beaked and spiral tasselweeds and two species of eelgrass. The invertebrate communities also are highly distinctive and include species found in few other British localities. Among the 23 species of fish recorded from the Fleet is the rare goby *Gobius couchii*, and the lagoon also acts as a nursery for bass.

Additional habitats present within the area include mudflats, saltmarsh, grassland, scrub and woodland. Both marshy and dry calcareous grasslands are present, including species-rich types, and containing scarce plants such as bulbous foxtail and marsh-mallow. There are extensive reedbeds, which hold populations of breeding birds.

Birds

The area supports nationally important numbers of breeding mute swan and little tern, and wintering mute swan, dark-bellied brent goose, wigeon and red-breasted merganser.

Numbers of breeding birds include 60+ pairs of **mute swans** (2% of British), 50 pairs of ringed plover and 37 pairs of **little terns** (in 1990, 1.5% of British). The reedbeds hold populations of sedge, reed and Cetti's warblers, and, occasionally, bearded tits.

In the five-winter period 1985/86 to 1989/90 the average peak counts were 680 **mute swans** (4% of British), 1000 **dark-bellied brent geese** (1% of British), 4860 **wigeon** (2% of British) and 115 **red-breasted merganser** (1% of British).

Conservation issues

Protection of tern colonies is essential because of their close proximity to carparks and areas of other public access. Recently brent geese have caused damage to farmland. This has highlighted the need to provide refuges for this species. The birds that use this area are vulnerable to oil spills.

Dorset Heathlands

	SPA/Ram Code	IBA Europe number
	1010A	188 (part)/189

County/Region	District(s)	OS sheet(s)	Grid Reference(s)	Maps 16, 18
Dorset	Bournemouth, Christchurch, East Dorset, Poole, Purbeck, West Dorset	194, 195	SY 9583	

Area (ha)	NNR	SPA		Ramsar	
1000-9999	Part	Designated	N	Designated	N
		Candidate	Y	Candidate	N

Lowland heathland and mires, with associated woodland and grassland, with important populations of specialist heathland birds.

Site description

The Dorset Heathlands extend over a large area in the east of the county, around Poole Harbour, and to the west of Wareham. They lie on the infertile and acidic Bagshot Beds, and although many areas have been lost to development, plantations or agricultural improvement, the total area of the remaining fragments is still considerable.

Dry heathland is dominated by heather, and with much bell heather, dwarf gorse and bristle bent. Patches of gorse are frequent, and locally bracken is abundant. Generally, the diversity of higher plants is low, but there may also be a high lichen cover, especially of *Cladonia portentosa*. All six species of British reptiles are found on the Dorset heaths, and the dry heaths are especially notable for the rare smooth snake and sand lizard.

As conditions become damper, species such as purple moor-grass and cross-leaved heath become dominant, often with *Sphagnum* mosses, and other characteristic species including deergrass, carnation sedge and round-leaved sundew. These humid heaths are notable for the presence of the nationally rare Dorset heath, and other scarce plants such as marsh gentian.

The wettest areas have mires in which *Sphagnum* carpets are well developed, often with substantial amounts of the scarce *Sphagnum pulchrum*. Other typical bog plants that grow in the mires include common cottongrass, bog pondweed, bogbean and bog asphodel. Several uncommon plants occur, including marsh clubmoss and bog orchid.

Communities transitional between the heaths and mires and other habitats provide additional variety. For example, where the heaths grade into reedbed or saltmarsh, there is often a more nutrient-rich zone characterised by black bog-rush or blunt-flowered rush. Reedbeds have developed in several areas, notably on the south-east side of the Arne peninsula. Where scrub or woodland has developed in wet areas, there is often a transitional zone in which bog-myrtle is abundant.

The wetter scrub and woodland is mostly of downy birch and sallow. The ground flora often has carpets of *Sphagnum fimbriatum*, and occasionally the local royal fern. The better established broad-leaved woodlands, such as those on Arne peninsula, seem to have developed on long abandoned fields. They are composed of oak, with an understorey of hazel or holly, but some areas have been planted with conifers and locally rhododendron invasion has been severe. On the dry heaths, Scots and maritime pines have invaded large areas.

Several different grassland communities are present, including both dry and wet acidic types. The damper acidic grasslands also are moderately species-rich, often dominated by bent grasses, but with a wide range of species such as sneezewort, devil's-bit scabious, saw-wort and lousewort.

The whole complex of heath, mire and associated habitats has an outstanding invertebrate fauna, involving many different groups. Many are specialists, strongly associated with or restricted to particular habitats.

Birds
This area supports nationally important numbers of breeding hobby, nightjar, wood-lark, Dartford warbler and wintering hen harrier.

Totals from surveys in recent years are up to 17 pairs of **hobbies** (2% of British), 135 pairs of **nightjars** (7% of British), about 16 pairs of **woodlarks** (7% of British) and about 125 pairs of **Dartford warblers** (25% of British). The numbers of each of these species fluctuate considerably from year to year. This site makes a substantial contribution to the maintenance of the traditional breeding ranges of these species within the EC.

In winter the site regularly holds 12 roosting **hen harriers** (2% of British).

Conservation issues
There has been a great deal of loss and fragmentation of lowland heathland during the present century. Sympathetic habitat management is required in order to maintain the wildlife interest of the remaining areas.

There are recreational pressures on the site and pollution is affecting bogs.

Further reading
Cadbury, C J 1989 What future for lowland heaths in southern Britain. *RSPB Conserv. Rev* 3: 61-67. RSPB, Sandy.
Dorset Heathland Strategy. Dorset Heathland Forum, Dorset County Council 1989.
Prendergast, E D V and Boys, J V 1983 *The Birds Of Dorset*. David and Charles, Newton Abbot.
Nature Conservancy Council *1988 The Conservation of the Dorset Heathlands*. Nature Conservancy Council, Taunton.
Webb, N (1986). *Heathlands*. Collins, London.

Poole Harbour

SPA/Ram Code	IBA Europe number
1011A	188 (part)

County/Region	District(s)	OS sheet(s)	Grid Reference(s)	Maps 16, 18
Dorset	Poole, Purbeck	195	SZ 000890	

Area (ha)	NNR	SPA		Ramsar	
4000	Part	Designated	N	Designated	N
		Candidate	Y	Candidate	Y

A large estuarine basin, comprising 83 km of shoreline and including extensive mudflats and saltmarshes and five islands, important for wintering waterfowl and breeding terns.

Site description

This drowned valley forms one of the largest natural harbours in the world, with the five islands representing high ground between former river valleys. These now have fringing marshes, and, in places, cliffs of sand and clay are present.

The relatively low volume of freshwater from several small rivers, the near landlocked entrance (350 m in width) to the sea and the shallow form of the harbour has allowed extensive saltmarshes and mudflats to develop. The tides show a 'double high' phenomenon, with the water held at or above mean level for 16 out of 24 hours.

The heathland landscape around the harbour has been much modified by human activity, particularly in the last 200 years, and the north-eastern shores of the harbour are heavily developed. Remaining natural transition from saltmarsh to bog and heathland still occurs, with some grazing marshes and fen and carr woodland also present.

Some 80% of the Harbour area comprises intertidal fine-grained mud, sandflats and marshes, with a widespread distribution of marine invertebrates, particularly large numbers of which are found in sheltered intertidal bays, and provide important feeding areas for wintering waders and wildfowl. Tube-worm beds dominate the fine sub-tidal sands of the central harbour and are particularly well developed at Poole Harbour. The mud- and sandflats grade into saltmarshes or stands of common reed on their landward side. These marshes are dominated by common cord-grass, a species which is undergoing dieback in some areas after rapid colonisation of estuaries in southern Britain. The higher marsh supports a more diverse plant community with a range of typical saltmarsh species, and in places includes the local shrubby sea-blite.

At Lytchett Bay, reedswamp merges with acidic bog communities which then grade into wet and dry heathland. Heather/western gorse dry heath occurs on the islands, although this has been reduced in extent by tree-planting and invasion. The open dry heathland of Brownsea Island is nationally important for its lichen assemblage.

Wetter grasslands are found along the harbour shore, with neutral, herb-rich swards at Lytchett, and more extensive brackish grazing marshes at Keysworth, dominated by creeping bent, with strawberry clover and narrow-leaved bird's-foot-trefoil. Grasslands at Keysworth and in the Lower Frome Valley are notable as feeding sites and as high water roosts. Adjacent to these areas are wet woodlands of birch and sallow. Stands of

Scots and maritime pine dominate the drier soils, particularly on the islands; the rare and protected red squirrel is found on Brownsea Island.

The range and continuity of habitats present supports several scarce and restricted species of insect, notably hairy dragonfly, small red damselfly, silver-studded blue butterfly and the shore bug *Saldula setulosa* (recorded only from Poole Harbour).

Birds
Poole Harbour supports internationally important numbers of wintering shelduck, black-tailed godwit and redshank, along with nationally important numbers of breeding black-headed gull and common tern and wintering pochard, goldeneye, red-breasted merganser, avocet, grey plover and curlew.

In the five-winter period 1985/86 to 1989/90 the average peak counts were 2470 **shelduck** (1% of NW European, 3% of British), 1200 **pochard** (2% of British), 190 **goldeneye** (1% of British), 365 **red-breasted merganser** (4% of British), 65 **avocet** (6.5% of British), 360 **grey plover** (2% of British), 1000 **black-tailed godwit** (1% of EAF, 20% of British), 1320 **curlew** (1% of British) and 1230 **redshank** (1% of EAF, 2% of British). Notable also are wintering dark-bellied brent goose, wigeon, gadwall, teal, pintail, shoveler, scaup, ringed plover and dunlin.

Breeding species include **black-headed gull** (over 3000 pairs, 1% of British) and **common tern** (130 pairs in 1989, 1% of British). Notable also are breeding grey heron, Sandwich tern (90 pairs in 1989) and redshank. Cetti's warblers breed in carr vegetation, especially along the River Frome.

Conservation issues
The area of water within the harbour is used for an ever increasing number and variety of recreational activities. This growth may lead to conflict with the wildlife. Controls on the use of the area of water are required and a management scheme for the site is essential. Attempts to prevent development in sensitive locations have been largely successful but occasional proposals seek to place development requiring water frontage in inappropriate locations. Development is confined to the northern shores allowing the southern shores to remain largely undisturbed.

The harbour is an important recreational site for the conurbation of Poole/ Bournemouth, as well as providing mooring facilities for boat owners from as far afield as Bristol. The increase in the number of boats, particularly power boats is placing pressure on the site. The expansion of the commercial port also has implications for the wildlife.

Oil extraction from within the harbour poses a potential threat to the harbour. Mineral extraction could damage areas of wet grassland.

Such diverse and conflicting activities within and adjacent to the site mean that a management plan is required to restrict and zone them.

Further reading
The New Dorset Bird Club. *Dorset Birds 1989.*
Prendergast, E D V and Boys, J V 1983 *The Birds of Dorset.* David and Charles, Newton Abbot.
Aspinall, S and Tasker, M L 1990 *Coastal birds of east Dorset.* Nature Conservancy Council, Peterborough.

East Devon Heaths

SPA/Ram Code	IBA Europe number
1012A	N/A

County/Region	District(s)	OS sheet(s)	Grid Reference(s)	Map 16
Devon	East Devon	192	SY 050880	

Area (ha)	NNR	SPA		Ramsar	
1000-9999	No	Designated	N	Designated	N
		Candidate	Y	Candidate	N

Lowland heathland, with characteristic breeding birds including hobby, nightjar and Dartford warbler.

Site description

Lying on the acidic Bunter Pebblebeds, these areas form the largest blocks of lowland heath in Devon. The higher areas have dry heath, while in shallow valleys wet heath and valley mires form a distinct contrast.

The dry heaths are dominated by heather, with bell heather, western gorse, bristle bent and purple moor-grass all frequent. There has been some invasion by pine and birch, and bracken is also locally abundant.

Wet heaths and mires are dominated by cross-leaved heath, purple moor-grass, heather, dwarf gorse and *Sphagnum* mosses, and with characteristic species such as meadow thistle, lesser butterfly-orchid, common sedge, and in the boggiest places, common cottongrass, bog asphodel and sundews. Patches of willow scrub have developed in some areas.

Invertebrate interest centres on butterflies, with this site reported to be the best lowland heath for butterflies in England.

Birds

These heaths support nationally important numbers of breeding nightjar and Dartford warbler.

The most recent survey, carried out in 1990, found 57 pairs of **nightjars** (3% of British) and 24 pairs of **Dartford warblers** (5% of British). Notable also are breeding hobby and curlew. Wintering species include hen harrier.

Conservation issues

There has been a great deal of loss and fragmentation of lowland heathland during the present century. Sympathetic habitat management is required in order to maintain the wildlife interest of the remaining areas. Management of the East Devon heaths is now being undertaken by the owners.

Further reading

Devon Bird Watching and Preservation Society. *Devon County Bird Reports.*
Sitters, H P 1988 *The Tetrad Atlas of the Breeding Birds of Devon.* DBWPS. Yelverton.

Tamar Complex

SPA/Ram Code	IBA Europe number
1014A	181

County/Region	District(s)	OS sheet(s)	Grid Reference(s)	Map 15
Cornwall	Caradon	201	SX 4361	
Devon	Plymouth,			
	South Hams,			
	West Devon			

Area (ha)	NNR	SPA		Ramsar	
1-999	No	Designated	N	Designated	N
		Candidate	Y	Candidate	N

An estuarine complex attracting important numbers of wintering avocets.

Site description

The Tamar estuary system is a large marine inlet on the English Channel coast comprising the estuaries of the rivers Tamar, Lynher and Tavy, which collectively drain an extensive part of Devon and Cornwall.

The Tamar river and its tributaries provide the main input of fresh water into the estuary complex, and form a ria (a drowned river valley) with Plymouth lying on the eastern shore. The broader, lower reaches of the rivers form extensive tidal mudflats bordered by saltmarsh communities. These support beds of algae, especially *Enteromorpha* species, eelgrasses, and moderately rich polychaete worm communities, all of which provide an important food source for wintering waders.

Saltmarsh communities, inundation grassland and, locally, rocky shores border these mudflats, the saltmarshes occurring upstream to Cotehele Quay. Saltmarshes are not usually extensive on rias, but there is a large area within the Lynher estuary, and smaller areas elsewhere. Typically these contain grasses such as common saltmarsh-grass, red fescue and sea couch, with associated species such as sea aster, sea-purslane and English scurvygrass.

In places the Tamar river has a rocky shore and subtidal habitats unusually far up the estuary. These support invertebrate communities that are considered to be the best examples of their type in tidal inlets in southern Britain.

Further upstream there are freshwater marshes and fen habitats in the alluvial river valley along with rush pasture and extensive banks of reedmace. The only known British population of triangular club-rush occurs among the common reed at one location.

Several areas of semi-natural sessile oak woodland reach to the shoreline, with Warleigh Point a good example of a western oak wood. Birch also occurs in the canopy, and the understorey of hazel, rowan and holly occasionally harbours a wild service tree.

Otters occur on undisturbed stretches of the river.

Birds
The Tamar is of national importance for wintering black-tailed godwit and avocet.

In the five-winter period 1985/86 to 1989/90 the average peak counts were 140 **avocets** (14% of British), 100 **black-tailed godwit** (2% of British), 24 spotted redshank and 22 greenshank. Notable also are wintering grey plover, dunlin, curlew, redshank, green sandpiper and common sandpiper. The numbers of dunlin, curlew and redshank fall just below the 1% British level.

Numbers of passage redshank regularly total over 1000 individuals.

Conservation issues
Threats from development are largely confined to sites close to Plymouth in particular on land surrounding the Plym estuary. There are several proposals to develop new marinas on the Tamar and these could require the loss of intertidal areas. Long-standing plans for a power station on the western shore of the Tamar remain.

A general increase in recreational activity within the estuary is of concern. Disturbance to the quieter areas may affect the wildlife. Demand for more moorings or marinas could result in the loss of the limited intertidal areas and a decline in water quality.

Further reading
Prater, A J 1981 *Estuary Birds of Britain and Ireland*. T and A D Poyser, Calton.
Reay, P 1988 *The Tamar Avocets*. Caradon Field and Natural History Club.

Bodmin Moor

SPA/Ram Code	IBA Europe number
1014B	182

County/Region	District(s)	OS sheet(s)	Grid Reference(s)	Map 15
Cornwall	North Cornwall	200, 201	SX 1681	

Area (ha)	NNR	SPA		Ramsar	
10,000+	No	Designated	N	Designated	N
		Candidate	Y	Candidate	N

Moorland and grassland important for golden plover in winter.

Site description
Occupying much of the central part of east Cornwall, Bodmin Moor is notable as a moorland for its low altitude (highest point is 420 m, Brown Willy) and for the Atlantic elements in its flora and fauna. The Moor is an eroded remnant of a massive granite boss, and is characterised by gently undulating hills, plateaux, broad valleys and scattered rocky slopes. Most hills are at 200–240 m above sea level, with 11% lying above 300 m. The two most widespread vegetation types are acid grassland dominated by sheep's-fescue, common bent and heath bedstraw, and heath of deergrass/cross-leaved heath. The acid grassland is often heavily grazed. Gorse scrub and both dry and wet heaths are present, as are bog and mire wetland communities, characterised by *Sphagnum* species, bottle sedge, star sedge and bog asphodel. Mixed broadleaved woodland is found, particularly in the marginal valleys, and willow carr is found along water courses. Conifer plantations, artificial open water areas, reservoirs, streams, rivers and rocky granite tors are other habitats found at this site.

Bodmin Moor is one of the best dragonfly and damselfly sites in Cornwall. Species recorded with a restricted range and distribution nationally are the black sympetrum, small red damselfly and the scarce blue-tailed damselfly. Silver-studded blue and marsh fritillary butterflies have both been recorded from the site.

Otters penetrate the Moor along watercourses.

Birds
Bodmin Moor is of international importance for wintering **golden plover** with over 10,000 birds recorded (1% of EAF, 5% of British). Other wintering species of note include hen harrier, merlin and peregrine.

Breeding species (as surveyed in 1984) include regionally important numbers of lapwing (77 pairs), dunlin (2 pairs), snipe (50 pairs), curlew (22 pairs) and wheatear (526 pairs).

Conservation issues
The birds that use Bodmin Moor are vulnerable to agricultural intensification, changing grazing regimes, winter shooting, afforestation and reservoir construction. China clay mining is carried out in the area. Proposed road schemes could cause further

fragmentation of the site. Recreational pressures include the use of microlight aircraft in the area.

Further reading

Chown, D J and Akers, P 1984 *A Survey of the Breeding Birds of Bodmin Moor*. Unpublished Report Cornwall Trust for Nature Conservation.

Chown, D J and Akers, P 1984 *A Survey of the Wintering Birds of Bodmin Moor*. Unpublished Report Cornwall Trust for Nature Conservation.

Chichester and
Langstone Harbours

SPA/Ram Code	IBA Europe number
1101A	196

County/Region	District(s)	OS sheet(s)	Grid Reference(s)	Maps 18, 19
Hampshire	Havant,	196, 197	SU 740010	
	Portsmouth			
West Sussex	Chichester			

Area (ha)	NNR	SPA	Ramsar
5764	No	Designated Y	Designated Y
		Candidate N/A	Candidate N/A

Large estuarine basins, with mudflats and associated saltmarshes, sand dunes and brackish marshes, of importance for wintering waterfowl and breeding terns.

Site description
The two harbours are joined by a stretch of water which separates Hayling Island from the mainland. Tidal channels drain the basins and penetrate far inland. The mudflats are rich in invertebrates, and also support extensive beds of algae, especially *Enteromorpha* species, and eelgrasses.

There are large areas of lower saltmarsh, dominated by common cord-grass, and also, at higher levels, mixed saltmarsh with sea-purslane, common sea-lavender and sea aster among the most abundant species.

Spits and islands of shingle and sand are present in several places, notably at the mouths of both harbours, but only at East Head of Chichester Harbour is the spit little modified from a natural state. The shingle beaches are unstable, and poorly vegetated, but sand dunes at East Head are colonised by marram.

Some of the periphery of the harbours, especially Langstone, has been modified through built development but some marshes and grasslands remain. The brackish and freshwater marshes include reedbeds, for example at Farlington Marshes and at the head of Fishbourne Channel, while at Thorney Deeps, on Thorney Island, reeds are surrounded by extensive rush beds and willow scrub. There are also ponds and lagoons at a number of places. Grasslands include species-poor types dominated by creeping bent, which are nonetheless important as feeding grounds for wildfowl, and also some unimproved species-rich areas, dominated by red fescue, and with old meadow plants also present. Adjoining Chichester Harbour are areas of hawthorn and blackthorn scrub and oak woodland.

Birds
The area supports internationally important numbers of wintering dark-bellied brent goose, shelduck, ringed plover, grey plover, dunlin, black-tailed godwit and redshank, and nationally important numbers of wintering black-necked grebe, pintail, shoveler, red-breasted merganser, golden plover, sanderling, bar-tailed godwit and curlew, and breeding little and common terns.

The site is a wetland of international importance by virtue of regularly supporting over 20,000 waterfowl. In the five-winter period 1985/86 to 1989/90 the average peak counts were 36 black-necked grebes, 11,000+ **dark-bellied brent geese** (6% of the world total, 12% of British), 3000+ **shelduck** (1% of NW European, 4% of British), 250+ **pintail** (1% of British), 125 **shoveler** (1% of British), 200+ **red-breasted merganser** (2% of British), 1000+ **ringed plover** (2% of EAF, 4% of British), 2140 **golden plover** (1% of British), 1900+ **grey plover** (1% of EAF, 9% of British), 310 **sanderling** (2% of British), 32,000+ **dunlin** (2% of EAF, 7% of British), 830+ **black-tailed godwit** (1% of EAF, 17% of British), 1100+ **bar-tailed godwit** (2% of British), 1600+ **curlew** (2% of British) and 1700+ **redshank** (1.5% of EAF, 2% of British).

Notable also are wintering mute swan, wigeon, goldeneye, oystercatcher, avocet, knot, ruff, greenshank and turnstone, and passage spotted redshank.

Nationally important numbers of **little tern** (154 pairs 1990, 1% of W European, 6.5% of British) and **common tern** (143 pairs 1990, 1% of British) breed at this site. Notable also are breeding black-headed gulls.

Conservation issues

Waterfowl that winter on estuaries are vulnerable to land-claim and other developments that would disturb or damage the existing ecology of these sites. Other human influences such as recreational disturbance, commercial exploitation of shellfish and worms, and oil and industrial pollution, are also potentially damaging to the conservation interest of estuaries.

The nature conservation importance of the Harbours has been well recognised in recent planning decisions. However, there are strong pressures for recreational development, usually in the form of small yacht harbours, slipways, pontoons and other shore facilities. Disturbance to high water wader roosts, rafted ducks and brent geese and breeding terns and waders by sailboards and water skiers is a problem, and jet-skis are becoming so. There are separate harbour authorities, with statutory advisory committees, for each Harbour with varying duties to nature conservation.

A notable physical threat to the Harbours (particularly Langstone) is from oyster and clam dredging, which disrupts sediments and invertebrate fauna below mean tide level. In Langstone Harbour the recent collapse of the sandeel population, which is commercially fished (for bait) may affect the size and success of tern colonies. At present there are no effective means of resolving these conservation problems.

Further reading

Kirby, J S and Tubbs, C R 1989 Wader populations in the Solent 1970/71 to 1987/88. *Hampshire Bird Report 1988*: 83-104.

Tubbs, C R and Tubbs, J M 1980 Wader and shelduck feeding distribution in Langstone Harbour, Hampshire. *Bird Study* 27: 239-248.

The New Forest

SPA/Ram Code	IBA Europe number
1103A	193

County/Region	District(s)	OS sheet(s)	Grid Reference(s)	Map 16, 18
Hampshire	New Forest, Test Valley	195, 196	SU 298081	

Area (ha)	NNR	SPA	Ramsar
27,734	No	Designated N Candidate Y	Designated N Candidate Y

A very large area of heath, grassland, mire and woodland, supporting nationally important populations of specialist birds.

Site description

The Forest is situated on acidic and mainly nutrient-poor soils, derived from plateau gravels and other deposits, and the underlying Tertiary strata which are exposed in valleys and hollows. More enriched conditions exist on marl clays in the south of the Forest.

The older, unenclosed, woodlands cover about 3800 ha and are mainly of oak and beech. The shrub layer is dominated by holly, with small amounts of other species such as hawthorn and field maple. Along streams, diversity is higher, with ash, alder and sallow all frequent. Many of the oldest stands of oak and beech, dating from the 17th century, were once pollarded. The restricted age structure, and impoverished ground flora, reflect a history of use as pasture woodland. Younger unenclosed woodland has arisen largely since the mid 19th century. A rich epiphytic lichen, fern and bryophyte flora is present. The large amounts of dead wood provide habitats for a great many dead-wood insects, especially beetles and flies.

The Forest includes 8000 ha of enclosed woodland, comprising fragments of former wood pasture dating from various periods since the early 18th century. Many of the plantations are of conifers, but about 40% are of native broadleaved species, again mainly oak and beech.

A range of heathland types is present. Humid heath of heather, cross-leaved heath and purple moor-grass occupies the greatest area, grading into wet heath of cross-leaved heath and purple moor-grass. These in turn may grade into mires. Acidic grasslands exist in a mosaic with the heaths, and also support patches of bracken and gorse, sometimes with colonising birch, rowan or oak.

The plant communities in the numerous valleys and seepage step mires, show considerable variation, being affected especially by the nutrient content of groundwater. In the most nutrient-poor zones, *Sphagnum* mosses, cross-leaved heath, bog asphodel, common cottongrass and similar species predominate. In more enriched conditions along the axis of the mires, there is often a fen-like community, with a central strip of alder or mixed carr.

The habitat mix within the New Forest owes much of its development to the traditions of common grazing by cattle and ponies, and of turning pigs out into the woodland. These practices continue, although modified, and form an essential element in the maintenance of the Forest's wildlife interest.

Birds

The area supports nationally important numbers of breeding hobby, nightjar, woodlark, Dartford warbler and wood warbler.

Recent estimates of breeding population sizes are up to 25 pairs of **hobbies** (3% of British), over 100 pairs of **nightjars** (more than 5% of British), 60 pairs of **woodlarks** (27% of British), a minimum of 400 pairs of **Dartford warblers** in 1989 (80% of British) and over 350 pairs of **wood warblers** (3% of British).

Notable also are breeding **honey buzzard** (1 pair, 3% of British), lapwing (c. 350 pairs), snipe (c. 160 pairs), curlew (c. 120 pairs), redshank (c. 120 pairs), kingfisher (up to 10 pairs), redstart (>400 pairs, with probably up to 1100 pairs in favourable years), stonechat (up to 430 pairs) and firecrest. **Hen harriers** (c. 15 individuals, 2% of British) regularly winter at the site.

Conservation issues

There has been a great deal of loss and fragmentation of lowland heathland during the present century. Sympathetic habitat management is required in order to maintain the wildlife interest of the remaining areas.

Threats to the Forest include a decline in commoning, disturbance through recreation, and development at the periphery of the Forest leading to increased pressure from recreation.

Conservation problems arise from the proximity of large urban areas and the consequential demands on the Forest for recreation and infrastructure (for example, roads, pipelines, reservoirs). Mechanisms exist to deflect proposals that might physically destroy parts of the area but recreational demands are less easily controllable and are posing acute problems. In the longer term the main problem confronting the area may be the collapse of the commoning system under which the Forest is grazed by commoners' livestock. The commoners' economy is threatened by soaring land prices that limit the establishment of successor holdings from which rights may be exercised, and poor market prices for Forest cattle and ponies.

Further reading

Tubbs, C R 1986 *The New Forest*. Collins (New Naturalist), London.

Westerhoff, D V 1989 Results of the 1988 survey of Dartford Warbler *Sylvia undata* in the New Forest. *Hampshire Bird Report* 1988: 77.

Westerhoff, D V and Tubbs, C R 1991 Dartford Warblers *Sylvia undata*, their Habitat and Conservation in the New Forest, Hampshire, England, in 1988. *Biol Conserv.* 56: 89–100.

Portsmouth Harbour

SPA/Ram Code	IBA Europe number
1105A	N/A

County/Region	District(s)	OS sheet(s)	Grid Reference(s)	Maps 18, 19
Hampshire	Fareham, Gosport, Portsmouth	196	SU 620035	

Area (ha)	NNR	SPA		Ramsar	
1121	No	Designated	N	Designated	N
		Candidate	Y	Candidate	N

A large estuary supporting important numbers of wintering wildfowl and waders.

Site Description

Portsmouth Harbour comprises a large industrialised estuary and includes one of the four largest expanses of mudflats and tidal creeks on the south coast of Britain. The Wallington River flows into the north-west corner of the estuary and gives rise to Fareham Creek, the most notable channel within the estuary. The harbour has only a narrow connection to the sea via the Solent, and receives comparatively little freshwater, thus giving it an unusual hydrology.

The mudflats support large beds of narrow-leaved and dwarf eelgrass, extensive green algae, predominantly *Enteromorpha* species, and sea lettuce. An area of cord-grass saltmarsh (170 ha) is now mostly degraded. Sea-purslane locally dominates saltmarsh at higher levels. There is a sea couch zone above high water mark.

Birds

The estuary supports internationally important numbers of wintering dark-bellied brent goose, and nationally important numbers of grey plover, dunlin and black-tailed godwit.

In the five-winter period 1985/86 to 1989/90, the average peak counts were 2080 **dark-bellied brent geese** (1% of the world total, 2% of British), 240 **grey plover** (1% of British), 7400 **dunlin** (2% of British) and 140 **black-tailed godwit** (3% of British).

Notable also are wintering teal, shoveler, red-breasted merganser, ringed plover and curlew.

Conservation issues

Waterfowl that winter on estuaries are vulnerable to land-claim and other developments that would disturb or damage the existing ecology of these sites. Other human influences such as recreational disturbance, commercial exploitation of shellfish and worms, and oil and industrial pollution, are also potentially damaging to the conservation interest of estuaries.

Southampton Water and Solent Marshes

SPA/Ram Code	IBA Europe number
1106A	194

County/Region	District(s)	OS sheet(s)	Grid Reference(s)	Map 18
Hampshire	Eastleigh, Fareham, Gosport, New Forest Southampton	196	SZ 4505	
Isle of Wight	Medina, South Wight			

Area (ha)	NNR	SPA		Ramsar	
1000-9999	Part	Designated	N	Designated	N
		Candidate	Y	Candidate	Y

A series of estuaries with extensive mudflats and associated saltmarshes, attracting large numbers of wintering waterfowl and breeding gulls and terns.

Site description

The area is intended to include the remaining intertidal areas of Southampton Water and the Solent. The mudflats support beds of *Enteromorpha* algae and eelgrass along with a rich invertebrate fauna that forms the food resource for the estuarine birds. Ledges of limestone which run out from the Isle of Wight shore support a different range of algae and marine invertebrates.

The saltmarsh on the Hampshire shore includes large areas dominated by cord-grass, but this is less evident on the Isle of Wight. The more species-rich mixed saltmarshes are dominated by common saltmarsh-grass, sea-purslane and common sea-lavender, and there are many associated species. At the upper limit of the saltings, there is often a belt of sea couch, with sea club-rush, sea aster and other species.

Along the west Solent there are several shingle spits, supporting a characteristic shingle beach flora. These include Hurst Spit, Needs Ore Point and Calshot Spit on the mainland and a spit at Newtown Bay on the Isle of Wight. Less common species found on the spits include sea-heath and sea spurge.

Just inland of the sea walls between Keyhaven and Lymington is a series of brackish lagoons, which were originally part of the local salt works.

A range of grassland types lie inshore of the intertidal zone. Around the arms of the Newtown estuary, there are unimproved neutral and calcareous grasslands. The former contain many species, including adder's-tongue, heath dog-violet and green-winged orchid, indicative of the long period since they were cultivated. Species rich limestone grassland, rough grassland and reed-dominated freshwater marshes also occur. The grasslands support Roesel's bush-cricket, well away from its Thames estuary stronghold.

Several woodlands adjoin the marshland on the Isle of Wight. They are mainly dominated by oak and ash, often with much field maple and hazel. Butterflies in these woods include white admiral and silver-washed fritillary.

Birds

The area supports internationally important numbers of wintering dark-bellied brent goose and nationally important numbers of wintering teal, ringed plover, grey plover, dunlin, ruff, black-tailed godwit and greenshank, and breeding black-headed gull, Sandwich tern, common tern and little tern.

In the five-winter period 1985/86 to 1989/90 the average peak counts were 2200 **dark-bellied brent geese** (1% of the world total, 2% of British), 1000+ **teal** (1% of British), 360 **ringed plover** (1.5% of British), 430 **grey plover** (2% of British), 5350 **dunlin** (1% of British), 26 ruff, 580 **black-tailed godwit** (12% of British) and 9 greenshank. Notable also are wintering curlew, redshank and turnstone.

Recent estimates for breeding species include **black-headed gull** (7250 pairs, 3% of British), **Sandwich tern** (175 pairs in 1990, 1% of British), **common tern** (316 pairs in 1990, 3% of British) and **little tern** (35 pairs in 1990, 1.5% of British).

Conservation issues

Waterfowl that winter on estuaries are vulnerable to land-claim and other developments that would disturb or damage the existing ecology of these sites. Other human influences such as recreational disturbance, commercial exploitation of shellfish and worms, and oil and industrial pollution, are also potentially damaging to the conservation interest of estuaries.

The main threats are increased recreational disturbance and land-claim for built development and marinas. Oil exploration and exploitation also pose a potential threat, similar to that in Poole Harbour (Site 1011A).

Local authority planning and other policies are highly protective, but the shore is nevertheless subject to planning applications for recreational and commercial development. The lower shore is also subject to damage by clam dredging. Recreational use is extensive and disturbance to wildfowl rafts and wader roosts at high water by jet-skis, board sailors and other craft is common. The gull and tern colonies require wardening against disturbance and trampling.

Further reading

Aspinall, S and Tasker, M L 1990 *Coastal birds of east Dorset.* Nature Conservancy Council, Peterborough.

Kirby, J S and Tubbs, C R 1989 Wader populations in the Solent 1970/71 to 1987/88. *Hampshire Bird Report* 1988: 83–104.

Avon Valley

SPA/Ram Code	IBA Europe number
1109A	192

County/Region	District(s)	OS sheet(s)	Grid Reference(s)	Maps 16, 18
Dorset	Christchurch, East Dorset	195	SZ 1499	
Hampshire	New Forest			
Wiltshire	Salisbury			

Area (ha)	NNR	SPA		Ramsar	
1-999	No	Designated	N	Designated	N
		Candidate	Y	Candidate	Y

Meadows, fen and carr in the flood plain of the River Avon, attracting a wide range of breeding and wintering wetland birds.

Site description

The area includes about 20 km of the Avon valley, the flood plain of which contains a variety of habitats. The river catchment is composed largely of chalk, but is supplemented by acid streams from the New Forest heaths. As a result, there is a particularly diverse aquatic flora, and the high water quality supports many species of invertebrates and fish. The river has both slow-flowing sections with meanders and backwaters, and faster flowing parts over gravels, and this variety adds to species diversity. Sixty-six aquatic plant species occur in the river and associated channels, including some which are nationally scarce such as mudwort. The mollusc fauna is well developed in chalky sections. Among the dragonflies is the nationally rare scarce chaser. The Avon is a famous fishing river, and species present include salmon.

The hay meadows and pastures that border the river are typically subject to low fertiliser and herbicide use, and have retained a diverse flora. In some areas, the fields still flood regularly.

Woodlands are scattered throughout the valley, notable amongst which, in wetter areas, is alder and willow carr, the latter originally derived from withy beds. Several species of willow occur within this carr woodland. On drier sandy soils, there is oak and birch woodland.

Birds

The area supports internationally important numbers of wintering Bewick's swan and gadwall, and nationally important numbers of wintering European white-fronted goose.

In the five-winter period 1985/86 to 1989/90 the average peak counts were 180 **Bewick's swans** (1% of NW European, 2.5% of British), 200 European **white-fronted geese** (3% of British) and 190 **gadwall** (1.5% of NW European, 3% of British). Notable also are wintering mute swan, wigeon, shoveler, pochard and smew.

The valley as a whole (Christchurch-Salisbury) supports a nationally important assemblage of breeding bird species typical of lowland wet meadow habitats. These include (1990 figures) lapwing (251 pairs), snipe (46 pairs), redshank (212 pairs) and **Cetti's warbler** (c. 40 pairs, 21% of British).

Conservation issues

There have been massive losses of lowland wet grassland habitat in Britain in recent decades as a result of drainage and agricultural intensification. Remaining areas need strong protection from such damage.

The main issues are agricultural changes, gravel extraction, water management and disturbance through recreational activities. There is some evidence that the valley flood plain has become drier since the 1950s, probably as a result of piecemeal drainage, and that the numbers of breeding birds associated with damp meadows have consequently declined. Yellow wagtails, for example, common in the 1960s, have declined to near extinction in the 1980s. Although numbers of breeding waders remain relatively high, their distribution in the valley is patchy. The main direct impact has probably been an increase in silage making, which destroys nests and young birds, and a decline in damp places where wader chicks can feed. These problems are being addressed by the EN, National Rivers Authority, RSPB and County Naturalists' Trusts.

Further reading

RSPB and WWA 1979 Avon and Stour Bird Survey.

Porton Down

	SPA/Ram Code	IBA Europe number
	1110A	190

County/Region	District(s)	OS sheet(s)	Grid Reference(s)	Maps 16, 18
Hampshire	Test Valley	184	SU 2436	
Wiltshire	Salisbury			

Area (ha)	NNR	SPA		Ramsar	
1000-9999	No	Designated N		Designated N	
		Candidate Y		Candidate N	

Chalk grassland with scrub and woodland, important for downland breeding birds, especially stone-curlew.

Site description

Porton Down, to the north-east of Salisbury, is part of Salisbury Plain, one of the largest uninterrupted tracts of semi-natural chalk grassland in Britain. The undulating plateau and shallow valleys also support chalk heath, scrub and woodland.

Several different grassland types are present, including two that are uncommon in Britain; one of these is more or less restricted to Porton Down. The grasslands have been uncultivated for between 40 and 200 years, and are grazed by rabbits and roe deer; fluctuations in numbers of the former have had a marked effect on the vegetation. Undergrazed areas tend to be less species-rich, and scrub may become established, but overgrazing also can lead to sward deterioration. Many areas are rich in typical chalk grassland plants, including several nationally scarce species, such as early gentian, bastard-toadflax, field fleawort and dwarf sedge.

Scattered shrubs, trees and patches of scrub are found throughout much of the grassland. Of particular note is the large amount of juniper, more than in any other site in southern England. In one place, chalk heath with heather grows alongside the juniper.

The downland is of outstanding entomological interest. Several groups are particularly well represented, including spiders, moths and butterflies, which include the silver-spotted skipper, Adonis blue and Duke of Burgundy butterflies, and species of moth which are dependent on juniper.

Plantations of beech, sycamore and Scots pine are widely distributed, and there are some areas of semi-natural woodland dominated by oak, ash and yew. There is a rich fungal flora.

Birds

This site supports nationally important numbers of **stone-curlew**, with 19 pairs recorded in 1990 (13% of British). Notable also are breeding buzzard, hobby and long-eared owl.

The area is also important for wintering raptors, with good numbers of hen harrier, merlin and short-eared owl taking advantage of the high densities of small mammals.

Conservation issues

Management is essential in order to maintain favourable conditions for stone-curlews. The creation of nesting areas on adjoining areas of arable land, supported by the MOD, has benefited this species.

Further reading

Buxton, J 1981 *The Birds of Wiltshire.* Wiltshire Library and Museum Service, Trowbridge.

Windsor Forest and Great Park

SPA/Ram Code	IBA Europe number
1111A	191

County/Region	District(s)	OS sheet(s)	Grid Reference(s)	Maps 18, 19
Berkshire	Bracknell Forest, Windsor and Maidenhead	175	SU 9472	
Surrey	Runnymede			

Area (ha)	NNR	SPA		Ramsar	
1000-9999	No	Designated	N	Designated	N
		Candidate	Y	Candidate	N

Ancient semi-natural woodland, parkland, plantations, lakes and ponds supporting important populations of breeding and wintering woodland and water birds.

Site description

A wide range of woodland types is found within the site. There are large areas of open parkland with scattered ancient oaks and oak pollards. Some of these oak pollards are at least 500 years old, and in all probability are primary woodland. Mature stands of beech and hornbeam also occur. Younger stands of woodland, including mixed deciduous, mixed deciduous/conifer and coniferous plantations are included within the area.

Open water is found at Virginia Water, which has margins partially overhung with rhododendron, and at the secluded Great Meadow Pond, which is surrounded by sallow, common reed and lesser bulrush. Patches of species-rich damp acidic grassland are present at Snow Hill.

The older trees have much dead and decaying timber, which supports an outstanding fauna of specialist invertebrates, including very rare species, some of which are restricted within Britain to Windsor Forest. The true flies and beetles are especially notable with about 2000 species of beetle having been recorded here. There is also a very diverse fungal community of over 1000 species, including scarce and rare taxa.

Birds

The area supports nationally important numbers of breeding sparrowhawk, hobby and firecrest.

The area has the highest density of breeding sparrowhawks recorded in Britain. Other breeding species include **mandarin duck**, (with the area being the breeding centre of Britain's main population and vital in winter with up to 400 individuals recorded), **hobby** (up to 8 pairs, 1% of British), **firecrest** (up to 30 singing males, 30% of British) and hawfinch (up to 10 pairs, with over 100 individuals recorded in winter). The heronry in Windsor Great Park held 24-53 pairs 1980-88. Notable also are breeding barn owl, kingfisher, lesser spotted woodpecker, siskin and crossbill.

Wintering species include large numbers of siskins, redpolls and crossbills.

Conservation issues

The major issues centre on increasing public use and recreational activities, both formal and informal. Horse riding and orienteering can cause problems.

Woolmer Forest

SPA/Ram Code	IBA Europe number
1112A	195

County/Region	District(s)	OS sheet(s)	Grid Reference(s)	Maps 18, 19
Hampshire	East Hampshire	186	SU 7932	

Area (ha)	NNR	SPA		Ramsar	
1-999	No	Designated	N	Designated	N
		Candidate	Y	Candidate	N

Lowland heath, with specialist heathland birds including nightjar, woodlark and Dartford warbler.

Site description
Located in eastern Hampshire, these heaths are about 10 km west of Haslemere on the Folkestone Beds of the lower greensand. These acidic and infertile soils produce typical conditions for heathland development. Heather dominated dry heath is extensive, with much bell heather, dwarf gorse and *Cladonia* lichens, and patches of gorse. There has been some invasion by birch and Scots pine, and of oak on Broxhead Common. Locally, the dry heathland is mixed with areas of acidic grassland.

In areas where drainage is impeded, such as on Blackmoor, humid heath dominated by cross-leaved heath, heather and purple moor-grass occurs.

In the wettest areas, there are valley mires and boggy pools. These have abundant *Sphagnum* mosses, together with cottongrasses, white beak-sedge, bog asphodel, bog pondweed and sundews. Woolmer Pond may have originated through peat cutting in one of the mires. It is extremely nutrient-poor, which is unusual for a water body in southern England, and is in the process of becoming colonised by vegetation.

The fauna of the heaths includes several vertebrates which are strongly associated with lowland heaths, including smooth snake, sand lizard and natterjack toad. The rich invertebrate fauna at the site is noteworthy for water beetles and butterflies, including the silver-studded blue.

Birds
Breeding species include nightjar, **woodlark** (8 pairs 1988, 4% of British) and Dartford warbler.

Conservation issues
There has been a great deal of loss and fragmentation of lowland heathland during the present century. Sympathetic habitat management is required in order to maintain the wildlife interest of the remaining areas.

Large areas of heathland have survived on MOD landholdings and the main threat at this site is successional changes to habitat through tree invasion. Military training does give rise to periodic conflict with nature conservation. The use of the MOD heathland for orienteering poses a threat to breeding species such as woodlark and Dartford warbler.

Further reading
Clark, J M 1984 *Birds of the Hants/Surrey Border*. Hobby Books, Fleet.

Woodlark

The Swale

SPA/Ram Code	IBA Europe number
1201A	208

County/Region	District(s)	OS sheet(s)	Grid Reference(s)	Maps 19, 20
Kent	Canterbury, Swale	178	TR 000670	

Area (ha)	NNR	SPA	Ramsar
6568	Part	Designated Y Candidate N/A	Designated Y Candidate N/A

Intertidal mudflats, with saltmarshes and extensive grazing marshes, important for wintering waterfowl, and also with notable breeding bird populations.

Site description
The area includes the mudflats and saltmarshes bordering the Swale, which separates the Isle of Sheppey from the Kent mainland, together with the extensive brackish and freshwater grazing marshes on both sides of the channel.

The intertidal flats are extensive, especially towards the east, and support a dense invertebrate fauna. These invertebrates, along with beds of algae and eelgrass, are important as food sources for waterfowl. Locally there are large mussel beds formed on harder areas of substrate.

There is a wide range of saltmarsh types dominated by common saltmarsh-grass and sea-purslane. Some nationally scarce plants such as small cord-grass and golden-samphire are present. The saltings are of entomological interest, for example as habitat for the ground lackey moth. In several places shell and sand beaches have formed. The saltmarshes and beaches are important roosting and nesting areas for birds.

The grazing marshes are the largest remaining in Kent, although they are much reduced compared with their former extent. They exhibit much variety both in the salinity of the dykes, which ranges from fresh to strongly brackish, and in the topography of the fields, where dry seawalls and counterwalls contrast with damp runnels and depressions. Both species-rich and species-poor grasslands are found here, with grazing mainly by sheep and cattle. A distinctive brackish dyke flora occurs in the dykes which intersect the grazing marshes. Smaller areas of other habitats include water-filled clay pits, scrub and woodland.

Birds
The area supports internationally important numbers of 5 species of wintering waterfowl, and nationally important numbers of 12 species of wintering waterfowl and five breeding species.

The site is a wetland of international importance by virtue of regularly supporting over 20,000 waterfowl. In the five-year period 1984/85 to 1988/89 the average peak count was 61,920 birds, comprising 22,905 wildfowl and 39,015 waders. Totals for individual species include 180 **great crested grebes** (2% of British), 1400 European **white-fronted** geese (23% of British), 1600 **dark-bellied brent geese** (2% of British), 1600 **shelduck** (2% of British), 10,500 **wigeon** (1% of NW European, 4% of British), 80 **gadwall** (1% of British), 2000 **teal** (2% of British), 400 **pintail** (2% of British), 410 **shoveler** (1% of NW European, 4% of British), 4800 **oystercatcher** (2% of British), 290 **ringed plover** (1% of British), 2200 **grey plover** (1% of EAF, 10% of British), 2900 **knot** (1% of British), 15,600 **dunlin** (1% of EAF, 4% of British), 210 **black-tailed godwit** (4% of British), 1900 **curlew** (2% of British) and 3100 **redshank** (3% of EAF, 4% of British).

Notable also are wintering golden plover, hen harrier, merlin and short-eared owl. During the autumn passage period the site supports internationally or nationally important numbers of oystercatcher, ringed plover, grey plover, dunlin, black-tailed godwit, curlew, spotted redshank, redshank, greenshank and Lapland bunting.

The Swale together with the Thames Estuary and Marshes (SPA/Ram 1202A) and the Medway Estuary and Marshes (SPA/Ram 1203A) is of international importance for the breeding bird assemblage of the grazing marshes. Breeding bird species recorded in recent years include **shoveler** (40 pairs, 3% of British), **pochard** (15 pairs, 4% of British), **avocet** (31 pairs, 8% of British), **black-headed gull** (4650 pairs, 2% of British) and **little tern** (24 pairs, 1% of British). Notable also are breeding gadwall, teal, oystercatcher, lapwing, snipe, redshank and common tern.

Conservation issues

Waterfowl that winter on estuaries are vulnerable to land-claim and other developments that would disturb or damage the existing ecology of these sites. Other human influences such as recreational disturbance, commercial exploitation of shellfish and worms, and oil and industrial pollution, are also potentially damaging to the conservation interest of estuaries.

Since 1930, 64% of the grazing marshes in the Greater Thames have been lost due to agricultural change and development.

The main threats to this site are habitat loss due to industrial development, roads and other infrastructure, marinas, recreational activities, land drainage and agricultural intensification.

Further reading

Gilham, E H and Holmes, R C 1950 *Birds of the North Kent Marshes*. Collins, London.
Harrison, J G and Grant, P 1976 *The Thames Transformed*. Deutsch, London.

Thames Estuary and Marshes

SPA/Ram Code	IBA Europe number
1202A	206

County/Region	District(s)	OS sheet(s)	Grid Reference(s)	Maps 19, 20
Essex	Thurrock	178	TQ 7678	
Kent	Gravesham,			
	Rochester-			
	upon-Medway			

Area (ha)	NNR	SPA		Ramsar	
1000-9999	Part	Designated	N	Designated	N
		Candidate	Y	Candidate	Y

Extensive grazing marshes with adjoining saltmarshes and mudflats, plus flooded clay and chalk pits, and woodland, attracting a wide range of estuarine and wetland birds, especially wintering waders.

Site description

These marshes extend for about 15 km along the coast on the south side of the Thames estuary, and also include marshes, intertidal areas and high tide roosts to the north of the estuary, for example, at Mucking Flats and West Thurrock Ash Lagoons, Essex.

To the south of the river, much of the area is brackish grazing marsh, although some of this has been converted to arable use. At Cliffe, there are flooded clay and chalk pits, some of which have been infilled with dredgings. Outside the sea wall, there is a small amount of saltmarsh, and broad intertidal flats.

The marsh grasslands are mainly dominated by mixed grasses including creeping bent, meadow barley, crested dog's-tail and perennial rye-grass.

The dykes and their margins support a diverse flora and fauna. Freshwater dykes are dominated by common reed, branched bur-reed and duckweeds, with sea club-rush, soft hornwort and fennel pondweed present in brackish dykes. Invertebrates within the site include noteworthy water beetles and flies. The scarce emerald damselfly is also present at this site.

At Northward Hill, woodland of oak, elm and sycamore, with large areas of hawthorn and blackthorn scrub and regenerating elm supports a notable heronry. White-letter hairstreak butterfly also occurs here.

Birds

The area supports internationally important numbers of wintering oystercatcher, ringed plover, grey plover, knot, dunlin, bar-tailed godwit, curlew, redshank and turnstone, and nationally important numbers of wintering European white-fronted goose, gadwall, teal, shoveler, black-tailed godwit and Lapland bunting.

The site is a wetland of international importance by virtue of regularly supporting over 20,000 waterfowl. In the five-winter period 1985/86 to 1989/90 the average peak was

58,900 birds, comprising 29,535 wildfowl and 29,365 waders. Counts for individual species were 250+ European **white-fronted geese** (4% of British), 70 **gadwall** (1% of British), 1200+ **teal** (1% of British), 120 **shoveler** (1% of British), 13,700 **oyster-catcher** (1.5% of EAF, 5% of British), 30 **avocets** (3% of British), 770 **ringed plover** (2% of EAF, 3% of British), 5100 **grey plover** (3% of EAF, 24% of British), 24,000 **knot** (7% of EAF, 11% of British), 24,300 **dunlin** (2% of EAF, 6% of British), 105 **black-tailed godwit** (2% of British), 3400 **bar-tailed godwit** (3% of EAF, 6% of British), 3700 **curlew** (1% of EAF, 4% of British), 3650 **redshank** (3% of EAF, 5% of British) and 730 **turnstone** (1% of EAF, 2% of British).

Notable also are wintering shelduck, pintail, hen harrier, merlin, short-eared owl and wintering/passage ruff, spotted redshank, greenshank and green sandpiper.

The Thames Estuary and Marshes together with The Swale (SPA/Ram 1201A) and the Medway Estuary and Marshes (SPA/Ram 1203A) are of international importance for the breeding bird assemblage of the grazing marshes. Breeding species present include shelduck, teal, mallard, garganey, shoveler, pochard, oystercatcher, avocet, ringed plover, lapwing, snipe, redshank and common tern (40-50 pairs). There is a large heronry at Northward Hill (174 nests in 1990, 1% of British).

Conservation issues
Waterfowl that winter on estuaries are vulnerable to land-claim and other developments that would disturb or damage the existing ecology of these sites. Other human influences such as recreational disturbance, commercial exploitation of shellfish and worms, and oil and industrial pollution, are also potentially damaging to the conservation interest of estuaries.

Since 1930, 64% of the grazing marshes in the Greater Thames have been lost due to agricultural change and development.

Existing threats to the grazing marshes within this area include major road proposals, disposal of dredgings, gravel extraction, recreation, land drainage and agricultural intensification.

Further reading
Cox, C J and Flegg, J J M 1967 The Birds of TQ77. *Kent Bird Report* 16: 76-82.
Gilham, E H and Holmes, R C 1950 *Birds of the North Kent Marshes*. Collins, London.
Harrison, J G and Grant, P 1976 *The Thames Transformed*. Deutsch, London.
Hudson, M J (1967). The Breeding Wildfowl of the North Kent Marshes 1961-64. *Kent Bird Report* 15: 85-98.

Medway Estuary and Marshes

SPA/Ram Code	IBA Europe number
1203A	207

County/Region	District(s)	OS sheet(s)	Grid Reference(s)	Maps 19, 20
Kent	Gillingham, Rochester-upon-Medway, Swale	178	TQ 610720	

Area (ha)	NNR	SPA		Ramsar	
5633	Part	Designated	N	Designated	N
		Candidate	Y	Candidate	Y

An estuary with extensive intertidal flats, saltmarshes and grazing marsh, holding important numbers of waterfowl on passage and in winter.

Site description

The Medway estuary forms a single tidal system with the Swale and joins the Thames estuary between the Isle of Grain and Sheerness. It has a complex arrangement of tidal channels, which drain around large islands of saltmarsh and peninsulas of grazing marsh.

The mudflats are rich in invertebrates, and also support extensive beds of *Enteromorpha* algae and some eelgrass. The pioneer saltmarsh zone is dominated by common cord-grass or by glassworts. Although there are large areas of accreting saltings, other areas are eroding and many saltmarshes are bounded by cliffs of up to 2 m. The better established marshes are dominated by common saltmarsh-grass, sea-purslane and common sea-lavender, with many other plant species also present The saltings have a diverse invertebrate fauna.

Small shell beaches are found throughout the estuary, with a larger one at Yantlet Creek on the Thames shore. The latter is well vegetated with a distinctive flora which includes sand couch, sea-holly, sea sandwort, sea rocket and prickly saltwort.

Grazing marshes are present inside the sea walls around the estuary, with the largest areas between Allhallows and Grain on the north side, and at Chetney Marshes to the south. The sheep-, cattle- and horse-grazed pastures separated by dykes and fleets are similar to those elsewhere in north Kent. These brackish marshes have a distinctive flora that includes species of restricted distribution both in the grassland and in the aquatic habitats. The area is also rich in invertebrates associated with the wetlands. Bugs, beetles and flies are especially well represented, with many uncommon species being recorded.

Birds

The area supports internationally important numbers of wintering dark-bellied brent goose, shelduck, pintail, ringed plover, grey plover, dunlin, redshank and turnstone, and nationally important numbers of wintering great crested grebe, wigeon, shoveler, black-tailed godwit, curlew and Lapland bunting and breeding avocet.

The site is a wetland of international importance by virtue of regularly supporting over 20,000 waterfowl. In the five-winter period 1985/86 to 1989/90 the average peak was 52,800 birds, comprising 36,400 waders and 16,400 wildfowl. Totals for individual species include 235 **great crested grebes** (3% of British), 2600 **dark-bellied brent geese** (1.5% of the world total, 3% of British), 4500 **shelduck** (2% of NW European, 6% of British), 3600 **wigeon** (1% of British), 830 **pintail** (1% of NW European, 3% of British), 135 **shoveler** (1.5% of British), 1000 **ringed plover** (2% of EAF, 4% of British), 6200 **grey plover** (4% of EAF, 29% of British), 21,200 **dunlin** (1.5% of EAF, 5% of British), 450 **black-tailed godwit** (9% of British), 1980 **curlew** (2% of British), 5100 **redshank** (5% of EAF, 7% of British) and 900 **turnstone** (1% of EAF, 2% of British).

Notable also are wintering goldeneye, oystercatcher, knot, hen harrier, merlin, short-eared owl and passage ruff, spotted redshank and greenshank.

The Medway Estuary and Marshes together with The Swale (SPA/Ram 1201A) and the Thames Estuary and Marshes (SPA/Ram 1202A) is of international importance for the breeding bird assemblage of the grazing marshes. Breeding birds include 34 pairs of **avocets** (9% of British) and 30 pairs of **little terns** (1% of British). Notable also are breeding shelduck, oystercatcher, ringed plover, redshank, black-headed gull and common tern.

Conservation issues

Waterfowl that winter on estuaries are vulnerable to land-claim and other developments that would disturb or damage the existing ecology of these sites. Other human influences such as recreational disturbance, commercial exploitation of shellfish and worms, and oil and industrial pollution, are also potentially damaging to the conservation interest of estuaries.

Since 1930, 64% of the grazing marshes in the Greater Thames have been lost due to agricultural change and development. The main current threats to this site are port expansion, power generation, landfill, road and other infrastructure developments, marinas, recreational activities and agricultural intensification.

Further reading

Gilham, E H and Holmes, R C 1950 *Birds of the North Kent Marshes*. Collins, London.
Gilham, E H (ed.) 1955 Report on breeding birds of the Medway Islands. Kent Ornithological Society.
Harrison, J G and Grant, P 1976 *The Thames Transformed*. Deutsch, London.
Harrison, J G, Humphries, J N and Graves, G 1972 *Breeding Birds of the Medway Estuary*. Kent Ornithological Society/Wildfowl Association of Great Britain and Ireland, Chester.

Pagham Harbour

SPA/Ram Code	IBA Europe number
1204A	202

County/Region	District(s)	OS sheet(s)	Grid Reference(s)	Maps 18, 19
West Sussex	Arun, Chichester	197	SZ 875970	

Area (ha)	NNR	SPA	Ramsar
616	No	Designated Y Candidate N/A	Designated Y Candidate N/A

An estuarine basin, with intertidal mudflats, saltmarsh, shingle, reedbeds and grazing marsh, attracting large numbers of wintering waterfowl.

Site description

Once subject to land-claim for agriculture, Pagham Harbour was flooded again early in the 20th century, and now consists of a central area of mudflats and saltmarsh, surrounded by brackish marsh and pasture. The harbour has a narrow opening to the sea, flanked by shingle beaches.

The intertidal mudflats are rich in invertebrates and algae, and provide important feeding areas for birds. The lower saltmarsh is dominated by common cord-grass but also includes patches of glasswort. At higher levels, sea-purslane is abundant, often with other species such as sea aster, common sea-lavender and greater sea-spurrey.

Behind the sea walls, there are damp unimproved and improved pastures, which attract breeding and wintering birds. Ditches and other low-lying areas are dominated by common reed, with some fairly extensive swamps.

Shingle beaches have in places developed a distinctive flora, with more diverse grass swards in sheltered areas, which include species such as early forget-me-not and biting stonecrop. A brackish lagoon is present behind the beach at Pagham.

There are small amounts of woodland and hawthorn scrub around the harbour. The woodland, some of which is ancient, is mainly of oak and willow, and has a diverse ground flora.

Invertebrates include a number of scarce coastal moth species.

Birds

The area supports internationally important numbers of wintering dark-bellied brent goose, and nationally important numbers of wintering pintail, grey plover and black-tailed godwit.

In the five-winter period 1985/86 to 1989/90 the average peak counts were 2740 **dark-bellied brent geese** (2% of the world total, 3% of British), 320 **pintail** (1% of British), 920 **grey plover** (4% of British), 210 **black-tailed godwit** (4% of British) and 35 ruff.

Notable also are wintering shelduck, wigeon, ringed plover, dunlin, curlew, redshank and turnstone.

Notable also are breeding little tern and passage spotted redshank and greenshank.

Conservation issues

Waterfowl that winter on estuaries are vulnerable to land-claim and other developments that would disturb or damage the existing ecology of these sites. Other human influences such as recreational disturbance, commercial exploitation of shellfish and worms, and oil and industrial pollution, are also potentially damaging to the conservation interest of estuaries.

Breeding terns are vulnerable to disturbance by uncontrolled recreational activities.

Thanet Coast

SPA/Ram Code	IBA Europe number
1207A	209

County/Region	District(s)	OS sheet(s)	Grid Reference(s)	Map 20
Kent	Canterbury, Dover, Thanet	179	TR360630	

Area (ha)	NNR	SPA		Ramsar	
2484	No	Designated	N	Designated	N
		Candidate	Y	Candidate	Y

Varied coastal habitats, especially important for wintering waders.

Site description

This area includes a wide range of habitats, with bird interest centred on the rocky coastline around Thanet. This site is regionally important for rocky shore habitats which are scarce along the south-east coast. These consist of a wave-cut chalk platform backed by chalk cliffs generally no more than 20 m high. Exposed chalk platforms, with abundant invertebrate and algal cover alternate with sandy beaches. This provides an important food source for waders. The natural structure of the shore has been affected by the construction of sea walls and the grading of cliffs, but some unmodified sections remain. A rich cliff and shore flora is found here. Nationally rare or scarce plants include hoary stock, wild cabbage and sea-heath.

Along the north coast, west of Thanet, the chalk gives way to a shingle beach before reaching a section where cliffs of London Clay and Thanet Sand back a muddy shore. The shingle beach is well vegetated in a few places and supports a characteristic flora. A brackish lagoon is present between the sea wall and the shingle beach. The sand and clay cliffs are poorly vegetated except at Bishopstone Glen, where there is scrub of hawthorn, blackthorn, elm and other species.

South of Thanet lies the estuary of the River Stour at Pegwell Bay. The mud and sand flats have abundant invertebrate life, and are fringed by saltmarshes.

Behind the dunes lies a broad area of marshes, including some grassland, but with many areas now converted to arable use. Fen communities and small areas of alder carr are present in the Hacklinge area.

Birds

The area supports internationally important numbers of wintering turnstone, and nationally important numbers of wintering ringed plover, golden plover, grey plover, sanderling and Lapland bunting, and breeding little tern.

In the five-winter period 1985/86 to 1989/90 the average peak counts were 370 **ringed plover** (2% of British), 1980 **golden plover** (1% of British), 530 **grey plover** (2% of British), 700 **sanderling** (5% of British), 1300 **turnstone** (2% of EAF, 3% of British), and 40 **Lapland buntings** (about 7% of British).

The site is notable for wintering purple sandpiper. In addition, large numbers of migratory passerine birds pass through the site during the spring and autumn passage periods.

In summer the area supports about 23 pairs of breeding **little terns** (1% of British).

Conservation issues

Birds that depend on these coastal habitats are vulnerable to land–claim, oil pollution and human disturbance.

Pevensey Levels

SPA/Ram Code	IBA Europe number
1208A	203

County/Region	District(s)	OS sheet(s)	Grid Reference(s)	Maps 19, 20
East Sussex	Rother, Wealden	199	TQ 6507	

Area (ha)	NNR	SPA		Ramsar	
1000-9999	Part	Designated	N	Designated	N
		Candidate	Y	Candidate	Y

An extensive area of grazing marsh, attracting important numbers of breeding and wintering waterfowl.

Site description

The Pevensey Levels are a large area of low-lying grazing marsh to the north-east of Eastbourne. Originally an area of intertidal mudflats, the Levels developed first to saltmarsh and then to freshwater marsh as a result of land-claim. The deposition of a shingle beach along the present coastline aided this process, and it now protects the Levels from sea water inundation. The maintenance of ditches helps to create a range of ditch types allowing a diverse floral and invertebrate community to become established. Several nationally scarce aquatic plant species are present, notably pondweed species. The main channels which carry water to the sea are less species-rich.

Most fields are of improved rye-grass leys with some creeping bent. A small area of shingle and intertidal mud and sand is included within the site.

The Pevensey Levels are of national importance for molluscs and aquatic beetles, including the rare great silver water beetle, Britain's largest water beetle. Over 15 species of dragonfly have been recorded from the Pevensey Levels including the nationally scarce hairy dragonfly and the variable damselfly.

Birds

The site supports an important assemblage of breeding bird species typical of lowland wet grassland. These include mute swan, mallard, lapwing, snipe, redshank, yellow wagtail, sedge warbler, reed warbler and reed bunting.

In winter the area is notable for supporting large numbers of lapwing and snipe.

Conservation issues

There have been massive losses of lowland wet grassland habitat in Britain in recent decades as a result of drainage and agricultural intensification. Remaining areas need strong protection from such damage. Much of the ornithological interest of the Pevensey Levels has been damaged in recent years due to increased drainage. Threats include further conversion to arable, road improvements, and lack of traditional management.

Further reading

The Sussex Ornithological Society. Sussex Bird Report.

Hitchings, S P 1987 The ornithological status of Pevensey Levels. *Sussex Bird Report* 40: 71–80.

Dungeness to Pett Levels

SPA/Ram Code	IBA Europe number
1209A	204

County/Region	District(s)	OS sheet(s)	Grid Reference(s)	Maps 19, 20
East Sussex	Rother	189, 199	TR 050180	
Kent	Shepway			

Area (ha)	NNR	SPA		Ramsar	
7838	No	Designated	N	Designated	N
		Candidate	Y	Candidate	Y

Extensive shingle beaches and grazing marshes, important for breeding and wintering waterfowl and breeding terns.

Site description

The area includes two shingle beaches, at Dungeness and Rye Harbour, which have a common origin, and the grazing marshes and arable land lying behind them. Also included are the Royal Military Canal, the Colonel Body Memorial Lakes on the Pett Level grazing marshes, the Pannel Valley wetlands and saltmarshes at the mouth of the River Rother. The Dungeness peninsula is a classic example of a large cuspate shingle foreland, of international geomorphological interest.

The distinct beach systems at Dungeness with variations in pebble size, age and exposure to maritime influence has allowed highly unusual vegetation types to develop. Many plant and animal species of restricted distribution occur here. The shingle system at Rye Harbour has similarities to that at Dungeness, though it is far less extensive.

Many uncommon species are found associated with the shingle ridge habitats. Invertebrates include scarce and rare species, with moths, true flies, bees, wasps, beetles and spiders especially well represented. Several invertebrates breeding nowhere else in Britain occur here, including the beetle *Omophron limbatum*, the Sussex emerald moth and a subspecies of the grass eggar which occurs nowhere else in the world. The moth *Coleophora otitae* is also restricted to Dungeness.

Natural wetlands within the Dungeness beach systems include a succession from species-rich sedge fen, through swamp to sallow carr at the Open Pits, although much of the fen has been lost in recent years.

Artificial lakes created through gravel extraction are important for birds, but, except at the marshland edge where nutrient levels are higher, have developed limited vegetation. Medicinal leeches have been recorded at Dungeness, Walland Marsh and Rye Harbour, with the largest known British population occurring on the former site.

Grazing marshes are found at Walland Marsh and at Pett Levels. The pastures are grazed mainly by sheep, and the dykes that separate them are of botanical and entomological importance. In places dense beds of common reed, or, in brackish conditions, sea club-rush occur.

Birds

The area supports internationally important numbers of wintering Bewick's swan, and nationally important numbers of breeding Sandwich tern, common tern and little tern, and wintering shoveler, pochard and sanderling.

Counts of wintering birds in recent years include 175 **Bewick's swans** (1% of NW European), 300 **shoveler** (3% of British), 570 **pochard** (1% of British), 26 smew and 285 **sanderling** (2% of British).

Counts of breeding species are **garganey** (2-6 pairs, min. 4% of British), **shoveler** (10-15 pairs, 1% of British), **Sandwich tern** (265 pairs in 1990, 2% of British), **common tern** (440 pairs in 1990, 3.5% of British) and **little tern** (40 pairs in 1990, 2% of British). Notable also are breeding lapwing, redshank and black-headed gulls.

Conservation issues

Birds that use this site are vulnerable to water management, recreation pressures and vehicle disturbance.

Threats to the site include land and water-based recreation, further mineral extraction, water abstraction, proposals for airport expansion and developments at Rye Harbour. There has been a 54% loss of wet grassland in Romney Marsh since 1930. The extension of Dungeness Nuclear Power Station is a potential threat.

Further reading

Ferry, B W and Waters, S J P (eds.) 1985 *Dungeness Ecology and Conservation*. Nature Conservancy Council, Focus on Nature Conservation series no. 12.

Ferry, B W, Waters, S J P and Jury, S L (eds.) 1989 Dungeness – The Ecology of a Shingle Beach. *Botanical Journal of the Linnean Society* 101 (1).

Ferry, B W, Lodge, N and Waters, S J P 1990 *Dungeness: a vegetation survey of a shingle beach*. Nature Conservancy Council, Research and survey in Nature Conservation series no. 26.

Lea Valley

SPA/Ram Code	IBA Europe number
1211A	197

County/Region	District(s)	OS sheet(s)	Grid Reference(s)	Map 19
Essex	Epping Forest	177	TQ 3795	
Greater London	Enfield, Hackney, Haringey, Waltham Forest			
Hertfordshire	East Hertfordshire, Broxbourne			

Area (ha)	NNR	SPA		Ramsar	
606	No	Designated	N	Designated	N
		Candidate	Y	Candidate	N

A complex of reservoirs, river valley and associated wetlands holding large numbers of moulting and wintering wildfowl, and breeding birds.

Site description

The series of wetlands and reservoirs along the River Lea, to the east of London, occupies about 10 km of the valley. The Walthamstow group was constructed during the 19th century, and is comparatively small, with sloping earth banks and scattered wooded islands. To the north, the more recently built Chingford reservoirs, King George's and William Girling, are larger, and have no islands, but are shallower than most of the large London reservoirs.

Included within the area are parts of the River Lea flood relief channel, and the Coppermill Stream. The aquatic and marginal flora of the reservoirs and streams is fairly rich, especially in the case of the Walthamstow reservoirs. Species include marsh-marigold, common club-rush, a large stand of lesser reedmace, and the hybrid sedge *Carex x subgracilis*.

Waltham Abbey is an area of alder woodland on damp alluvial soils overlying fluvio-glacial gravel in the valley of the River Lee. The woodland was planted in about 1700 and was coppiced to produce charcoal for gunpowder manufacture. Planting ceased around 1914-18 and the present canopy has largely regenerated from coppice stools. The trees support a large heronry.

The Rye Meads meadows are the last substantial remnants of ancient flood meadows on the rich alluvial soils of the Lea Valley. The site supports one of the largest areas of tall fen vegetation in Hertfordshire. This habitat has been substantially reduced in extent, both locally and nationally, by drainage and agricultural intensification. Habitats include tall mixed fen, marshy grassland, willow carr and open water lagoons.

Birds

The area supports nationally important numbers of wintering great crested grebe, gadwall, shoveler, pochard, tufted duck, goosander and coot, and of breeding grey heron.

In winter, nationally important populations of the following migratory waterfowl occur: 140 **great crested grebes** (1% of British), 95 **gadwall** (2% of British), 310 **shoveler** (3% of British), 560 **pochard** (1% of British), 1800 **tufted duck** (3% of British), 50 **goosander** (1% of British) and 1000 **coot** (1% of British). Notable also are wintering black-necked grebe, cormorant, grey heron and gulls.

A large moult concentration of up to 2200 tufted duck occurs during the late summer and autumn.

In summer there is a large breeding population of **grey heron** (160 pairs, 1% of British). Notable also are breeding great crested grebe, common tern and kingfisher.

Conservation issues
The birds that use this area are vulnerable to recreational disturbance and changes in the management of the water regime.

Further reading
The Essex Birdwatching Society. Essex Bird Reports.
The London Natural History Society. London Bird Reports.

Stodmarsh

	SPA/Ram Code	IBA Europe number
	1212A	205

County/Region	District(s)	OS sheet(s)	Grid Reference(s)	Map 20
Kent	Canterbury	179	TR 2261	

Area (ha)	NNR	SPA		Ramsar	
1-999	Part	Designated	N	Designated	N
		Candidate	Y	Candidate	Y

Wetlands including reedbeds, lagoons, grasslands and gravel pits, supporting a wide range of wetland birds including important populations of breeding and wintering reedbed birds.

Site description

The area covers about 6 km of the Stour valley flood plain, downstream of Canterbury. It includes flooded gravel pits, reedbeds and lagoons in an area which has undergone colliery subsidence, cattle and sheep grazed pastures, and smaller areas of scrub and alder carr.

The gravel pits in the upper part of the area have well vegetated margins, including extensive stands of common reed, and also dense scrub of bramble, sallow and willow. Also in this part of the valley are semi-natural alder carrs, which have a rich ground flora.

Very large reedbeds exist in the central section of the area, and in cut areas and along dykes, species-rich fen communities exist. Some of the dykes have a diverse aquatic flora including scarce species.

Grasslands within the site include fields that are periodically cut for turf.

Birds

The area supports nationally important numbers of wintering **hen harrier**, with a maximum of 9 roosting birds in 1987 (1% of British). Notable also in winter are mute swan, gadwall, teal and shoveler. Breeding species include gadwall, shoveler, pochard, Cetti's and Savi's warblers (both now recently gone) and **bearded tit** (65 pairs in 1990, 11% of British). Bittern has bred in the past and has been recorded annually (1980-87) in the Stour valley, where there have been some records of booming birds. Spotted crake has also bred in the past.

Conservation issues

Threats to this site include further gravel extraction, water abstraction and storage, and recreation.

Thursley, Hankley and Frensham Commons

SPA/Ram Code	IBA Europe number
1213A	200

County/Region	District(s)	OS sheet(s)	Grid Reference(s)	Maps 18, 19
Hampshire	East Hampshire	186	SU 8840	
Surrey	Waverley			

Area (ha)	NNR	SPA		Ramsar	
1551	Part	Designated	N	Designated	N
		Candidate	Y	Candidate	Y

Heaths, mire and woodland, with breeding populations of specialist heathland birds.

Site description

These extensive heaths lie between Farnham and Milford on the acidic soils of the Folkestone and Sandgate Beds. The vegetation types present include dry and wet heaths, and valley mires, together with some grasslands and wetlands, and substantial areas of woodland. The diversity of habitats supports a rich flora and fauna.

Dry heath occurs on all three commons, but is best represented on Hankley Common. Heather is dominant, often with much bell heather, and some dwarf gorse and petty whin. Wetter heaths are dominated by heather, purple moor-grass and cross-leaved heath. Gorse scrub is scattered throughout the heaths. The heathlands are important for their reptile populations, including those of smooth snake and sand lizard, as well as their invertebrate fauna, which includes many uncommon species, such as the silver-studded blue and grayling butterflies.

The wet heaths grade into mires, of which those on Thursley Common are the best examples. *Sphagnum* mosses of several species are abundant. Less common species include cranberry, many-stalked spike-rush and brown beak-sedge. Peatlands developing over open water include bottle sedge, bogbean and lesser bladderwort. The invertebrate fauna of the mires includes specialist species, such as the nationally rare large marsh grasshopper and white-faced darter.

Grassland types present include neutral, and both wet and dry types of acidic grassland. Associated scrub includes hawthorn, blackthorn, sallow and gorse.

Woodlands include mature areas of beech, ash, oak, birch, holly and hazel, and in wetter places, alder carr is present. There has been recent invasion of heathland by silver and downy birches, oak and Scots pine. Two notable butterflies associated with trees are found within the area, the purple emperor and white-letter hairstreak.

In addition to the highly acidic bog pools, there are larger ponds, with fringing swamps and fen communities mainly on the peripheries of the heaths. Being more nutrient-rich than the bog pools, they support a more varied aquatic flora.

Birds
The area supports nationally important numbers of breeding nightjar, woodlark and Dartford warbler.

Recent estimates of breeding population sizes are about 20 pairs of **nightjars** (1% of British), up to 27 pairs of **woodlarks** (12% of British), and in excess of 20 pairs of **Dartford warblers** (4% of the British breeding population in 1984). The numbers of these species fluctuate considerably from year to year; the figures given above relate to peak numbers recorded over the last 10–15 years. This site makes a substantial contribution to the maintenance of the traditional breeding ranges of these species within the EC.

Notable also are breeding kingfisher and wintering hen harrier.

Conservation issues
There has been a great deal of loss and fragmentation of lowland heathland during the present century. Sympathetic habitat management is required in order to maintain the wildlife interest of the remaining areas.

The birds that use this area are subjected to disturbance from recreational activities and the accidental/deliberate lighting of fires. Part of the site is a military training area.

Chobham to Yateley Commons

SPA/Ram Code	IBA Europe number
1214A	199

County/Region	District(s)	OS sheet(s)	Grid Reference(s)	Maps 18, 19
Berkshire	Bracknell Forest	175, 186	SU 9764	
Hampshire	Hart			
Surrey	Surrey Heath			
	Guildford			

Area (ha)	NNR	SPA		Ramsar	
1000-9999	No	Designated	N	Designated	N
		Candidate	Y	Candidate	N

Heath, mire and woodland, with breeding populations of specialist heathland birds.

Site description

This area consists of several widely separated fragments of the once almost continuous block of heathland around Camberley. Situated on the Bagshot, Bracklesham and other tertiary strata of the Thames Basin, the soils are acidic and nutrient-poor, typical conditions for heathland development. In Crowthorne Forest at Broadmoor there are areas of heathland with valley mires which comprise 60% of all the bog and open heath in Berkshire. The site includes the majority of the remaining Thames Basin heathland and mire in Surrey and north Hampshire.

On higher ground, there is heather-dominated dry heath, with bell heather, bilberry, dwarf gorse and bristle bent. Lichens are also frequent. Invasion of the heaths by bracken, gorse, or by mixed woodland of birch, oak and Scots pine has been frequent. Locally, for example along paths, there is acidic grassland with a range of characteristic species.

Where drainage is impeded, the dry heath grades into humid heath of heather, cross-leaved heath and purple moor-grass, and eventually into mires. The latter tend to be dominated by purple moor-grass and cross-leaved heath, over a carpet of *Sphagnum* mosses. The valley mires support typical plant communities with several scarce flowering plants and bryophytes.

The invertebrate fauna includes many species which are strongly associated with heath and mire, such as the silver-studded blue butterfly, the bog bush-cricket and the raft spider.

In addition to the recently invasive woodland, the site contains some mature woodland, mainly of oak, but with alder and willow in wetter areas. There are also scattered ponds, most of which have now largely succeeded to woodland. The whole complex of heaths, woods and wetlands supports an impressive range of fungi, which is especially well-developed in the birch and pine woodlands.

Birds

Breeding species include nightjar, **woodlark** (min. 9 pairs 1991, 4% of British) and

Dartford warbler, whilst hen harrier and merlin winter here. Migratory and feeding hobbies use this site, and breed within the surrounding area.

Conservation issues
There has been a great deal of loss and fragmentation of lowland heathland during the present century. Sympathetic habitat management is required in order to maintain the wildlife interest of the remaining areas.

Large parts of Chobham-Yateley are included in military training areas, and locally, habitat has been damaged by motorcycle scrambling. Further damage is caused by summer fires on heathland and scrub. Invasion of open ground and heathland by birch, pine and gorse affects the habitat of woodlark.

Further reading
Clark, J M 1984 *Birds of the Hants/Surrey Border*. Hobby books, Fleet.
Surrey Bird Club. Surrey Bird Report.

Amberley

SPA/Ram Code	IBA Europe number
1216A	201

County/Region	District(s)	OS sheet(s)	Grid Reference(s)	Maps 18, 19
West Sussex	Chichester, Horsham	197	TQ 033142	

Area (ha)	NNR	SPA		Ramsar	
1-999	No	Designated	N	Designated	N
		Candidate	Y	Candidate	Y

Alluvial grazing marsh, which attracts important numbers of wildfowl including Bewick's swans in winter.

Site description
Lying in the valley of the River Arun, just north of the South Downs escarpment, the Amberley Wild Brooks show an unusual range of physical and chemical conditions, and a correspondingly high floristic diversity. The soils are principally alluvial, but include a peaty area which is a relict raised bog. The southern parts of the Wild Brooks are fed by calcareous springs, but to the north, where the underlying geology is Greensand, the water is more acidic.

Drier fields are dominated by species such as meadow-grasses, crested dog's-tail and perennial rye-grass. In wetter areas, rushes, sedges and tufted hair-grass are more frequent.

Ungrazed fields have developed into fen, scrub or woodland. Fen areas consist of common reed, reed sweet-grass and greater tussock-sedge, often with scattered elder and sallow scrub. On firmer ground there is alder, willow, birch and sallow, with oak and hazel woodland on the driest ground.

The ditches separating grazing marsh fields have an outstanding flora. Species present include many of the British species of pondweeds, duckweeds, yellow-cresses, and water-milfoils. Seventeen species of dragonfly are present including downy emerald, along with several species of molluscs.

Birds
The area supports nationally important numbers of wintering Bewick's swan and shoveler.

In the five-winter period 1985/86 to 1989/90 the average peak counts included 120 **Bewick's swans** (2% of British) and 100 **shoveler** (1% of British). Another notable species is wintering teal.

Breeding species (1991 data) include lapwing (15 pairs), snipe (26 pairs) and redshank (17 pairs).

Conservation issues
Birds that use this site are vulnerable to drainage and agricultural intensification.

Although a pump drainage scheme for Amberley Wild Brooks was rejected following a public inquiry in 1978, gravity drainage works have taken place. Since that time, there have been significant declines in breeding waders, other ground nesting species and wintering birds within the SSSI.

South-West London
Reservoirs and Gravel Pits

SPA/Ram Code	IBA Europe number
1217A	198

County/Region	District(s)	OS sheet(s)	Grid Reference(s)	Maps 18, 19
Berkshire	Windsor and Maidenhead	176	TQ 0573	
Greater London	Hounslow			
Surrey	Elmbridge, Runnymede, Spelthorne			

Area (ha)	NNR	SPA		Ramsar	
1000-9999	No	Designated	N	Designated	N
		Candidate	Y	Candidate	Y

A wetland complex comprising reservoirs, gravel pits and alluvial grassland, attracting large numbers of wintering waterfowl.

Site description

These widely scattered water bodies on the south-west margins of London are primarily water supply reservoirs but include two areas of flooded gravel pits.

The gravel pits are principally of interest for their birds, but do have well vegetated shorelines and islands, including dense cover of willows and sallows, and locally marshy areas. Scrub and woodland, of hawthorn, willow, oak and other species are present along some ditches and on disused railway embankments.

Staines Moor consists of alluvial grassland through which the River Colne flows. The river and adjacent ditches support a diverse aquatic flora. Dry grassland is also found at Staines Moor and is notable for the antiquity of its anthills, believed to be up to 180 years old.

Birds

The area supports internationally important numbers of wintering **gadwall** and **shoveler**, and nationally important numbers of wintering **great crested grebe**, **teal**, **pochard**, **tufted duck** and **goosander**. Wintering black-necked grebe and smew are also notable.

There is a major gull roost at Queen Mary Reservoir.

Conservation issues

The birds that use these reservoirs are dependent upon the water management regimes. The redundant Kempton Park Reservoir may be developed at a later date. Previous plans for a theme park and business park have never reached fruition. Potentially damaging changes including infilling have been proposed for Wraysbury Gravel Pits.

The complex is vulnerable to recreational pressures, industrial/residential and infrastructure developments, the change in nature of the use of the reservoirs for public water supply and disturbance arising from maintenance works, unconsented access etc.

Further reading
Taylor, D, Wheatley, J and Prater, A J 1987 *Where to watch birds in Kent, Surrey and Sussex*,
  pp 85-89. Christopher Helm, London.

SITE ACCOUNTS:
WALES

Dee Estuary

SPA/Ram Code	IBA Europe number
1301A	210

County/Region	District(s)	OS sheet(s)	Grid Reference(s)	Maps 11, 21
Cheshire	Chester, Ellesmere Port and Neston	108, 116, 117	SJ 2380	
Clwyd	Alyn and Deeside, Delyn;			
Merseyside	Wirral			

Area (ha)	NNR	SPA	Ramsar
13,055	No	Designated Y Candidate N/A	Designated Y Candidate N/A

A large estuary with extensive intertidal flats and saltmarshes, of great importance for passage and wintering wildfowl and waders.

Site description

The Dee estuary lies between the Wirral peninsula and the north Wales coast, and consists of a very large intertidal area, some 20 km long and up to 9 km wide. The mud and sand flats exposed at low tide contain abundant invertebrates, on which many of the wintering birds feed. The estuary is important for the large numbers of grey seals, representing about 15% of the Welsh population, which haul out on sandbanks in the outer estuary.

Saltmarsh covers large areas, especially on the English side at the head of the estuary. Much of this is dominated by common cord-grass, but there is also more mature marsh nearer the shore. This marsh is heavily sheep grazed. At Neston, there is a transition to brackish marsh dominated by common reed.

Hilbre Islands, in the north of the estuary, are three low-lying sandstone islands, which are important as a wader roost. There is limited maritime vegetation, including cliff flora dominated by sea campion and common scurvygrass on the sheltered eastern side.

Relevant also are the dunes and foreshore of the north Wales coast to the west of the estuary mouth. Many of these dunes have been lost through development, but between the Point of Air and Prestatyn, a narrow strip remains. Breeding little terns occur on shingle spits on the foreshore. There are only small areas of more fixed dunes, but dune slacks are well developed at Talacre Warren.

Birds

The area supports internationally important numbers of wintering shelduck, teal, pintail, oystercatcher, knot, dunlin, black-tailed godwit, curlew, redshank and turnstone, nationally important numbers of wintering scaup, grey plover and sanderling, and nationally important numbers of breeding little tern.

The site is a wetland of international importance by virtue of regularly supporting over 20,000 waterfowl. In the five-winter period 1985/86 to 1989/90 the average peak was 117,070 birds, comprising 90,800 waders and 26,270 wildfowl. Totals for individual species include 5650 **shelduck** (2% of NW European, 8% of British), 5360 **teal** (1% of NW European, 5% of British), 8300 **pintail** (12% of NW European, 33% of British), 140 **scaup** (3% of British), 30,400 **oystercatcher** (3.5% of EAF, 11% of British), 1550 **grey plover** (7% of British), 22,200 **knot** (6% of EAF, 10% of British), 425 **sanderling** (3% of British), 15,100 **dunlin** (1% of EAF, 3.5% of British), 750 **black-tailed godwit** (1% of EAF, 16% of British), 3500 **curlew** (1% of EAF, 4% of British), 7900 **redshank** (7% of EAF, 10% of British) and 930 **turnstone** (1% of EAF, 2% of British).

Breeding species include **little tern** (51 pairs in 1990, 2% of British).

Notable also are wintering and passage wigeon, mallard, ringed plover, lapwing, bar-tailed godwit, spotted redshank and greenshank.

Conservation issues
Waterfowl that winter on estuaries are vulnerable to land-claim and other developments that would disturb or damage the existing ecology of these sites. Other human influences such as recreational disturbance, commercial exploitation of shellfish and worms, and oil and industrial pollution, are also potentially damaging to the conservation interest of estuaries.

Much of the adjoining land is urban or industrial and pollution or development proposals such as tipping, coastal protection works, road schemes and new industrial sites are a continuing threat.

Increased recreational pressure, in particular windsurfing, puts pressure on birds at roost sites, for example, at Little Eye (smallest of Hilbre group) and at West Kirby. Disturbance to roosting and feeding birds is also caused through the presence of horse riders, dogs, pedestrians and off road vehicles and motorcycles at a number of locations within the estuary, and by the action of cockle collectors, who harvest cockles once every four years. The control of cord-grass is practised on parts of the estuary in order to maintain the marsh in its current state. The tipping of coal waste and the spread of caravan sites onto dune slacks also poses problems at this site.

Traeth Lafan (Lavan Sands), Conway Bay

SPA/Ram Code	IBA Europe number
1303A	212

County/Region	District(s)	OS sheet(s)	Grid Reference(s)	Maps 11, 21
Gwynedd	Aberconwy, Arfon	115	SH 630750	

Area (ha)	NNR	SPA		Ramsar	
2700	No	Designated	N	Designated	N
		Candidate	Y	Candidate	N

A large intertidal area of sand, and mudflats, attracting important populations of moulting, passage and wintering wildfowl and waders.

Site description

At the eastern edge of the Menai Straits, this large intertidal area contains a range of habitats from exposed sands to sheltered sands and mudflats. Freshwater streams flowing across the flats add to the habitat diversity.

Birds

The area supports nationally important numbers of moulting great crested grebe and wintering oystercatcher and curlew.

Traeth Lafan holds up to 500 **great crested grebes** (about 5% of the British population) during the autumn moult period. This represents the largest known regular coastal moulting concentration in Britain.

In the five-winter period 1985/86 to 1989/90 the average peak counts were 4000 **oystercatcher** (1% of British) and 1380 **curlew** (1.5% of British). Notable also are wintering/passage shelduck, goldeneye, red-breasted merganser, ringed plover, dunlin, spotted redshank, redshank and greenshank.

Conservation issues

Waterfowl that winter on estuaries are vulnerable to land-claim and other developments, that would disturb or damage the existing ecology of these sites. Other human influences such as recreational disturbance, commercial exploitation of shellfish and worms, and oil and industrial pollution, are also potentially damaging to the conservation interest of estuaries.

At Traeth Lafan, Gwynedd County Council organises meetings of the LNR Committee to oversee conservation of the area. Common cord-grass has become established very locally in a sheltered bay. Commercial cockling has increased in recent years. A study of the possible effects on birds is being carried out. A significant oil pollution incident occurred in the 1970s.

Ynys Feurig, Cemlyn Bay and The Skerries

	SPA/Ram Code 1306A	IBA Europe number 213

County/Region	District(s)	OS sheet(s)	Grid Reference(s)	Map 21
Gwynedd	Ynys Mon/ Anglesey	114	SH 2694	

Area (ha) 86	NNR No	SPA Designated N Candidate Y	Ramsar Designated N Candidate N

Small islands and a coastal lagoon with islet on the west and north coasts of Anglesey, holding large tern colonies.

Site description

This area includes three widely separated sites. On the west coast lies Ynys Feurig, close to Valley airfield, while Cemlyn Bay is on the north coast about 20 km away. The Skerries lie 3 km off Carmel Head.

Ynys Feurig consists of a series of small low-lying islands, extending about 1 km out to sea from a sandy shore. There is little vegetation, except on the highest outer islands. The flora is maritime and includes marram, red fescue and thrift.

At Cemlyn Bay, a shingle storm beach forms a bar between a tidal lagoon and the open shore. The shingle habitats, together with saltmarsh developing around the lagoon and brackish pools further inland make an unusual combination of habitats.

The Skerries are a group of sparsely vegetated small islets, 17 ha in extent. They are protected by strong currents but are very exposed to strong westerly and northerly winds. There is an automated lighthouse and associated buildings.

Birds

The area supports internationally important numbers of breeding Sandwich tern and roseate tern, and nationally important numbers of breeding common and arctic terns.

A survey in 1990 found 517 pairs of **Sandwich terns** (1% of Western European, 3.5% of British), 45 pairs of **roseate terns** (3% of EC, 53% of British), c. 840 pairs of **arctic terns** (1% of British) and c. 170 pairs of **common terns** (1.5% of British). Notable also are breeding lesser black-backed gull and herring gull on the Skerries.

In winter, up to 1000 curlew are present.

Conservation issues

Seabirds are sensitive to changes in the quality of the marine environment, especially to changes in fish stocks and to oil pollution. Ground-nesting seabirds on offshore islands are vulnerable to the introduction of predatory mammals. The breeding terns are vulnerable to predation of eggs and young, and to human disturbance. The experimental use of tern boxes and planting of tree-mallow to shelter nesting adults and young terns from predators is meeting with some success. The three sites are wardened during the nesting season.

Common tern

Glannau Ynys Gybi (Holy Island Coast)

SPA/Ram Code	IBA Europe number
1310A	214

County/Region	District(s)	OS sheet(s)	Grid Reference(s)	Map 21
Gwynedd	Ynys Mon/ Anglesey	114	SH 210820	

Area (ha)	NNR	SPA		Ramsar	
351	No	Designated	N	Designated	N
		Candidate	Y	Candidate	N

Sea cliffs with cliff-top heath and grassland, important for breeding choughs and colonies of seabirds.

Site description

The cliffs of the western side of Holy Island are formed from geologically complex and impressively folded strata, comprising grits, greywackes and sandstones with interbedded shales. The cliffs rise to 120 m, and the hinterland rises to 220 m on Holyhead Mountain. There are many small offshore stacks and islets.

The cliff vegetation includes nationally scarce plants such as rock sea-lavender, spotted rock-rose and golden-samphire, and also a form of field fleawort which is endemic to this site.

The maritime heath is dominated by heather, bell heather and western gorse. Exposure to strong on-shore winds has resulted in an unusual 'wave' formation in places. The vegetation is fairly species-rich, and includes a number of locally and nationally scarce plants as well as bryophytes which occur in sheltered gullies and on screes. The heathland supports populations of marsh fritillary and silver-studded blue butterflies, the latter of a race which is restricted to north Wales.

Birds

The area supports nationally important numbers of breeding chough.

Up to 6 breeding pairs of **choughs** (2% of British) are present. Notable also are breeding peregrine, herring gull, kittiwake, guillemot, razorbill and puffin.

Conservation issues

Rock climbing caused some disturbance of birds in the early 1970s, but this problem was resolved by means of a voluntary seasonal ban agreed with the British Mountaineering Council. Visitor use is heavy but is controlled by provision of car parks and footpaths. Management of the heath and grassland for chough feeding is taken into account by the RSPB, who also provide an information centre and viewing facilities for the main seabird colony.

Berwyn

SPA/Ram Code	IBA Europe number
1311A	211

County/Region	District(s)	OS sheet(s)	Grid Reference(s)	Map 21
Clwyd	Glyndwr	125	SJ 0030	
Gwynedd	Montgomery			
Powys	Meirionnydd			

Area (ha)	NNR	SPA		Ramsar	
20,000+	N	Designated	N	Designated	N
		Candidate	Y	Candidate	N

A large area of blanket mire and heath, supporting a wide range of upland birds including birds of prey.

Site description

Berwyn contains one of the largest areas of heather-dominated heath and blanket mire remaining in Wales. It is an upland block, rising to 827 m, which runs south-west from near Llangollen. On steeper, better drained slopes, heathland predominates, but on more gently sloping land, blanket mire occurs. The heath is dominated by heather, with associated bilberry and other species.

Heather, hare's-tail cottongrass and *Sphagnum* mosses dominate the blanket mires, and frequently occurring associated species include cross-leaved heath, cranberry, cowberry and deergrass. There are also some acidic grasslands and bracken-dominated areas, and areas where rushes are dominant.

Birds

The area supports nationally important numbers of breeding hen harrier, merlin and peregrine.

Estimates of population sizes from a survey in 1990 include 14 pairs of **hen harriers** (2% of British), 15 pairs of **merlins** (2.5% of British) and 18 pairs of **peregrines** (2% of British).

Notable also are breeding red grouse, black grouse, golden plover, curlew, short-eared owl, whinchat, ring ousel and raven.

Conservation issues

Birds that depend on moorland areas are vulnerable to widescale habitat change, especially afforestation and agricultural intensification.

Since 1946, the Berwyn Mountains have lost 44% of their heather cover, about two-thirds to agriculture and one-third to forestry. At present, the main threat to continued heather cover is overgrazing. Good grouse-moor management helps to maintain suitable habitat for upland birds, but there are problems both with the economics of keepering and ensuring that predatory birds are not persecuted.

Glannau Aberdaron and Ynys Enlli (Aberdaron Coast and Bardsey Island)

SPA/Ram Code	IBA Europe number
1312A	215

County/Region	District(s)	OS sheet(s)	Grid Reference(s)	Map 21
Gwynedd	Dwyfor	123	SH 120220	

Area (ha)	NNR	SPA		Ramsar	
512	Yes	Designated N		Designated N	
		Candidate Y		Candidate N	

Rocky coastline and islands, with maritime grassland and heath, important for choughs and breeding seabirds.

Site description

This area includes part of the coast at the tip of the Lleyn peninsula, together with the island of Bardsey, and two smaller islands – the Gwylans. This is a rocky coastline with many crags, screes and low cliffs.

The Aberdaron coast consists of a series of heather covered hills, rising to about 190 m, separated by valleys occupied by pastures. The maritime heaths dominated by heather, bell heather and western gorse are exposed to strong westerly winds, and show 'wave' formation. Flushes and adjoining grassland add to the habitat diversity.

The Mountain on Bardsey has similar heathland to the mainland. Sheltered screes on the north-east side of the island have a rich fern and bryophyte flora including Wilson's filmy-fern.

On the Gwylans, which rise to only 33 m, the vegetation is heavily influenced by salt spray and by the breeding seabirds. Dominant plants include tree-mallow and oraches.

Birds

The area supports nationally important numbers of breeding Manx shearwater and chough.

Breeding birds in the area include about 4300 pairs of **Manx shearwaters** (2% of British) and 14 pairs of **choughs** (5% of British). Notable also are breeding cormorant, shag, peregrine, herring gull and puffin.

Conservation issues

Seabirds are sensitive to changes in the quality of the marine environment, especially to changes in fish stocks and to oil pollution. Ground-nesting seabirds on offshore islands are vulnerable to the introduction of predatory mammals.

Maintenance of suitable heath and grassland is important for the well-being of choughs. Control of overgrazing and avoidance of disturbance to seabird colonies are being tackled by the National Trust and Bardsey Island Trust.

Further reading

Jones, P H 1988 *The Natural History of Bardsey*. National Museum of Wales, Cardiff.
Roberts, P 1985 *The Birds of Bardsey*. Bardsey Bird and Field Observatory, Pwllheli.

Cors Fochno and Dyfi

SPA/Ram Code	IBA Europe number
1401A	216

County/Region	District(s)	OS sheet(s)	Grid Reference(s)	Map 21
Dyfed	Ceredigion	135	SN 6595	
Gwynedd	Merionnydd			
Powys	Montgomery			

Area (ha)	NNR	SPA		Ramsar	
2715+	Part	Designated	N	Designated	Y
		Candidate	Y	Candidate	N/A

An estuary with adjoining saltmarsh and a large raised bog, important for wintering waterfowl.

Site description

A west coast estuary of outstanding physiographic interest, an area of sand dunes, an extensive tract of unmodified actively growing raised mire, important for plants, insects and wintering wildfowl, and diverse flood plain habitats.

The estuary includes a range of habitats with sandbanks, mudflats, saltmarsh, river channels and creeks. Cord-grass is widespread in the saltmarsh. The sand dunes at Ynyslas, which are part of the estuarine complex, show all the stages of dune formation and growth, from sandy shore with strand line, fore dunes, mobile dunes and fixed dunes to scrub dominated by burnet rose.

The raised bog, Cors Fochno, is a mosaic of hummocks and hollows. Bog-myrtle and flowering plants occur on the hummocks, while *Sphagnum* bogmosses occur in the hollows.

Birds

The area supports nationally important numbers of wintering Greenland white-fronted goose and wigeon.

In the five-winter period 1985/86 to 1989/90 the average peak counts were 110 **Greenland white-fronted geese** (1% of British) and 4040 **wigeon** (2% of British). Notable also are wintering shelduck, teal, red-breasted merganser, curlew and various birds of prey. Large numbers of red-throated divers and great crested grebes occur in winter off the mouth of the Dyfi.

Conservation issues

Waterfowl that winter on estuaries are vulnerable to land-claim and other developments that would disturb or damage the existing ecology of these sites. Other human influences such as recreational disturbance, commercial exploitation of shellfish and worms, and oil and industrial pollution, are also potentially damaging to the conservation interest of estuaries.

Further reading

Fox, A D 1986 The breeding teal (*Anas crecca*) of a central raised mire in central west Wales. *Bird Study* 33: 18-23.

Fox, A D and Stroud, D A 1986 The Greenland White-fronted Goose in Wales. *Nature in Wales* (New Series) 4: 20-27.

Grassholm

SPA/Ram Code	IBA Europe number
1404A	220

County/Region	District(s)	OS sheet(s)	Grid Reference(s)	Map 21
Dyfed	Preseli	157	SM 598093	

Area (ha)	NNR	SPA	Ramsar
9	No	Designated Y Candidate N/A	Designated N Candidate N

A small island, most notable for its very large gannetry.

Site description

Grassholm is a rather low, flat-topped, basalt island which lies about 18 km west of the mainland coast of Dyfed. The terrestrial vegetation is limited, due to the effects of the large numbers of seabirds, and the salt-spray and wind exposure.

Away from the gannetry, there is grassland dominated by red fescue, but containing species typical of the exposed and nutrient-enriched conditions, such as tree-mallow and the maritime variety of buck's-horn plantain.

The foreshore and sublittoral zones are of interest for their communities of plants and animals adapted to the extreme degree of wave and tide exposure. Grey seals haul out on to the rocks, but they do not breed here.

Birds

The area supports internationally important numbers of breeding **gannet**. A survey in 1987 found 28,535 pairs, representing 11% of the North Atlantic population and 18% of the number breeding in Britain.

Also present are small numbers of other breeding seabirds, including shag, herring gull, great black-backed gull, kittiwake, guillemot and razorbill.

Conservation issues

Seabirds are sensitive to changes in the quality of the marine environment, especially to changes in fish stocks and to oil pollution. Netting and discarded waste also pose a threat to breeding gannets. Visitors can cause disturbance to the birds.

Skokholm and Skomer

SPA/Ram Code	IBA Europe number
1405A	219

County/Region	District(s)	OS sheet(s)	Grid Reference(s)	Map 21
Dyfed	Preseli	157	SM 725095 (=Skomer)	

Area (ha)	NNR	SPA		Ramsar	
422	Part (Skomer)	Designated Y		Designated N	
		Candidate N/A		Candidate N	

These islands lie off the south-western coast of Dyfed and support large seabird colonies.

Site description

The islands have a plateau-like form bounded by cliffs which reach 70 m on Skomer. The plateau vegetation is much affected by salt spray, rabbit grazing and nutrient enrichment from the seabirds. The grasslands with strongest maritime influence contain much thrift and sea campion. On Skokholm, there is more extensive red fescue dominated grassland on old field systems. Flushes on Skokholm have stands of rushes and sedges with much marsh pennywort, while on Skomer, there are areas dominated by purple moor-grass in the valleys. Both islands have small areas of maritime heath, but bracken now occupies large areas, especially on Skomer.

The ecology of the islands has been well studied, and a number of scarce species are known to occur. Rocky outcrops also have a rich lichen flora, with marked marine and bird-influenced characteristics.

The invertebrates found on the islands include many coastal species of restricted distribution. The rabbits on Skokholm are free of the flea which carries myxomatosis, as a consequence of which the vegetation is especially strongly affected by rabbit grazing. Skomer has an endemic race of the bank vole, and grey seals breed on the islands.

Both islands have small ponds which are used by passage wildfowl.

Birds

The area supports internationally important numbers of breeding Manx shearwater and lesser black-backed gull, and nationally important numbers of breeding storm petrel, razorbill and puffin.

Recent estimates of seabird colony sizes from the Seabird Colony Register include 130,000–140,000 pairs of **Manx shearwaters** (46% of Western European, 57% of British), 5000–7000 pairs of **storm petrels** (10% of British), 16,300 pairs of **lesser black-backed gulls** (9% of Western and Central European, 20% of British), 3430 individual **razorbills** (2% of British) and 13,200 individual **puffins** (2% of British).

Notable also are breeding fulmar, shag, peregrine, herring gull, kittiwake, guillemot, short-eared owl and chough.

In winter up to 100 barnacle geese (probably from the Greenland population) winter on Skomer. They also occur on the nearby mainland, at Marloes.

Conservation issues

Seabirds are sensitive to changes in the quality of the marine environment, especially to changes in fish stocks and to oil pollution. Ground-nesting seabirds on offshore islands are vulnerable to the introduction of predatory mammals. Visitor pressure may cause disturbance to breeding birds, and there is overgrazing by rabbits.

Pembrokeshire Cliffs

SPA/Ram Code	IBA Europe number
1406A	218

County/Region	District(s)	OS sheet(s)	Grid Reference(s)	Map 21
Dyfed	Preseli	157	SM 7328	

Area (ha)	NNR	SPA		Ramsar	
1000-9999	No	Designated	N	Designated	N
		Candidate	Y	Candidate	N

Rocky coastline and an offshore island with breeding choughs and seabirds.

Site description
The varied coastline around St David's and Strumble Heads is highly indented, with many offshore islets and stacks. The cliffs have varied aspects, with consequent variations in exposure to the prevailing winds. Some near-vertical faces, up to 140 m, are present, but there are also more broken slopes with many ledges, and screes. A characteristic cliff ledge flora also supports the endemic sea-lavender *Limonium paradoxum* at St David's Head. On the nutrient-enriched soils where seabirds congregate there is much tree-mallow and sea beet.

Maritime heaths on the cliff tops are dominated by heather, bell heather and western gorse. The cliff-top grasslands are generally dominated by red fescue. There are many springs and small streams, around which flush vegetation adds to the diversity of species; cowslip and early-purple orchid are a feature of these flushes.

Ramsey, which measures about 280 ha including its islets, is heavily grazed by rabbits and sheep, and recently also by red deer. This has produced the tightly cropped sward favoured by choughs. The maritime-influenced acidic grasslands are dominated by bents, crested dog's-tail, Yorkshire-fog and red fescue. There are also areas of maritime heathland and flushes similar to those on the mainland. On the sheltered east side of the island, there is scrub dominated by blackthorn and wild privet with a few juniper bushes.

The complex of cliff, maritime heathlands and grasslands supports a wealth of invertebrates including grayling and small blue butterflies, and several nationally scarce moths, beetles and flies belonging to coastal habitats.

Both Ramsey and the caves and beaches of the mainland hold breeding grey seals. Ramsey holds the largest colony of grey seals in south-west Britain.

Birds
The area supports nationally important numbers of breeding peregrine, herring gull, razorbill and chough.

Recent estimates include c. 30 pairs of **peregrines** (2% of NW European, 4% of British), 1460 pairs of **herring gulls** (1% of British), 1660 individual **razorbills** (1% of British) and 50 pairs of **choughs** (19% of British). Notable also are breeding fulmar, great black-backed gull and guillemot.

Conservation issues

Maintenance of suitable heath and grassland is important for the well-being of choughs.

Seabirds are sensitive to changes in the quality of the marine environment, especially to changes in fish stocks and to oil pollution.

Carmarthen Bay

SPA/Ram Code	IBA Europe number
1409A	221, 240

County/Region	District(s)	OS sheet(s)	Grid Reference(s)	Map 21
Dyfed	Carmarthen, Llanelli, South Pembrokeshire	158, 159	SN 3000	

Area (ha)	NNR	SPA		Ramsar	
10,000+	No	Designated	N	Designated	N
		Candidate	Y	Candidate	Y

A large bay with sandy beaches, sand dunes, saltmarshes, and low cliffs, important for wintering waterfowl and breeding seabirds.

Site description

This area comprises three broad estuaries (the Taf, Tywi and Gwendraeth) which drain into the Bay, in addition to the bay itself, Laugharne Burrows, St Margaret's Island and part of the Pembrey coast. As a whole, the area contains a wide range of coastal habitats.

The open shore consists of broad sandy beaches, backed by actively accreting major dune systems, which hold varied duneland plant communities ranging from dry dune areas to wet slacks and fen habitats. Many uncommon or scarce plants occur, including the nationally rare fen orchid and dune gentian, and sand catchfly in dry areas; these dune systems also hold many notable invertebrates.

The estuaries show full successions from open mud to saltmarsh, and include large areas of ungrazed marsh. Rock sea-lavender is an important constituent of the Pembrey saltings, in a very different habitat from its usual rocky shores.

Laugharne Burrows is an extensive sand dune system, notable for its diversity of plants, and includes Witchett Pool (9 ha), which supports breeding and wintering waterfowl and reedbed species. The pool is rich in dragonflies, the most notable of which are the hairy dragonfly and the migrant hawker.

St Margaret's Island is a small limestone island, joined to Caldey Island at low tide. The top of the island forms a plateau at about 30 m, and has been partly quarried in the past. Maritime grassland predominates, much modified by nutrient-enrichment by seabirds, and by sheep- and rabbit- grazing. The steep cliffs have some vegetation which includes nationally scarce plants such as tree-mallow and golden-samphire.

Birds

The area supports nationally important numbers of breeding cormorant and wintering common scoter, oystercatcher and sanderling.

In winter the bay regularly supports in the order of 11,000 **common scoter** (31% of British). Wintering **oystercatcher** (peak average 3100 birds, 1% of British) and **sanderling** are also regularly present in nationally important numbers (Prys-Jones and

Davis 1990). Notable also are wintering wigeon, ringed plover, golden plover, bar-tailed godwit, curlew, redshank and green sandpiper.

St Margaret's Island holds a large colony of breeding **cormorants** with 270 pairs recorded in 1989 (4% of British). Notable also are breeding great black-backed gull, kittiwake, guillemot and razorbill.

Conservation issues
Much of the interest of this site is associated with wintering common scoter. These birds frequent the shallow inshore waters of the bay and are, therefore, outwith the remit of SSSI protection.

In coastal areas sea-buckthorn is invading throughout the dune system, and dune erosion between Tywyn and Pembrey is bringing increasing pressure for coastal defences. It is to be hoped that motorcycle scrambling on Pembrey saltings and uncontrolled shooting on Tywyn saltings will be controlled as part of management proposals.

Further reading
Prys-Jones, R P and Davis, P E 1990 *The abundance of wildfowl and waders on Carmarthen Bay (Taf/Tywi/Gwendraeth).* BTO report to NCC. (BTO Research Report No. 55).

Elenydd – Mallaen

SPA/Ram Code	IBA Europe number
1411A	217

County/Region	District(s)	OS sheet(s)	Grid Reference(s)	Map 21
Dyfed	Ceredigion, Dinefwr	146, 147	SN 8766 (Elenydd)	
Powys	Brecknock, Radnor			

Area (ha)	NNR	SPA		Ramsar	
10,000+	Part	Designated	N	Designated	N
		Candidate	Y	Candidate	N

Uplands covered by heath and mire, and valleys with woodland and grassland, supporting a wide range of breeding birds, including raptors and upland waders.

Site description
One of the most important areas of hill land in Wales this area is dominated by blocks of upland rising to about 460 m separated by steep-sided valleys. The higher ground has heath and blanket mire, characterised by heather and hare's-tail cottongrass or deergrass, and in places acidic grassland dominated by mat-grass, heath rush or purple moor grass. Crags are frequent, and these hold interesting cliff plant communities, including some calcareous types. Pool and hummock bog is found at Cors Lwyd.

The valley sides are clothed with sessile oak woodland, which in places has a ground flora rich in mosses and liverworts. The occurrence of occasional ash, alder, birch, elm and rowan adds to variety in these woods. There is a rich epiphytic lichen flora.

Fast-flowing rivers run down the valleys and are often lined by alder. Some of the valley floor grasslands are rich in herbs.

Birds
The area supports nationally important numbers of **red kite** and **raven** throughout the year.

The large numbers of sheep help to support a large community of carrion-feeding birds, including a very high density of ravens, and the feeding range of a large part of the British population of red kite.

Notable also are breeding red grouse, golden plover, dunlin, snipe, curlew, short-eared owl and ring ousel. Breeding species along the rivers include goosander, common sandpiper, grey wagtail and dipper.

Conservation issues
Birds that depend on moorland areas are vulnerable to widescale habitat change, especially afforestation and agricultural intensification.

The site is vulnerable to overgrazing by sheep, which affects breeding waders and is damaging broadleaved woodland, through preventing regeneration of oaks. Recreational pressures, for example, the use of four-wheel-drive vehicles and motorcycles cause disturbance in certain areas. This site also suffers from the illegal burning of moorlands, afforestation and the drainage of peatlands.

Red kite

Burry Inlet

SPA/Ram Code	IBA Europe number
1501A	222

County/Region	District(s)	OS sheet(s)	Grid Reference(s)	Map 21
Dyfed	Llanelli	159	SS 500970	
West Glamorgan	Lliw Valley, Swansea			

Area (ha)	NNR	SPA		Ramsar	
6660	Part	Designated	N	Designated	N
		Candidate	Y	Candidate	Y

A large estuary surrounded by saltmarshes and sand dunes, attracting internationally important numbers of wintering wildfowl and waders.

Site description

The Burry Inlet forms a large intertidal area between the Gower peninsula and Llanelli. Large sand dune systems flank the mouth of the estuary, while there is extensive saltmarsh (2200 ha, the largest in Wales) in the inner parts. The Inlet experiences wide tidal fluctuations (about 8 m), and large expanses of sediments are exposed at low water. Mostly, these are fine sands, but more muddy substrates are found in sheltered areas. The abundant invertebrate fauna of the sand, and mudflats, and the vegetation of the saltmarshes provide food for the many wintering birds.

Many different saltmarsh communities are present. Pioneer communities include stands of glassworts and annual sea-blite, and large areas of common cord-grass. At higher levels, common saltmarsh-grass is abundant with sea-purslane along the creek sides wherever grazing pressure is low. Much of the area is, however, grazed, and the predominant community at the mid-upper levels is common saltmarsh-grass and red fescue, with smaller amounts of other species. At its uppermost limit, the saltmarsh is fringed by a belt of sea rush.

The dunes to north and south of the Inlet mouth contain a succession of dune communities, from fore-dunes and mobile dunes, through fixed 'grey' dunes, to dune grassland and dune slacks. The dune ridges and associated dune slacks support a very rich flora including many scarce and rare species.

Birds

The area supports internationally important numbers of wintering shelduck, wigeon, teal, pintail, oystercatcher and knot, and nationally important numbers of wintering shoveler, golden plover, grey plover, sanderling, curlew and turnstone, and passage waders and terns.

The site is a wetland of international importance by virtue of regularly supporting over 20,000 waterfowl. In the five-winter period 1983/84 to 1987/88 the average peak count was 46,850 birds, comprising 11,900 wildfowl and 34,950 waders. Totals for individual species include 1390 **shelduck** (1% of NW European, 2% of British), 5350 **wigeon** (1% of NW European, 3% of British), 2080 **teal** (1% of NW European, 2% of British), 1890

pintail (3% of NW European, 8% of British), 220 **shoveler** (2% of British), 17,810 **oystercatcher** (2% of EAF, 6% of British), in excess of 2000 **golden plover** (1% of British), 710 **grey plover** (3% of British), 5490 **knot** (2% of EAF, 3% of British), 170 **sanderling** (1% of British), 1310 **curlew** (1% of British) and 580 **turnstone** (1% of British).

In addition, during passage periods, the site supports nationally important numbers of whimbrel (average of nearly 100 birds in autumn), greenshank (average of 30 birds in September), Sandwich tern, common tern, arctic tern, little tern and black tern. Redshank breed in good numbers.

Conservation issues

Waterfowl that winter on estuaries are vulnerable to land-claim and other developments, such as the construction of barrages that would disturb or damage the existing ecology of these sites. Other human influences such as recreational disturbance, commercial exploitation of shellfish and worms, and oil and industrial pollution, are also potentially damaging to the conservation interest of estuaries.

Development proposals include marinas at various locations bordering the estuary and the redevelopment of the Machynys Peninsula which will require associated sea defences. There are also proposals to modify the sewage disposal system, and the threat of landfill associated with waste disposal (Upper Loughor only). Unregulated shooting takes place on the north shore, and there are problems with bait digging throughout the site. Sand winning takes place within the estuary, with offloading facilities at Carmarthen Bay Power Station. Much of the estuary is of importance as a cockle fishery with stocks being managed by the South Wales Sea Fisheries Committee under the 1965 Burry Inlet Cockle Fishery Regulating Order.

Severn Estuary

SPA/Ram Code	IBA Europe number
1502A	224

County/Region	District(s)	OS sheet(s)	Grid Reference(s)	Maps 16,
Avon	Bristol, Northavon, Woodspring	162, 171, 172, 182	ST 480830	**17, 18**
Gloucestershire	Forest of Dean, Stroud			
Gwent	Monmouth, Newport			
Somerset	Sedgemoor			
South Glamorgan	Cardiff, Vale of Glamorgan			

Area (ha)	NNR	SPA		Ramsar	
21,200	Part	Designated	Y	Designated	Y
		Candidate	Y	Candidate	Y

A large, complex, coastal plain estuary attracting internationally important numbers of wintering and passage wildfowl and waders and holding important breeding bird populations.

Site description

Fed by five major rivers (the Severn itself, the Wye, the Usk, the Parrett and the Avon), and numerous lesser rivers, the Severn estuary provides the outlet to the Bristol Channel. The estuary's classic funnel shape, unique in Britain, is a factor in causing the Severn to have the second highest tidal range in the world (after the Bay of Fundy, Canada). This unique tidal regime leads to strong currents, mobile sediments and high turbidity which results in a plant and animal community typical of extreme physical conditions of liquid mud and tide swept sand and rock. The species-poor invertebrate community includes high densities of ragworms, lugworms and other invertebrates forming an important food source for passage and wintering waders.

A further consequence of the large tidal range is the extensive intertidal zone, one of the largest in the UK, comprising mudflats, sand banks, shingle, and rocky platforms.

Glassworts and annual sea-blite colonise the open mud, with beds of all three species of eelgrass occurring on more sheltered mud- and sandbanks. Large expanses of common cord-grass also occur on the outer marshes. Extensive areas of saltmarsh, much of it heavily grazed by sheep and cattle, fringe the estuary, with a range of saltmarsh types present. The middle marsh sward is dominated by common saltmarsh-grass, with typical associated species. In the upper marsh, red fescue and saltmarsh rush become more prominent. Highly saline salt pans have abundant reflexed saltmarsh-grass and lesser sea-spurrey. Sea couch dominates the highest saltmarsh around the driftline, and brackish marsh pools and depressions on the upper marshes have small stands of common reed or sea club-rush. Parts of the Upper Severn Estuary comprise reclaimed grassland dominated by perennial rye-grass.

Several islands are included within the site, notably Flat Holm, Steep Holm and Sully Island. The first two hold breeding seabirds. Flat Holm is a low limestone island of 24 ha, clothed by coarse grassland, bracken, and scrub of bramble and other species. Along the western cliffs there is maritime grassland, and in a few other places, species-rich communities remain on the calcareous soils. Steep Holm is also a small limestone island (26 ha) but unlike Flat Holm it is surrounded by precipitous cliffs. The cliffs are partially vegetated with scrub and immature woodland. The plateau of the island is occupied by dense thickets of alexanders, a community that is extremely scarce in Britain.

Sully Island provides the main roost site for wintering waders feeding in the Taff/Ely Estuary. The roost holds up to 100% of the dunlin, grey plover and ringed plover of the Taff/Ely, and over 50% of the redshank and knot.

A notable run of migratory fish occurs between the sea and the estuary complex, including salmon, sea trout, river lamprey and eel. Sea lamprey, twaite shad and allis shad also occur.

Birds

The area supports nationally or internationally important numbers of 17 species of wintering and passage waterfowl, together with nationally important numbers of breeding shelduck and lesser black-backed gull.

The site is a wetland of international importance by virtue of regularly supporting over 20,000 waterfowl. In the five-winter period 1984/85 to 1988/89 the average peak was 77,445 birds, comprising 51,215 waders and 26,230 wildfowl. Totals for individual species include 360 **Bewick's swans** (2% of NW European, 5% of British,), 4100 European **white-fronted geese** (1% of NW European, 68% of British), 2400 **shelduck** (1% of NW European, 3% of British), 8500 **wigeon** (1% of NW European, 3% of British), 290 **gadwall** (2% of NW European, 5% of British), 2300 **teal** (2% of British), 450 **pintail** (2% of British), 170 **shoveler** (2% of British), 1900 **pochard** (4% of British), 1500 **tufted duck** (2% of British), 250 **ringed plover** (1% of British), 440 **grey plover** (2% of British), 44,400 **dunlin** (3% of EAF, 10% of British), 3600 **curlew** (1% of EAF, 4% of British) and 3000 **redshank** (3% of EAF, 4% of British).

Golden plover occur in large numbers in winter on the coastal levels adjacent to the estuary, but make use of the estuary especially in hard weather.

Increased numbers of birds may be present in cold weather when the estuary functions as a cold weather refuge, for example, for European white-fronted geese, and also for golden plover.

Over 2000 **whimbrel** (3% of EAF, c. 50% of British) occur here on passage, using fields adjacent to the estuary for feeding during the day, and roosting on the estuary at night, particularly at Collister Pill and Stert Island (the largest roost in Britain). Ruff occur regularly as passage migrants (max. 64 April 1987) and small numbers also occur in winter. During spring and autumn there is a considerable passage of **ringed plover** through the Severn Estuary with up to 1500 birds recorded in recent years (>1% of EAF).

Breeding species include **shelduck** (94 territory-holding pairs, c. 1% of the British breeding population) and redshank (estimated 100-200 pairs). The islands of Flat Holm and Steep Holm hold breeding **lesser black-backed gull** (2100 pairs, 1% of Western and Central European, 3% of British). Notable also are breeding cormorant, herring gull and great black-backed gull.

Bridgwater Bay, a long-established traditional shelduck moulting area, represents the largest single moulting area for shelduck in Europe away from the Waddenzee, with a peak count of just under 2000 birds recorded in July 1988.

Conservation issues

Waterfowl that winter on estuaries are vulnerable to land-claim and other developments, such as the construction of barrages that would disturb or damage the existing ecology of these sites. Other human influences such as recreational disturbance, commercial exploitation of shellfish and worms, and oil and industrial pollution, are also potentially damaging to the conservation interest of estuaries.

The rivers Severn, Usk, Taff, Ely and Parrett (Bridgwater Bay) are subject to proposed tidal barrage schemes. There are also pressures from recreational use, sand dredging, pollution, port, industrial and housing developments and major engineering works (for example, the second Severn crossing and sea defences). There has been a recent airport proposal in Gwent.

Swansea Bay – Blackpill

SPA/Ram Code	IBA Europe number
1503A	223

County/Region	District(s)	OS sheet(s)	Grid Reference(s)	Map 21
West Glamorgan	Swansea	159	SS 6290	

Area (ha)	NNR	SPA		Ramsar	
1-999	No	Designated	N	Designated	N
		Candidate	Y	Candidate	N

Broad intertidal flats, and adjacent sand dunes, attracting important numbers of wintering and passage waders.

Site description

This area comprises parts of Swansea Bay, and includes the intertidal flats of sand and mud at the western and eastern ends of the bay which are over 1 km wide at low water. Dunes that back Swansea Bay are small in extent and rather degraded, and part of these dunes is now a golf course. The dunes bordering the River Neath are a botanical SSSI.

Birds

The area supports nationally important numbers of wintering ringed plover and sanderling. In the five-winter period 1985/86 to 1989/90 the average peak counts were 270 **ringed plover** (1% of British) and 230 **sanderling** (2% of British).

Notable also are wintering oystercatcher, grey plover, knot, dunlin, bar-tailed godwit and turnstone, and passage ringed plover and whimbrel.

Conservation issues

Waterfowl that winter on estuaries are vulnerable to land-claim and other developments that would disturb or damage the existing ecology of these sites. Other human influences such as recreational disturbance, commercial exploitation of shellfish and worms, and oil and industrial pollution, are also potentially damaging to the conservation interest of estuaries.

At Blackpill, there is disturbance to birds through the activities of baitdiggers, and dogs running loose on the foreshore. The foreshore is currently under threat of infilling to make way for commercial developments. Cord-grass is invading the saltmarsh, but growth is currently limited to the area immediately adjacent to Blackpill.

SITE ACCOUNTS:
NORTHERN IRELAND

Rathlin Island

SPA/Ram Code	IBA Europe number
2001A	247

County/Region	District(s)	NI OS sheet(s)	Grid Reference(s)	Map 22
Antrim	N/A	5	D 130520	

Area (ha)	NNR	SPA		Ramsar	
1500	Part	Designated	N	Designated	N
		Candidate	Y	Candidate	N

Site description

A large island with important seabird cliffs and stacks on the north and west shores. Inland there are wetlands, a limited amount of maritime heath and a mosaic of unimproved and improved grazing.

Birds

These cliffs support nationally important numbers of breeding kittiwake and guillemot.

The cliffs on the north and west shores support important seabird populations including fulmar (1223 pairs), Manx shearwater (250–350 pairs), shag (104 pairs), herring gull (4037 pairs), **kittiwake** (6420 pairs, 1% of British), **guillemot** (39,840 individuals, 1% of Western European, 4% of British), razorbill (9071 birds), black guillemot (46 pairs) and puffin (2896 birds). Also breeding are peregrine (6 pairs) and chough (which declined to one pair in 1990).

Conservation issues

Seabird colonies and other ground nesting species on the island are threatened by a recently introduced feral ferret population. Elimination by trapping is being attempted. Agricultural intensification and reclamation has reduced the area of unimproved grazing with repercussions for the chough population.

Sheep Island

SPA/Ram Code	IBA Europe number
2002A	246

County/Region	District(s)	NI OS sheet(s)	Grid Reference(s)	Map 22
Antrim	N/A	5	D 048458	

Area (ha)	NNR	SPA		Ramsar	
4	No	Designated	N	Designated	N
		Candidate	Y	Candidate	N

Site description
Exposed marine island with steep cliffs and rocky shores, important for breeding cormorants.

Birds
Sheep Island supports a nationally important breeding colony of cormorant of the sub-species *carbo*.

This island supports one of the larger **cormorant** colonies of the sub-species *carbo* in the European Community. The population peaked at 371 pairs in 1988 and had declined to 317 pairs (4.5% of British) by 1990.

Conservation issues
Birds from this colony have traditionally posed a predation problem on the nearby River Bush, which is a noted salmon fishery and has a salmon rearing station. Since 1987, when a total of 90 birds were shot on the river, the fishery has adopted a 'shoot to scare' policy commencing well in advance of the smolt run and release times. This appears to be a satisfactory solution. Pressure to cull the colony has been resisted by the owners (the National Trust), other NGOs, and the licensing authority, DoE(NI).

Lough Foyle

SPA/Ram Code	IBA Europe number
2003A	245

County/Region	District(s)	NI OS sheet(s)	Grid Reference(s)	Map 22
Londonderry	N/A	4, 7	C 560300	
Republic of Ireland				

Area (ha)	NNR	SPA		Ramsar	
20,000	Part	Designated	N	Designated	N
		Candidate	Y	Candidate	Y

Site description

A large, shallow estuary with extensive mudflats, shell ridges and mussel beds, low-lying reclaimed agricultural land, partly arable, partly grazing, and limited saltwater marsh.

Birds

Lough Foyle supports internationally important numbers of whooper swan, light-bellied brent goose, wigeon and bar-tailed godwit, and nationally important numbers of Bewick's swan, Greenland white-fronted goose, curlew and redshank.

The site is a wetland of international importance by virtue of regularly supporting over 20,000 waterfowl. In the five-winter period 1984/85 to 1988/89 the average peak count for total waterfowl was 40,895 birds, comprising 25,520 wildfowl and 15,375 waders. Totals for individual species were 163 **Bewick's swans** (2% of British), 1607 **whooper swans** (9% of world population, 27% of British), 2113 **light-bellied brent geese** (11% of Canada/Greenland population), 110 **Greenland white-fronted geese** (1% of British), 16,959 **wigeon** (2% of NW European, 7% of British), 2704 **bar-tailed godwit** (3% of EAF, 4% of British), 2832 **curlew** (3% of British), 1051 **redshank** (1% of British) and 47 greenshank.

Conservation issues

Mudflat is being lost through disposal of rubbish on the foreshore at Culmore, and there have been proposals to expand this along the Co. Donegal shore. Shooting and commercial shellfisheries are unregulated and are sources of disturbance. The estuary is exposed to large quantities of raw and partially treated sewage and pollution with oil and chemicals from lough-side heavy industry. A potential threat exists from the expansion of port activities. Agricultural intensification and field drainage along the south shore has led to loss of breeding wader habitats.

Larne Lough and Swan Island

SPA/Ram Code	IBA Europe number
2004A	248

County/Region	District(s)	NI OS sheet(s)	Grid Reference(s)	Map 22
Antrim	N/A	9, 15	D 430000 (Larne Lough)	
			D 423997 (Swan Island)	

Area (ha)	NNR	SPA		Ramsar	
1000	Part	Designated	N	Designated	N
		Candidate	Y	Candidate	Y

Site description

Sea lough with mudflats, mussel-beds and a small area of saltings important for wintering light-bellied brent geese. Swan Island is a small vegetated island, supporting an important mixed tern colony.

Birds

This site supports internationally important numbers of wintering light-bellied brent geese and breeding roseate terns, and nationally important numbers of breeding common terns.

Swan Island has an important tern colony, which in 1990 held Sandwich tern (130 pairs), **roseate tern** (19 pairs, 1% of EC, 23% of British), **common tern** (250 pairs, 2% of British), and arctic tern (4 pairs).

Wintering species at Larne Lough include between 252-295 **light-bellied brent geese** during the winters 1983/84-1985/86 (min. 1% of Canada/Greenland population) and 20-30 greenshank.

Conservation issues

The area is threatened by proposals for fish farming, and pollution from the port and a possible refuse disposal site. Breeding terns are vulnerable to disturbance.

Pettigoe Plateau

SPA/Ram Code	IBA Europe number
2005A	261

County/Region	District(s)	NI OS sheet(s)	Grid Reference(s)	Map 22
Fermanagh	N/A	17	H 010650	
Republic of Ireland				

Area (ha)	NNR	SPA		Ramsar	
2700	part proposed	Designated	N	Designated	N
		Candidate	Y	Candidate	N

Site description
Low-lying blanket bog with rocky outcrops, small lakes and farmland interspersed with small patches of forestry, important for breeding upland birds.

Birds
This site is important for a range of upland breeding species the most notable being a few pairs of hen harriers and 12 pairs of golden plover.

Up to 50 Greenland white-fronted geese winter at the site.

Conservation issues
Problems at the site include afforestation, peat extraction, drainage, poor moorland management, shooting and agricultural improvement.

Lower Lough Erne

SPA/Ram Code	IBA Europe number
2006A	258

County/Region	District(s)	NI OS sheet(s)	Grid Reference(s)	Map 22
Fermanagh	N/A	17, 18	H 130600	

Area (ha)	NNR	SPA		Ramsar	
3300	Part	Designated	N	Designated	N
		Candidate	Y	Candidate	Y

Site description
A large lake in limestone country, with an indented shoreline, marshes, wet meadows, and agriculturally unimproved islands. The hinterland on the east shore includes traditional hay-meadow and unimproved grazing land.

Birds
The site is important for breeding wildfowl and waders. Key species include a declining population of **common scoter** (10 pairs in 1987, 10% of British), 164+ pairs of snipe, 74+ pairs of curlew, 84 pairs of redshank, 78 pairs of Sandwich terns and 5 pairs of common terns. A population of **corncrakes** occurs in the Kesh/Ederney area, but these are in long-term decline, numbering only 23 calling males (4% of British) in 1990.

Wintering waterfowl include irregular parties of up to 100 whooper swans.

Conservation issues
The Lough suffers from eutrophication as a result of increasing amounts of agricultural and domestic effluents in recent years. Leisure and cruising activity, and the disturbance they cause are increasing. Colonisation by feral mink is thought to have been a contributory factor to the decline in breeding waterfowl since 1970.

Many of the breeding species at this site, particularly corncrake, are vulnerable to changes in agricultural practices.

Further reading
Partridge, J K 1989 Lower Lough Erne's Common Scoters. *RSPB Conserv. Rev.* 3, 25-28.

Upper Lough Erne

	SPA/Ram Code	IBA Europe number
	2007A	259

County/Region	District(s)	NI OS sheet(s)	Grid Reference(s)	Map 22
Fermanagh	N/A	27	H 300320	

Area (ha)	NNR	SPA		Ramsar	
11,300	Part	Designated	N	Designated	N
		Candidate	Y	Candidate	Y

Site description
Flooded drumlins in the course of River Erne, giving rise to a complex of islands, bays, and many lakes bordered by damp pastures, fens and reedswamp.

Birds
Upper Lough Erne is of international importance for wintering whooper swan and of national importance for breeding great crested grebe.

Upper Lough Erne is very important for breeding waders, especially snipe (630+ pairs), curlew (173+ pairs) and redshank (146 pairs). Other breeding species include **great crested grebe** (c. 300 pairs, 5% of British), corncrake (4 calling males in 1990 and declining) and common tern.

Wintering wildfowl include 876 **whooper swans** (5% of world total, 15% of British) and up to 50 Greenland white-fronted geese.

Conservation issues
Problems at this site include field drainage and consequent agricultural intensification, shooting disturbance, eutrophication, and recreation developments, with proposed marinas and a large projected increase in cruiser traffic, in part due to the reopening of the Ballyconnell Canal linking the Shannon and Erne systems.

Further reading
Partridge, J K 1988 Breeding waders in Northern Ireland. *RSPB Conserv. Rev.* 2: 69-71.

Lower Lough Macnean

SPA/Ram Code	IBA Europe number
2008A	260

County/Region	District(s)	NI OS sheet(s)	Grid Reference(s)	Map 22
Fermanagh	N/A	26	H 120380	

Area (ha)	NNR	SPA		Ramsar	
500	No	Designated	N	Designated	N
		Candidate	Y	Candidate	Y

Site description
A freshwater lake with islands.

Birds
The lake supports wintering wildfowl important in a Northern Ireland context including whooper swans and 50 Greenland white-fronted geese. This site is most important as a roost for these geese.

Conservation issues
Problems include drainage, tourism and marina development, and unregulated shooting.

Lough Neagh and Lough Beg

SPA/Ram Code	IBA Europe number
2009A	257

County/Region	District(s)	NI OS sheet(s)	Grid Reference(s)	Map 22
Antrim	N/A	14, 19, 20	J 030760	
Armagh	N/A			
Down	N/A			
Londonderry	N/A			
Tyrone	N/A			

Area (ha)	NNR	SPA		Ramsar	
39,500	Part	Designated	N	Designated	Y
		Candidate	Y	Candidate	N

Site description

These lakes form relatively shallow bodies of water with associated damp grassland, reedbeds, islands, fens and pasture. Lough Neagh is the largest freshwater lake in the UK. The most significant area of wet grassland in Northern Ireland lies south and west of Lough Beg. In areas the shoreline has a screen of alder and willow carr. Water levels in Lough Neagh and Lough Beg have been significantly lowered during the last 50 years, and are subject to erratic, artificial change.

Birds

The area supports internationally important numbers of wintering Bewick's swan, whooper swan, pochard, tufted duck, scaup and goldeneye and nationally important numbers of breeding and wintering great crested grebe.

The site is a wetland of international importance by virtue of regularly supporting over 20,000 waterfowl, and is one of the most important in the UK for wintering waterfowl. In the five-winter period 1984/85 to 1988/89 the average peak count for total waterfowl was 67,924. Totals for individual species include 1293 **great-crested grebes** (13% of British), 271 **Bewick's swans** (1% of NW European, 4% of British), 1072 **whooper swans** (6% of world total, 18% of British), 24,417 **pochard** (7% of NW European, 49% of British), 12,900 **tufted duck** (2% of NW European, 21% of British), 1720 **scaup** (1% of NW European, 34% of British) and 9365 **goldeneye** (3% of NW European, 62% of British).

Breeding species include **great-crested grebe** (750 pairs, 12% of British), small numbers of pochard, lapwing (175 pairs), snipe (350 pairs), curlew (46 pairs) and redshank (215 pairs).

Conservation issues

The Lough drains some 40% of Northern Ireland and has been subject to severe eutrophication as a result of increased nutrient inputs. Phosphate reduction at sewage works has to some extent reduced this problem. The ecology of the very large wintering waterfowl populations is largely unstudied but the Lough is now counted regularly and

451

population trends have been recently reviewed (Winfield *et al* 1989). Wildfowling is poorly regulated and there are very few refuges. Disturbance from other sources is not yet problematical.

The size of the Lough makes it susceptible to a wide range of actual and potential threats and pressures including lignite mining, sand and gravel extraction, pollution, recreational activities, water abstraction and arterial drainage. It is suspected that the important breeding wader population is declining, probably due to agricultural intensification. Lough Neagh supports an important commercial eel fishery. Management of water levels within the Lough Neagh basin can have a deleterious impact on birds at Lough Beg.

Further reading
Winfield, D K, Davidson, R D and Winfield, I J 1989 Long term trends (1965–1988) in the numbers of waterfowl overwintering on Lough Neagh and Lough Beg, Northern Ireland. *Irish Birds* 4 (1), 19–42.

Pochard

Belfast Lough

SPA/Ram Code	IBA Europe number
2010A	249

County/Region	District(s)	DNI OS sheet(s)	Grid Reference(s)	Map 22
Antrim	N/A	15	J 410830	
Belfast City	N/A			
Down	N/A			

Area (ha)	NNR	SPA		Ramsar	
2000	No	Designated	N	Designated	N
		Candidate	Y	Candidate	Y

Site description
Belfast Lough is a sea lough with a greatly reduced area of tidal mudflats following 150 years of land-claim for development. The outer lough shores are mainly rocky with a few sandy bays. Two man-made lagoons in the Inner Harbour provide the main wader roost.

Birds
Belfast Lough is of international importance for wintering redshank and turnstone, and of national importance for wintering great crested grebes, scaup, goldeneye, oyster-catcher, black-tailed godwit and curlew.

In the five-winter period 1984/85 to 1988/89, the average peak wader counts totalled 12,687 individuals. Totals for individual species include 512 (minimum figure) **great crested grebe** (5% of British), 204 **scaup** (4% of British), 419 **goldeneye** (3% of British), 5867 **oystercatcher** (2% of British), 89 **black-tailed godwit** (2% of British), 1082 **curlew** (1% of British), 2102 **redshank** (1% of EAF, 3% of British) and 752 **turnstone** (1% of EAF, 2% of British).

Conservation issues
Problems include land-claim, industrial and port development (involving domestic refuse disposal and hard-core tipping), pollution from a landfill site and Ireland's largest port, and assorted sources of disturbance including motorcycling on the foreshore. In 1990, an agreement was reached between the Belfast Harbour Commissioners and various conservation groups to safeguard 81 ha of intertidal flats, lagoons and land for wildlife conservation purposes and to undertake appropriate management. This area had previously been earmarked for development and includes the key high-tide wader roost.

Strangford Lough and Islands

SPA/Ram Code 2011A	IBA Europe number 252

County/Region Down	District(s) N/A	NI OS sheet(s) 15, 21	Grid Reference(s) J 560600	Map 22

Area (ha) 13,700	NNR Part	SPA Designated N Candidate Y	Ramsar Designated N Candidate Y

Site description

A shallow sea lough with an indented shoreline and a wide variety of marine and intertidal habitats. The west shore has numerous islands typical of flooded drumlin topography. The Lough contains extensive areas of mudflat, saltmarsh and rocky coastline.

Birds

This is Northern Ireland's most important coastal site for wintering waterfowl, and it is important for breeding terns and other birds.

The site is of international importance for wintering light-bellied brent goose, knot, bar-tailed godwit and redshank and for breeding Sandwich tern; nationally important wintering numbers of 7 species of wildfowl and 6 species of waders also occur here.

Strangford Lough is a wetland of international importance by virtue of regularly supporting over 20,000 waterfowl. In the five-winter period 1984/85 to 1988/89 the average peak total of waterfowl was 74,139, comprising 25,111 wildfowl and 49,028 waders. Totals for individual species include 214 **mute swans** (1% of British), 91 **whooper swans** (2% of British), 13,455 **light-bellied brent geese** (67% of Canada/Greenland population), 2186 **shelduck** (3% of British), 92 **gadwall** (2% of British, but not all of wild origin), 131 **shoveler** (1% of British), 409 **goldeneye** (3% of British), 283 **red-breasted merganser** (3% of British), 4587 **oystercatcher** (2% of British), 9082 **golden plover** (5% of British), 13,883 **lapwing** (1% of British), 9824 **knot** (3% of EAF, 4% of British), 5704 **dunlin** (1% of British), 172 **black-tailed godwit** (3% of British), 1057 **bar-tailed godwit** (1% of EAF, 2% of British), 1682 **curlew** (2% of British), 3100 **redshank** (2% of EAF, 4% of British) and 38 greenshank.

The site is important for breeding birds including the **cormorant** subspecies *carbo* (150 pairs, 2% of British), **Sandwich tern** (1571 pairs in 1990, 4% of Western European population, 10% of British), **common tern** (650 pairs, 5% of British), roseate tern (1 pair) and arctic tern (133 pairs).

Conservation issues

Situated close to the Greater Belfast conurbation, the Lough is subject to a range of largely uncontrolled recreational pressures, including sailing, water skiing, windsurfing, boating, walking and horse riding. Marinas have been proposed for several sites but none has been approved in recent years. Strangford Lough's environs are a much sought-after residential area and there have been large population increases within the lough catchment, with attendant eutrophication. In the past few years there have been proposals for a tidal power barrage at the mouth of the Lough; land-claim, which would have affected the NNR at the northern end; and a commercial fin-fish farm. All have been rejected. Agricultural land use around the shore of the Lough has also become more intensive in recent years.

The foreshore and some islands are managed under the National Trust's Wildlife Scheme, which also provides for the regulation of wildfowling. The Scheme has recently been the subject of a comprehensive Review (Jepsen, 1990) and the implementation of a wide range of recommendations is awaited.

Strangford Lough was identified by the 1984 All Ireland RSPB/IWC Tern Survey as the most important site for nesting terns in Ireland, with about one-third of the Irish population. Since then roseate tern has become a rare breeder on the Lough and Sandwich tern numbers have fallen from 2300 pairs in 1985. The reasons for this are not clear.

Further reading
Jepsen, P U 1990 *A review of the Strangford Lough Wildlife Scheme, final report and recommendations* IWRB, Slimbridge. 43pp.

Annaghroe, River Blackwater

SPA/Ram Code 2012A	IBA Europe number 256

County/Region	District(s)	NI OS sheet(s)	Grid Reference(s)	Map 22
Tyrone	N/A	19	H 737440	

Area (ha)	NNR	SPA	Ramsar
50	No	Designated N Candidate Y	Designated N Candidate Y

Site description
Grazed, periodically flooded meadow along the River Blackwater.

Birds
The site is important in a Northern Ireland context for wintering wildfowl which include 50 whooper swans and 90 Greenland white-fronted geese.

Conservation issues
This site was affected by the recent Blackwater River Arterial Drainage Scheme. An artificial embankment and sluices were constructed, in order to control water levels, which are monitored and currently adjusted by the Department of Agriculture with the agreement of the landowners.

Gun's Island including Sandy Island

SPA/Ram Code	IBA Europe number
2013A	255

County/Region	District(s)	NI OS sheet(s)	Grid Reference(s)	Map 22
Down	N/A	21	J 598414	

Area (ha)	NNR	SPA		Ramsar	
35	No	Designated N		Designated N	
		Candidate Y		Candidate N	

Site description

Sandy Island is low and sandy with sparse maritime vegetation, and is linked by a narrow causeway to Gun's Island, which is well vegetated and grazed.

Birds

These two islands support a breeding tern colony of variable size which in 1989 included 2 pairs of **roseate terns** (2% of British), 20-25 pairs of common terns, 15 pairs of arctic terns and 1-2 pairs of little terns. It is the only breeding site for the latter species in Northern Ireland.

Conservation issues

Recreational pressure, especially day visitors, affects the site and mammalian predation is a problem.

Dundrum Inner Bay

SPA/Ram Code	IBA Europe number
2014A	253

County/Region	District(s)	NI OS sheet(s)	Grid Reference(s)	Map 22
Down	N/A	21, 29	J 415370	

Area (ha)	NNR	SPA		Ramsar	
350	No	Designated N		Designated N	
		Candidate Y		Candidate Y	

Site description

An enclosed sandy bay with extensive mudflats, fed by four small rivers.

Birds

Dundrum Bay supports internationally important numbers of wintering light-bellied brent geese.

Light-bellied brent geese winter in internationally important numbers with between 212–226 (min. c. 1% of Canada/Greenland population) wintering during the winters of 1985/86 to 1987/88, in addition to significant numbers of oystercatchers, which have peaked at 1960 birds.

Conservation issues

Threats to the site include disturbance from commercial shellfish gathering and recreational pressure, fly tipping and pollution from sewage.

Killough Harbour and Coney Island Bay

SPA/Ram Code	IBA Europe number
2015A	251

County/Region	District(s)	NI OS sheet(s)	Grid Reference(s)	Map 22
Down	N/A	21	J 540365	

Area (ha)	NNR	SPA		Ramsar	
130	No	Designated N Candidate Y		Designated N Candidate Y	

Site description
A small estuary with tidal mudflats and shingle banks.

Birds
Light-bellied brent geese winter in internationally important numbers with an average maximum of 235 during the winters 1987/88–88/89 (1% of Greenland/Canada population). This site is of particular importance in late winter.

Conservation issues
The site has been threatened by marina proposals and associated land-claim.

Carlingford Lough including Green Island

SPA/Ram Code	IBA Europe number
2016A	254

County/Region	District(s)	NI OS sheet(s)	Grid Reference(s)	Map 22
Down	N/A	29	J 220135 (Carlingford	
Republic of Ireland			Lough),	
			J 240110 (Green Island)	

Area (ha)	NNR	SPA		Ramsar	
3800	No	Designated	N	Designated	N
		Candidate	Y	Candidate	Y

Site description

A narrow sea lough surrounded by mountains. The northern shore is in Northern Ireland and includes the most significant mudflats in the lough, and an area of saltmarsh. At the mouth of the Lough are several small rock and shingle islands which are of importance to terns.

Birds

The site supports internationally important numbers of wintering light-bellied brent geese and nationally important numbers of wintering scaup and breeding common terns.

Green Island has an important tern colony which is in long-term decline. Counts in 1990 were 59 pairs Sandwich tern, 3 pairs **roseate tern** (4% of British), 217 pairs **common tern** (2% of British) and 9 pairs of arctic tern.

Wintering species include **light-bellied brent goose** which ranged between 365 and 407 during the winters 1984/85 and 1986/87 (2% of Greenland/Canada population). **Scaup** winter in nationally important numbers (325, 7% of British, 1985/6 to 1989/90).

Conservation issues

Green Island is a small island, subject to chronic natural erosion and in danger of disappearing. Threats to the mudflats include sewage pollution, leisure developments and shellfish culture.

Outer Ards Peninsula

SPA/Ram Code	IBA Europe number
2017A	250

County/Region	District(s)	NI OS Sheet(s)	Grid Reference(s)	Map 22
Down	N/A	15, 21	J 558838 to J 625454	

Area (ha)	NNR	SPA		Ramsar	
1300	Part	Designated	N	Designated	N
		Candidate	Y	Candidate	N

Rocky and sandy shoreline of importance for wintering waders.

Site description
A flat, eastern-facing shoreline of the Irish Sea with rocky outcrops, a number of islands and long sandy beaches.

Birds
Count data is available from 1985/86 onwards: however from winter 1989/90 the area counted was reduced in size so reference is made here to the four years' data that preceded this change.

The site is important for wintering waders, with internationally important numbers of **turnstone** present during the four winters of 1985/89 at an average of 1405 (2% of EAF, 3% of British). The count information indicates that this shoreline regularly held nationally important numbers of **ringed plovers** over this period, counts averaging 477 (2% of British). **Redshank** also averaged above GB nationally important threshold levels during these winters, an average of 768 birds being counted (1% of British).

Breeding birds include three colonies of cormorant of the subspecies *carbo*, amounting to 133 pairs in 1990 (2% of British); the largest colony, on North Rock (Portavogie), held 51 pairs. The islands are used by small numbers of breeding common terns and two colonies of arctic terns. The largest arctic tern colony in 1990, on Cockle Island, held 140 pairs.

Conservation issues
Breeding birds at this site are vulnerable to disturbance. Illegal shooting of shags and cormorants has occurred on a number of occasions.

SITE ACCOUNTS: THE CHANNEL ISLANDS

THE CHANNEL ISLANDS

Introduction

Located off the north-west coast of France, within the Gulf of St Malo, the Channel Islands lie some 130 km from the English coast and, in places, less than 12 km from the coast of Normandy. They are a dependency of the British Crown, covering a total area of 195 square km, and with a human population of 138,000 (1986).

Administratively, the Islands are divided into two Bailiwicks. The Bailiwick of Guernsey is formed, in turn, of two island groups: the more northerly comprises Alderney, with the rocks of the Casquets, Burhou and Ortac; the more southerly, Guernsey itself, Sark, Herm, Jethou, Lihou and Brecqhou. The Bailiwick of Jersey consists of Jersey and the islets of the Minquiers Reef and the Ecréhous.

The Channel Islands are not part of the United Kingdom, and are not represented in the UK Parliament at Westminster. Each Bailiwick is self-governing with its own legislative assembly: the States of Jersey and the States of Guernsey. Foreign policy and defence matters, however, are handled by the UK Government on behalf of the States. Jersey and Guernsey are not members of the European Community, and are therefore not covered by EC Directives (such as the EC Directive on the Conservation of Wild Birds 79/409). Instead, the Channel Islands enjoy a 'special relationship' with the EC arising from Article 227(5) of the EEC Treaty and Protocol No. 3 to the Treaty of Accession. This places the Islands within the tariff barrier applied by the EC to its trade with non-EC countries, although the Channel Islands contributes nothing to the EC budget, and receives no grants or payments from the EC.

International wildlife conventions ratified by the UK Government on behalf of both the States of Guernsey and the States of Jersey are the 'Bonn' Convention on the Conservation of Migratory Species of Wild Animals and the 'Washington' Convention on International Trade in Endangered Species of Wild Fauna and Flora. In addition, the UK Government has ratified the 'Ramsar' Convention on Wetlands of International Importance especially as Waterfowl Habitat on behalf of the States of Jersey (HoL 1991).

Being outside the UK, the Channel Islands have their own conservation legislation. Relevant bird and habitat conservation legislation for the States is, for Guernsey, the Protection of Wild Birds Ordinance 1949, amended 1974: and for Alderney, the Protection of Wild Birds Ordinance 1950. Neither state has legislated to protect wildlife habitats. The corresponding States of Jersey legislation is the Protection of Birds Law 1963, amended 1972. The Island Planning (Amendment No. 3) (Jersey) Law 1983 provides for the protection of ecologically important habitats through the designation of Sites of Special Interest (SSI). These are equivalent to Sites of Special Scientific Interest (SSSIs) notified under the British Wildlife and Countryside Act 1981.

The European IBA book (Grimmett and Jones 1989) listed only one site in the Channel Islands, the gannetries of Les Etacs and Ortac, although it recognised that it was 'likely that other important bird areas exist in the Channel Islands which need to be identified and evaluated.' Work conducted for the present book has identified a total of 13 sites of 'importance at UK and Channel Islands level'. It is possible that other sites may meet the qualification criteria (such as outlying islets and reefs for wintering waders) where the necessary survey work has not yet been undertaken.

THE STATES OF GUERNSEY
(includes : Alderney, Guernsey, Jethou, Sark)

ALDERNEY

Introduction
The most northerly of the Channel Islands, Alderney lies 12.8 km west of Cap de la Hague (the north-western promontory of the Cherbourg peninsula). About 5.6 km long, 2 km across at its widest point, and 1554 ha in area, the island rises to a maximum height of 90 m. The western two-thirds of the island consists of an elevated plateau, surrounded by granite cliffs to the west and south. The remainder is low-lying, with sand-dunes around the bays of Braye, Saye and Longis, and underlying Longis Common. Coastal heathland is found in the west and south of Alderney. Extensive heathland used to be present at Mannez Garenne, in the east of the island, but has been degraded by bracken invasion.

Birds
Species included in *Red Data Birds in Britain* (Batten *et al*, 1990) for which Alderney supports more than 1% of the British and Channel Islands population, and may therefore be considered to be of 'national' importance at 'British and Channel Islands level', include **gannet** (4900 pairs in the two colonies of Les Etacs and Ortac, 3% of British and CI) and **Dartford warbler**. In the period 1973–84, the coastal heathland of Alderney supported c. 15 pairs of Dartford warbler (2.5% of British and CI). Since the hard winters of 1984/85, 1985/86 and 1986/87, however, there have been no breeding records. In more recent years, Dartford warblers have been recorded during the summer and recolonisation might be expected (Mendham, pers comm).

Other species of interest at Channel Islands level include storm petrel and puffin colonies on the small island of Burhou, 1.6 km off the north-west shore of Alderney. In the 1960s, the storm petrel colony was estimated to contain many thousands of birds; four consecutive trapping nights in 1963 caught 1100 (Long 1981). The colony has now declined to 15 pairs (Mendham, pers comm). The main puffin colony on Burhou is in the same area as the storm petrels and has suffered a comparable decline. Described as 'an enormous colony' in about 1950 (Dobson 1952), it was estimated to be well under 1000 individuals in 1978 (Long, 1981), and numbered some 280 individuals in 1988 (Hill, pers comm). As in the other Channel Islands, short-toed treecreeper replaces treecreeper.

Site Descriptions and Conservation Issues
001 Les Etacs (The Garden Rocks)
Area (ha): c. 0.6. WA 550062 (Note: this site is included with Ortac as Channel Islands site 001 in the European IBA book). Map 23.

These two groups of igneous rocks rise to 39 m above LWOST, c. 200 m off the west coast of Alderney. The gannetry, which was founded in the early 1940s, had grown to c. 200 pairs in 1946 (Dobson and Lockley 1946), 1010 pairs in 1960, 2000 pairs in 1969 (Cramp *et al* 1974), and 2810 pairs (2% of British and CI) by 1989 (Hill 1989).

Discarded nylon fishing nets used by gannets for nests snare birds, particularly nestlings.

002 Ortac
Area (ha): c. 0.1. Lat 49°43′27″N Long 2°17′30″W. (Note: this site is included with Les Etacs as Channel Islands site 001 in the European IBA book). Map 23.

This Cambrian sandstone rock rises to 24 m above LWOST and is located c. 4.5 km off the west coast of Alderney. The gannetry, founded in the 1940s, had expanded to c. 250 pairs in 1946 (Dobson and Lockley 1946), 925 pairs in 1960, 1000 pairs in 1969 (Cramp et al 1974), and 2106 pairs (1% of British and CI) by 1989 (Hill 1989). It is now thought to have reached saturation point (Bourgaize, pers comm).

Discarded nylon fishing nets, used by gannets for nests, snare birds, particularly nestlings.

003 Alderney Heathland
Area (ha): 93. WA 557066 (Le Giffione) and WA 590073 (Trois Vaux). Map 23.

Heathland dominated by heather and gorse at Le Giffione in the west of Alderney and at Trois Vaux on the south coast. This site has held resident Dartford warblers.

Threats to the heathland include agricultural land-claim, invasion by bracken and lack of management, especially of gorse.

GUERNSEY

Introduction
Guernsey is a triangular island, measuring c. 15 km along the longest north-west facing coast and 10 km along the shorter south- and east- facing coasts. Totalling 6340 ha in area, the island slopes from granite cliffs in the south and south-east, rising to 107 m, to low-lying areas in the north. Guernsey experiences a slightly cooler climate than Jersey, due in part to the island sloping from south to north. Coastal heathland associated with cliffs occurs along the south coast, sand dune areas (mainly golf course) at L'Ancresse in the north, and there is a large area of reedbed at Les Grands Marais beside the north-west coast. There are also extensive intertidal areas along the north-west coast, with rocks, sand and mud. The interior of the island is divided into small fields, with small-scale cultivation, livestock farming and an extensive glasshouse industry.

Birds
Turnstone is the only species included in the British Red Data Book for which Guernsey supports more than 1% of the British and Channel Islands population. The average winter peak count for 1985/86–1989/90 was 672 (1.5% of British and CI). The species is only absent from the southern coastline associated with cliffs between Pleinmont in the east and La Vallette in the west. The main areas for turnstone (clockwise from Pleinmont Point) are: L'Erée, Perelle, Fort de Crocq, Vazon, the area between Rousse and Portinfer, and Bellegreve Bay.

Guernsey has supported more than 1% of the British and Channel Islands population of **Dartford warbler**. Following a long absence of records between 1875 and 1960, it was recorded breeding in 1961. Increased to peak of c. 20 pairs in 1984 (3% of British and CI), before sharp and progressive decline following hard winters of 1984/85, 1985/86 and

1986/87. Absent as a breeding species 1989/91, but has now recolonised (Bisson 1989, Bourgaize, pers comm). The main breeding area is along the south coast in remnant coastal heathland associated with cliffs. Dartford warbler has also been recorded breeding in small numbers on heath/dune areas in the northern part of the island from 1976, following an autumn influx of birds in 1975, possibly from north-west France (Bisson 1989).

Other species of importance at Channel Islands level include wintering divers and grebes in the coastal waters surrounding Guernsey (c. 40 black-throated divers, c. 40 great northern divers and c. 20 Slavonian grebes) and breeding common terns (c. 70 pairs) (Bourgaize in Grimmett and Jones 1989). Cetti's warblers probably bred in 1982, 1983 and 1984. Serins were suspected of breeding in 1976 and some following years, and confirmed in 1983 and 1984, but breeding has not been recorded since then (Bisson 1989). The narrow coastal strip on the north-west coast and northern heath/dune area at Vale is an important staging area for migrants.

Site Descriptions and Conservation Issues
004 Guernsey Shoreline
Area (ha): 1050. WV 236755 in the west to WV 343773 in the east. Map 24.

A rocky shoreline, indented with many small bays of rocks, sand and shingle, along the north-west and northern part of the east coast of Guernsey. This area is of national importance for wintering turnstone. At low tide, rocky sites are favoured feeding areas for turnstone, with high tide roosts located on shingle and grassy beach tops. Vazon Bay is sandier than the other sites listed above, but is rocky at each end.

This coastline is under threat from land-claim for development and tidal barrage schemes.

005 Guernsey Heathland
Area (ha): 280. WV 350838 (L'Ancresse Common) and WV 762238 (Les Pezeries) in the west to WV 341752 (Jerbourg) in the east. Map 24.

This area of heathland is in two parts. One part is located to the west of L'Ancresse Common in the north-eastern corner of the island, and comprises coastal heath dominated by gorse and heather. Bracken incursion is checked by cattle grazing.

The second part consists of land at the cliff top, between the cliff edge and agricultural fields, along the south coast of the island from Les Pezeries in the west to Jerbourg in the east. This area is primarily remnant coastal heathland, dominated by gorse and heather with associated scrub (particularly hawthorn and blackthorn). The site holds resident Dartford warblers.

The major threat to the site is lack of management, especially of gorse. Bracken invasion is of local impact. Scrub invasion is very damaging in some localities. Recreational pressure is considerable. Development threats and pressure arising from tourism are of lesser significance, but still of concern.

JETHOU

Introduction
Jethou lies 4.5 km east of Guernsey. Roughly circular in shape at 455 m across, it is steep-sided, with a partly cultivated plateau and some woodland.

Birds
A Manx Shearwater colony is of interest at Channel Islands level of importance; 5–10 apparently occupied burrows were recorded in 1989 (Hill in Lloyd *et al* 1991).

SARK

Introduction
Lying 12 km east of Guernsey, the island consists of Great Sark and Little Sark, which are connected by an isthmus. The island is 4.8 km by 2.4 km, with an area of only 1165 ha, and reaches 110 m at its highest point. Sark consists principally of coastal heathland and small scale cultivation, with a coastline of cliffs.

Birds
A Manx shearwater colony is of interest at Channel Islands level of importance. In 1989, 10–20 burrows in the southernmost part of Little Sark were apparently occupied, one of only two breeding colonies in the Channel Islands (Hill in Lloyd *et al* 1991).

STATES OF JERSEY
(includes: Jersey)

JERSEY

Introduction
The largest of the Channel Islands at 11,630 ha, Jersey lies c. 30 km from the French coast. Rectangular in shape, the island measures c. 16 km from east to west, and c. 9 km north to south. Over 140 m at its highest point, Jersey slopes from north to south. The climate of Jersey is mild compared with similar inland locations at the same latitude. Snow is relatively rare and ground frosts occur, on average, about 50 days each year.

A large tidal range of up to 12 m uncovers an extensive intertidal area of sand, mud and rock along the east, south and west coasts of the island. The north coast is mainly granite cliffs with an associated thick strip of coastal heath. The east coast is low-lying and has mainly been developed. However, there is a relic dune system at Gorey which now forms part of a golf course. North of Gorey, the coast takes on a wooded character. The south coast is also mainly developed. The south-west coast consists of a granite cliff with associated heathland (La Corbiere-La Lande du Ouest-Portelet Common-Noirmont), with sand dunes, scrub and heathland at Ouaisne. The west coast ranges from low-lying dry grassland with sand dunes at Les Blanches Banques at the southern end, to reedbeds and open freshwater, La Mare au Seigneur, in the centre of the coastal plain, rising to a granite headland with the associated coastal heath of Les Landes at the northern end. The interior of the island is divided by an extensive network of hedgerows, and is mainly under small-scale cultivation (especially for potatoes), with some livestock farming (mainly dairy). Several small wooded valleys dissect the island.

Birds

Species included in Red Data Birds in Britain (Batten et al, 1990) for which Jersey supports more than 1% of the British and Channel Islands population, and may therefore be considered to be of 'national' importance at British and Channel Islands level, include **ringed plover, grey plover, sanderling** and **turnstone**.

Passerine species for which Jersey supports more than 1% of the British and Channel Islands population include:

Cetti's warbler: Breeding first proven 1973, although probably first bred 1971. Increased to an estimated 30 pairs in 1978 (14% of British and CI). Population now c. 10 pairs (5% of British and CI), recovering after a trough in 1985-87 due to hard winter weather (Long, pers comm).

Dartford warbler: Total population of estimated at a peak of c. 100 pairs (17% of British and CI) in mid 1980s, but declined dramatically following intense cold spells during 1989/90 and 1990/91 winters. Population now estimated at 15+ pairs.

Serin: Breeding first suspected 1972, population now increased to over 20 pairs (60–100% of British and CI) (Long, pers comm).

Cirl bunting: Population remained stable at one or two pairs until the 1970s after which it increased to 14 pairs by 1982 (Long 1981, Sitters 1985). Current population estimated at c. 20 pairs (9% of British and CI).

Jersey also has a breeding population of 300–400 pairs of **shags** (1% of British and CI), which are mainly situated along the north and south-west coasts. Species of importance in the context of the Channel Islands include wintering divers, bearded tit (an occasional breeder in small numbers), common tern (120 pairs, including the reef of Les Ecréhous), razorbill (5-10 pairs) and puffin (20 pairs). Lying on main migration routes, Jersey, like the other Channel Islands, provides a staging post for many spring and autumn migrants.

The reef of Les Ecréhous, 14 km east-north-east of Jersey and unvegetated apart from extensive tree mallow on the largest island of Maître Ile, is of interest for breeding cormorants (c. 50 pairs), shags (c. 100 pairs), herring gulls (c. 400 pairs) and common terns (c. 70 pairs).

The Plateau des Minquiers is also of importance for breeding cormorant and shag. An extensive area of rocks and sand, with an area in excess of 80 square km being uncovered at spring low tides, the reef is located 25 km due south of Jersey. The largest island, Maîtresse Ile, is only 91 m by 27 m in size, and only 0.1 ha of land remains exposed at high tide. It is likely that the extensive intertidal area is used by considerable numbers of waders on passage and in winter, but detailed survey is required.

(References cited above, and in the site accounts which follow, can be found at the end of the site accounts).

Site Descriptions and Conservation Issues

The island's habitats, though individually relatively small, consist of a wide range of different plant communities with each merging into the next along different environmental gradients. It is thus difficult to identify important sites individually. The following are sites considered to be specifically important for birds.

Heathland
006 Les Landes
Area (ha): 99. WV 550555. Map 24.

Diverse coastal heath in the north-west of the island which held resident Dartford warblers until the winter of 1990/91, and holds resident stonechats and breeding wheatears.

The main threat to Les Landes is recreational pressure. Current uses include a horse racing track, model aircraft airfield and rifle range. Threatened uses include a golf course and car-rally area. Les Landes is a proposed Site of Special Interest (SSI).

007 Jardin d'Olivet
Area (ha): 25. WV 673542. Map 24.

Coastal heath above granite cliffs (c. 60 m) at the north end of the island, holding resident Dartford warbler. Jardin d'Olivet is also a major site for wall lizard.

This area is under recreational pressure. Jardin d'Olivet is a proposed SSI.

008 Noirmont
Area (ha): 39. WV 607471. Map 24.

Gorse heathland with large areas of bracken adjacent to granite cliffs in the south-west of the island. This site holds resident Dartford warblers, and is also an important site for migratory birds.

There is pressure from increased agricultural activity and growing associated edge effects. Noirmont is a proposed SSI.

009 Portelet Common
Area (ha): c. 27. WV 596474. Map 24.

Gorse heathland c. 60 m above mean sea level in the south-west of the island. Portelet Common is connected to Ouaisne and Noirmont by gorse/conifer plantation providing a refuge and escape corridor in case of fire. The site holds resident Dartford warblers and cirl buntings.

The site suffers from minor recreational pressure. Proposed SSI.

010 Ouaisne
Area (ha): 10. WV 596479. Map 24.

Stabilised sand dune with slacks, with managed gorse and dry heath in the south-west of the island. This site has supported a high density of resident Dartford warblers (Milton

1988), as well as serins and cirl buntings. In 1991, c. 5 pairs of Dartford warblers bred. It is also a major site for breeding agile frog. The *astreptophorus* form of grass snake, in which the white collar is missing, and green lizard also occur.

Ouaisne is threatened by increased recreational pressures, building development and drainage. It is a proposed SSI.

011 La Lande du Ouest (La Moye)
Area (ha): c. 20. WV 565475. Map 24.

Gorse heathland above granite cliffs in the south-west of the island. The site supports resident Dartford warblers, serins and cirl buntings.

La Lande du Ouest is under pressure from building development, notably a proposed extension to an adjacent housing estate. This site also suffered severe fire damage in the summer of 1989. La Lande du Ouest is a proposed SSI.

012 La Mare au Seigneur (St Ouen's Pond)
Area (ha): c. 5. WV 567520. Map 24.

St Ouen's Pond is 5 ha of open freshwater, fringed by an extensive bed of common reed. This site supports breeding Cetti's warblers, and is a valuable migrant refuge.

The site is under pressure from increased water abstraction. Recent expansion of a golf course may also lead to deterioration of the site.

013 Jersey Shoreline
Area (ha): c. 3100. WV 546552 in west to WV 715530 in east. Map 24.
These extensive intertidal zones on the west, south and east coasts of Jersey stretch from L'Etacq in the west to St Catherine's Bay in the east. The south and east coasts are more sheltered than the exposed west coast. There are extensive areas of sand and silt at St Ouen's Bay (west), St Aubin's Bay (south) and Grouville Bay (east), and of rocks at L'Etacq (west), La Pulente (south-west) and in the south-east, between St Helier and La Rocque.

Jersey Shoreline is a site of national importance for wintering **ringed plover** (average winter peak count 1987-1991: 353, 1.5% of British and CI. Wintering population may exceed 400 (Buxton, pers comm)), **grey plover** (average winter peak count 1987-1991: 398, 2% of British and CI. Wintering population estimated at 550 (Buxton, pers comm)), **sanderling** (average winter peak count 1987-1991: 241, 2% of British and CI. Wintering population probably exceeds 285 (Buxton, pers comm)) and **turnstone** (average winter peak count 1987-1991: 556, 1% of British and CI). The wintering population of turnstone may exceed 1000 (Buxton, pers comm), in which case Jersey would be of international significance for this species.

Ringed plover and grey plover occur mainly along the south-east coast of the island, ringed plover between Le Hocq and Le Hurel, and grey plover between Green Island and Gorey Harbour. Sanderling are found mainly at St Aubins Bay and at L'Etacq, and turnstone occur on the west coast at L'Etacq and in the south-east between Le Hocq and Gorey Harbour.

Other species of importance in the context of the Channel Islands include wintering wildfowl and waders, for example, 1000-1200 dark-bellied brent geese, up to 100 light-bellied brent geese, 1749 oystercatcher (average winter peak count 1987-1991), 2722 dunlin (average winter peak count 1987-1991), 259 bar-tailed godwit (average winter peak count 1987-1991) and 373 redshank (average winter peak count 1987-1991) (Long 1981, Buxton, pers comm).

The Jersey Shoreline is threatened by increased coastal pollution, shell fish farming, marina development and land reclamation.

References
(References cited in the text and not listed can be found at the end of chapter 1).
Anderson, P A 1984 *The Heathlands of Jersey*. Unpublished report for Island Development Committee, States of Jersey.
Bisson, A J 1989 *A List of the Birds of Guernsey*. Guernsey.
Buxton, I J 1986 Winter shorebirds in Jersey. *Annual Bulletin Société Jersiaise* 24: 265-269.
Cramp, S, Bourne, W R P and Saunders, D 1974 *The Seabirds of Britain and Ireland*. Collins, London.
Dobson, R 1952 *The Birds of the Channel Islands*. Staples Press, Newton Abbot.
Dobson, R and Lockley, R M 1946 Gannets breeding in the Channel Isles: two new colonies. *British Birds* 39: 309-312.
Hill, M 1989 The Alderney gannetries – photographic counts of Ortac and Les Etacs, Channel Islands, 1979-1989. *Seabird* 12: 45-52.
House Of Lords *Official Report*, 29 January 1991, Column WA 25.
Long, R 1981 Review of birds in the Channel Isles, 1951-80. *British Birds* 74: 327-344.
Mendham, M L 1990 *A List of the Birds of Alderney*.
Milton, N 1988 *Habitat Management of Gorse for the Dartford Warbler on Jersey*. Unpublished report for Island Development Committee, States of Jersey.
Sitters, H P 1985 Cirl buntings in Britain in 1982. *Bird Study* 32: 1-10.

Cirl bunting

SITE ACCOUNTS:
THE ISLE OF MAN

THE ISLE OF MAN

Introduction

The Isle of Man lies in the northern part of the Irish Sea. The nearest coast is that of Scotland: Burrow Head, Galloway is 29 km north from the Point of Ayre. The Island is 51 km long, has a maximum width of 21 km, covers an area of 58,793 ha and has a coastline 160 km long. In 1986, the population was 64,282, of whom 20,368 resided in Douglas, the capital.

The Isle of Man consists of a central highland mass, set on a south-west to north-east axis. Snaefell, at 621 m, is the highest point. In the north and south-east, the hills give way to lowland areas. Two subsidiary islets, the Calf of Man and Kitterland, lie to the south of the Isle of Man mainland.

Agricultural habitats account for 86% of the Island's area; urban habitats 7%, forest and woodland 5% and non-agricultural rural habitats 2% (NCC/ITE 1975). The agricultural land is utilised as arable, permanent grass and extensive rough grazing in equal proportions (DAFF 1988). The Isle of Man holds more than 1% of the British and Isle of Man population of four bird species included in *Red Data Birds in Britain* (Batten *et al* 1990), and which may therefore be considered to be of 'national' importance at British and Isle of Man level. These are **hen harrier** (minimum 40 occupied territories (1990), c. 6% of British and Manx population), **peregrine** (9-13 pairs (1986), c. 1% of British and Manx population), **little tern** (57-60 pairs (1985), c. 2.5% of British and Manx population) and **chough** (60 pairs (1982), 18% of British and Manx population) (Cullen and Jennings 1986, Batten *et al* 1990, RSPB 1990). The Isle of Man supports more than 1% of the British and Isle of Man population of two species not listed in *Red Data Birds in Britain*: shag (650 pairs, 1985-6) and black guillemot (334 individuals, 1989) Moore (1987,1989).

Administratively, like the Channel Islands, the Isle of Man is a self-Governing Crown dependency. The Lieutenant-Governor is the Queen's personal representative on the Island. The legislature, the Tynwald, is responsible for all matters other than foreign policy and defence. These are handled by the UK Government on behalf of the Isle of Man Government. The Isle of Man is not a member of the European Community: it enjoys a special relationship with the EC arising from the EEC Treaty and Protocol No 3 to the Treaty of Accession (see Channel Islands section). Thus the EC Directive on the Conservation of Wild Birds 79/409 does not apply to the Isle of Man.

The UK Government has ratified two international wildlife conventions on behalf of the Isle of Man Government: the Convention concerning the Protection of the World Cultural and Natural Heritage, and the 'Washington' Convention on International Trade in Endangered Species of Wild Fauna and Flora. The UK Government hopes 'soon' to extend the UK's ratification of the 'Berne' Convention on the Conservation of European Wildlife and Natural Habitats, and the 'Bonn' Convention on the Conservation of Migratory Species of Wild Animals, to include the Isle of Man (HoL 1991).

Being outside the UK, the Isle of Man has its own conservation legislation. The Wild Birds Protection Act 1887 was the first legislation passed by Tynwald to protect wild birds. Protection was extended and consolidated by subsequent Acts in 1932, 1955 and 1975. In general, this bird protection legislation parallels that of the (now repealed) British Protection of Birds Acts 1954–67. During 1990, Tynwald enacted the Wildlife Act 1990. This Act incorporates and updates the Protection of Birds Acts; extends protection to specified mammals and plants; and permits the creation of National Nature Reserves, Marine Nature Reserves and the notification of Areas of Special Scientific Interest. It is based on the British Wildlife and Countryside Acts 1981–5, and the Northern Ireland Nature Conservation and Amenity Lands Order 1985.

At the time of writing, however, it is not yet in force, as the necessary commencement orders have not yet been made. It is anticipated that the Act will be brought into force once additional secondary Regulations (such as the financial guidelines for the determination of management agreements in respect of ASSIs) have been made.

The European IBA book (Grimmett and Jones 1989) listed three sites for the Isle of Man: the Isle of Man Sea Cliffs (001), Calf of Man (002) and The Ayres (003). Two additional areas have been identified in respect of this book: 'Ballaugh Curraghs' and 'The Isle of Man Hills'.

(References cited above can be found at the end of the site accounts).

Chough

SITE ACCOUNTS

001 Isle of Man Sea Cliffs

IBA Europe number
001

Sheading(s):	OS Sheet	Grid reference(s)	Length	Map 23
Garff, Glenfaba,	95	East Coast SC 461934 to	East 64 km;	
Middle, Rushen		SC 256661; West Coast	West 33 km	
		SC 242847 to SC 210675		

Sea cliffs with adjacent upland heather and grass moorland and agricultural land, important for breeding and wintering chough and breeding peregrine and seabirds.

Site description
Ordovician Manx slate cliffs of varying profile, some high, steep and vertical (from 150–300 m) as at Spanish Head and The Sugar Loaf at the south of the island; elsewhere more rounded with low cliffs below and maritime heath above. The adjacent land-use also varies; at some locations agricultural land extends to the cliff edge. Many sections, however, grade into upland heather or grass moorland. The site is divided. The eastern section extends from Ballure, near Ramsey, in the north to Scarlett Point, near Castletown, in the south. The south and western part stretches between St Patrick's Isle, Peel, in the north and Port St Mary in the south. About 260 ha of cliff and associated land is owned by the Manx National Trust at six locations.

Species of interest include a subspecies of grey moth *Hadera caesia mananii*, which is of local distribution in the British Isles, always associated with the splash zone of cliffs within 50 m of high water mark. As well as the Isle of Man, it is known from south and east Ireland, Islay, Rhum, Canna and Mull (Heath and Maitland 1979).

Birds
An important breeding area for peregrine (5+ pairs), **chough** (50+ pairs, 16% of British and IoM), raven (15–20 pairs) and breeding seabirds, including fulmar (2100 pairs), cormorant (50 pairs), **shag** (400 pairs, 1% of British and IoM), kittiwake (1300 pairs), guillemot (1854 birds), razorbill (237 birds), **black guillemot** (334 birds, 1% of British and IoM) and puffin (60 pairs).

Wintering species include purple sandpiper (max 120) and **chough** (25–40, max 60, min. 3% of British and IoM) (Bullock *et al* 1983, Cullen and Jennings 1986, Hopson and Moore 1989, Moore 1989).

Conservation issues
Some peregrine nests are robbed. Maintenance of the chough population is dependent on the retention of maritime heath and well-grazed, traditionally managed permanent pasture at the cliff edge.

002 Calf of Man

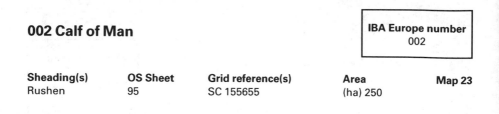

IBA Europe number
002

Sheading(s)	OS Sheet	Grid reference(s)	Area	Map 23
Rushen	95	SC 155655	(ha) 250	

An offshore island with cliffs important for breeding seabirds and chough.

Site description
An offshore island with slate cliffs and boulder areas providing suitable sites for breeding seabirds. The grazed maritime turf provides important feeding areas for choughs. It is wholly owned by the Manx National Trust.

The Calf of Man lies 400 m off the south-westernmost tip of the Isle of Man. Formed of Ordovician Manx slates, the island rises to 128 m above sea-level, and is dissected by a valley, which runs on a north-south axis through its centre. The coastline is rugged with steep slate cliffs of varying height topped with maritime turf, heather and bracken covered slopes. The island was farmed until 1958. Remnants of the old farm system are still identifiable; small fields, once arable but now permanent pasture being invaded by bracken, divided by stone walls. Outside the enclosed land is maritime heath, with bell heather, heather, western gorse and bracken. The island continues to be grazed by rabbits and a flock of Manx loaghtan sheep.

Birds
The Calf is of importance for breeding **chough** (6-10 pairs, min. 2% of British and IoM), peregrine (1 pair), short-eared owl (up to 3 pairs) and breeding seabirds, including shag (250 pairs), guillemot (490 birds), razorbill (225 birds) and puffin (40 pairs) (Bullock *et al* 1983, Cullen and Jennings 1986, Moore 1987, 1989). Manx shearwaters probably breed annually in small numbers (up to 10-12 pairs). Storm petrels are present during the breeding season. A population of up to 50 breeding pairs has been suggested, although conclusive evidence of breeding has yet to be obtained (Cullen and Jennings 1986).

In addition, the island is an important site for migrant birds; large numbers of thrushes and warblers occur on spring and autumn passage. A bird observatory has been operated on the Calf of Man since 1959, and was recognised by the BTO in 1962.

Conservation issues
Controlled burning of heather assists the maintenance of maritime heath. Continued grazing by sheep is of importance in maintaining the chough populations: the densest population recorded anywhere in north-west Europe. Following cessation of farming in 1958, which permitted bracken to spread into the old pastures, and the remaining grass to grow long, the chough population dwindled from 10 pairs to just four in 1967. The introduction of Loaghtan sheep in 1969, together with the constantly high rabbit population in more recent years, stimulated a recovery to 9 pairs in 1981.

Further reading
Calf of Man Bird Observatory Reports.

003 The Ayres

IBA Europe number
003

Sheading(s)	OS Sheet	Grid reference(s)	Area	Map 23
Ayre	95	NX 430035	(ha) c. 800	

A series of shingle ridges, with adjacent heathland, important for breeding waders and terns.

Site description

Shingle beach, sand dunes and lichen heath holding breeding terns and waders. Ownership of the site is divided between the Manx National Trust (18 ha), private landowners (c. 550 ha) and the Isle of Man Government (250 ha), the latter managed by the Department of Agriculture, Fisheries and Forestry.

The Ayres extend 8 km between The Lhen in the west and the Point of Ayre in the east; the site includes the coast and adjacent heath. The Ayres consist of a series of shingle ridges, over which blown-sand has accumulated. At the western end the beach is sandy but grades into shingle towards the east. A line of marram-covered sand dunes separates the beach from an area of heath, approximately 1.5 km deep in the east, but narrowing towards the west. Vegetation types on the heath include western gorse/mixed heather heath, lichen heath (which includes *Usnea articulata*, which normally grows on trees, this change of habit being unique in the British Isles), and grass heath. The inland margin of the Ayres is being invaded by gorse, bracken and bramble. There are no dune slacks, although low areas may hold water in winter after heavy rain; several small ponds are present which may have been created by marl digging. The flora of the Ayres is rich: as well as the nationally important lichen communities, burnet rose, common twayblade, pyramidal, early-purple, early-marsh and dense-flowered orchids are present. The last species is only known elsewhere in the British Isles in the west of Ireland.

Birds

The Ayres is of importance for breeding terns. **Little terns** increased from 43 pairs in 1979 to 57-60 pairs (min. 2.5% of British and IoM) in 1985. Arctic terns number 15-30 pairs, and up to 7 pairs of common terns nest. One pair of roseate terns was thought to have bred in 1975. Breeding waders include 70-100 pairs of oystercatcher and about 100 pairs of ringed plover.

In winter, the site supports 300-1000 golden plover, several flocks of up to 300 curlew and 1 or 2 short-eared owls (Cullen and Jennings 1986, Moore 1987).

Conservation issues

Sand and gravel extraction has damaged the eastern end of the site. Recreational use, including motorcycles, has damaged the heath vegetation in parts. Recreational disturbance also affects ground-nesting birds. Of concern is the invasion of the inland margin of the heath by gorse, bracken and bramble due to the cessation of grazing. Previously cattle (rabbits prior to the 1820s) kept this in check.

The site was recommended for protection as a Manx Nature Reserve by the NCC and Institute of Terrestrial Ecology in 1975 (NCC/ITE 1975).

004 Ballaugh Curraghs

IBA Europe number
N/A

Sheading(s)	OS Sheet	Grid reference(s)	Area	Map 23
Ayre, Michael	95	SC 365950	(ha) 374	

Bog with low shrubs, willow carr and some open water, of importance for its hen harrier roost and breeding bird community.

Site description

'Curragh' is the Manx Gaelic word for willow carr. Ballaugh Curraghs is the largest such area in the Isle of Man. It covers flat glacial moraine deposits of the northern plain, occupying part of the site of Lake Andreas, which was formed in glacial times. Impeded drainage encouraged peat formation. There is dense growth of willow and birch over much of the Curragh. Other areas of bog are dominated by low shrubs, including creeping willow and bog-myrtle. Open water is now scarce. Surrounding the Curraghs proper is a network of small rushy fields, divided by boundary 'hedges' of willow and alder.

Plants of interest include marsh cinquefoil, common twayblade, lesser and greater butterfly-orchids, fragrant orchid, common cottongrass, greater bladderwort, frogbit, bogbean and royal fern. The site is also of interest for insects, including the Diptera *Epitriptus cowini*, first named after specimens collected in the area.

A very small part of the site is owned by the Manx National Trust (4.5 ha).

Birds

Ballaugh Curragh provides a communal winter roost for **hen harriers**. The roost was first discovered in December 1986 when up to 23 birds (3% of British and IoM) were noted. Since then, up to 80 birds (9% of British and IoM, January and October 1990) have been recorded, making it the largest roost in western Europe. Over 40 species have bred on the site during the last decade including shoveler, water rail, long-eared owl and grasshopper warbler. The wet rushy meadows hold breeding lapwing, snipe and curlew.

Conservation issues

Historically, peat has been cut from Ballaugh Curraghs for fuel. From the 16th century onwards, land marginal to the Curraghs was drained for agriculture by improvements to the main drainage channels – the Lhen Trench and Killane River, which connect to minor drainage ditches. Until the last century, however, drainage was checked by the need to maintain water levels in the Curraghs to enable mills on the Lhen and Killane rivers to operate. Following closure of the mills, much more extensive drainage took place, resulting in considerable reduction of the open water area. Since the 1860s, willow carr has colonised many of the fields at the margin of the Curraghs, presumably due to reductions in grazing intensity and changes in water management.

The site was recommended for protection as a Manx Nature Reserve in 1975 (NCC/ITE 1975).

005 The Isle of Man Hills

IBA Europe number
N/A

Sheading(s)	OS Sheet	Grid reference(s)	Area	Map 23
Ayre, Garff,	95	SC 330840	(ha) 8650	
Glenfaba, Michael,				
Middle, Rushen				

Upland heather and grass moorland, with some conifer afforestation, of importance for breeding hen harrier, merlin, red grouse, short-eared owl and chough.

Site description

The Isle of Man hills are composed of Ordovician Manx slates. Snaefell, at 621 m above sea level, is the highest point, although in all there are 19 peaks in excess of 400 m asl. The hills lie on a north-east to south-west axis, divided by a central valley formed by the rivers Dhoo and Neb. Historically, many areas have suffered from overgrazing by sheep and cattle and these are characterised by the grass moorland, which predominates in the central and northern hills. Bell heather and heather, however, still dominate some hills in this area, and most of the southern hills. Botanically, overgrazing has reduced the diversity of flora in the uplands. Dwarf willow is still found on Snaefell, while North and South Barrule have cowberry.

The site is owned by the Isle of Man Government and managed by the Department of Agriculture, Fisheries and Forestry.

Birds

The Isle of Man uplands are of particular importance for **hen harrier**. A survey in 1990 found a minimum of 40 occupied territories, including 34 nests (6% of British and IoM), (RSPB 1990). Other species of interest include merlin (1-2 pairs), red grouse (60-90 pairs), curlew (40 pairs), short-eared owl (2-5 pairs), chough (1-2 pairs) and raven (20 pairs).

Conservation issues

Only a small area of heather moorland is routinely managed by controlled burning. The Department of Agriculture, Fisheries and Forestry lets out the grazing and shooting rights separately to agricultural and shooting tenants, hindering the adoption of positive measures to manage and re-generate heather moorland.

During the last century, some 2400 ha has been planted by the Department of Agriculture, Fisheries and Forestry with conifers, in some 50 plantations. Hen harriers have taken advantage of some plantations for nesting sites as enclosure has reduced grazing pressure and permitted the growth of tall heather, so providing cover for nest sites. Suitable conditions for hen harrier have been perpetuated by default, as inadequate ground preparation has caused several areas of plantation to fail or grow only very poorly.

Plans approved by Tynwald in 1985 propose doubling the area of conifer afforestation, by planting a further 2833 ha by the year 2000. Since then, the target has been reduced to

2024 ha over a longer timescale. This is due to be accompanied by re-planting of areas of failed plantation, and some improvements to hill land have been made to compensate the agricultural tenants for land lost to forestry. Such work has mainly consisted of improvements to fencing and access, but some heather moorland has already been re-seeded and converted to grass. If implemented fully, these proposals could lead to the loss of an estimated 1600 ha of heather moorland (Williams 1989).

The growth in the hen harrier population from first breeding in 1977, to 6-10 pairs in the early 1980s, to about 40 occupied territories now, illustrates how successful this species can be when it is not persecuted.

References
(References cited in the text and not listed here can be found at the end of Chapter 1).

Bullock, I D, Drewett, D and Mickleburgh, S P 1983 The chough on the Isle of Man. *Peregrine* 5: 229-237.

Cullen, J P and Jennings, P P 1986 *The Birds of the Isle of Man.* Bridgeen Publications, Douglas.

Department of Agriculture, Fisheries and Forestry 1988 *June 1988 Agricultural Returns.* Isle of Man Government.

Garrard, L S 1972 *The Naturalist in the Isle of Man.* David and Charles, Newton Abbot.

Heath, J and Maitland, E 1979 *The Moths and Butterflies of Great Britain and Ireland. Volume 9.* Curwen Books, Plaistow, London.

Hopson, T and Moore, A 1989 The Manx Bird Report 1988. *Peregrine* 6(3): 36-65.

House Of Lords *Official Report,* 29 January 1991, Column WA 25.

Moore, A S 1987 The numbers and distribution of seabirds breeding on the Isle of Man during 1985-86. *Peregrine* 6(2): 64-80.

Moore, A S 1989 Black guillemots (*Cepphus grylle*) in the Isle of Man in 1987. *Peregrine* 6(3): 71-73.

Nature Conservancy Council and Institute of Terrestrial Ecology 1975. *Nature Conservation in the Isle of Man.* A Report by the NCC and ITE to the Isle of Man Local Government Board. IoMLGB.

Williams, G 1989 Land use and birds in the Isle of Man. *RSPB Conserv. Rev.* 3: 45-49.

APPENDICES

APPENDIX I:
LIST OF BIRD SPECIES MENTIONED IN TEXT

Red-throated Diver	*Gavia stellata*
Black-throated Diver	*G. arctica*
Great Northern Diver	*G. immer*
Little Grebe	*Tachybaptus ruficollis*
Great Crested Grebe	*Podiceps cristatus*
Slavonian Grebe	*P. auritus*
Black-necked Grebe	*P. nigricollis*
Fulmar	*Fulmarus glacialis*
Manx Shearwater	*Puffinus puffinus*
Storm Petrel	*Hydrobates pelagicus*
Leach's Petrel	*Oceanodroma leucorhoa*
Gannet	*Sula bassana*
Cormorant	*Phalacrocorax carbo*
Shag	*P. aristotelis*
Bittern	*Botaurus stellaris*
Little Egret	*Egretta garzetta*
Grey Heron	*Ardea cinera*
Mute Swan	*Cygnus olor*
Bewick's Swan	*C. columbianus*
Whooper Swan	*C. cygnus*
Bean Goose	*Anser fabalis*
Pink-footed Goose	*A. brachyrhynchus*
White-fronted Goose	*A. albifrons (flavirostris)*
Greylag Goose	*A. anser*
Canada Goose	*Branta canadensis*
Barnacle Goose	*B. leucopsis*
Brent Goose	*B. bernicla*
Shelduck	*Tadorna tadorna*
Mandarin Duck	*Aix galericulata*
Wigeon	*Anas penelope*
Gadwall	*A. strepera*
Teal	*A. crecca*
Mallard	*A. platyrhynchos*
Pintail	*A. acuta*
Garganey	*A. querquedula*
Shoveler	*A. clypeata*
Pochard	*Aythya ferina*
Tufted Duck	*A. fuligula*
Scaup	*A. marila*
Eider	*Somateria mollissima*
Long-tailed Duck	*Clangula hyemalis*
Common Scoter	*Melanitta nigra*
Velvet Scoter	*M. fusca*
Goldeneye	*Bucephala clangula*
Smew	*Mergus albellus*
Red-breasted Merganser	*M. serrator*

Goosander	*M. merganser*
Ruddy Duck	*Oxyura jamaicensis*
Honey Buzzard	*Pernis apivorus*
Red Kite	*Milvus milvus*
White-tailed Eagle	*Haliaeetus albicilla*
Marsh Harrier	*Circus aeruginosus*
Hen Harrier	*C. cyaneus*
Goshawk	*Accipiter gentilis*
Sparrowhawk	*A. nisus*
Buzzard	*Buteo buteo*
Golden Eagle	*Aquila chrysaetos*
Osprey	*Pandion haliaetus*
Kestrel	*Falco tinnunculus*
Merlin	*F. columbarius*
Hobby	*F. subbuteo*
Peregrine	*F. peregrinus*
Red Grouse	*Lagopus lagopus*
Ptarmigan	*L. mutus*
Black Grouse	*Tetrao tetrix*
Capercaillie	*T. urogallus*
Quail	*Coturnix coturnix*
Water Rail	*Rallus aquaticus*
Spotted Crake	*Porzana porzana*
Corncrake	*Crex crex*
Coot	*Fulica atra*
Oystercatcher	*Haematopus ostralegus*
Avocet	*Recurvirostra avosetta*
Stone-curlew	*Burhinus oedicnemus*
Little Ringed Plover	*Charadrius dubius*
Ringed Plover	*C. hiaticula*
Dotterel	*C. morinellus*
Golden Plover	*Pluvialis apricaria*
Grey Plover	*P. squatarola*
Lapwing	*Vanellus vanellus*
Knot	*Calidris canutus*
Sanderling	*C. alba*
Little Stint	*C. minuta*
Curlew Sandpiper	*C. ferruginea*
Purple Sandpiper	*C. maritima*
Dunlin	*C. alpina*
Ruff	*Philomachus pugnax*
Snipe	*Gallinago gallinago*
Black-tailed Godwit	*Limosa limosa*
Bar-tailed Godwit	*L. lapponica*
Whimbrel	*Numenius phaeopus*
Curlew	*N. arquata*
Spotted Redshank	*Tringa erythropus*
Redshank	*T. totanus*
Greenshank	*T. nebularia*
Green Sandpiper	*T. ochropus*

Common Sandpiper	*Actitis hypoleucos*
Turnstone	*Arenaria interpres*
Red-necked Phalarope	*Phalaropus lobatus*
Arctic Skua	*Stercorarius parasiticus*
Great Skua	*S. skua*
Little Gull	*Larus minutus*
Black-headed Gull	*L. ridibundus*
Common Gull	*L. canus*
Lesser Black-backed Gull	*L. fuscus*
Herring Gull	*L. argentatus*
Great Black-backed Gull	*L. marinus*
Kittiwake	*Rissa tridactyla*
Sandwich Tern	*Sterna sandvicensis*
Roseate Tern	*S. dougallii*
Common Tern	*S. hirundo*
Arctic Tern	*S. paradisaea*
Little Tern	*S. albifrons*
Black Tern	*Chlidonias niger*
Guillemot	*Uria aalge*
Razorbill	*Alca torda*
Black Guillemot	*Cepphus grylle*
Puffin	*Fratercula arctica*
Barn Owl	*Tyto alba*
Snowy Owl	*Nyctea scandiaca*
Long-eared Owl	*Asio otus*
Short-eared Owl	*A. flammeus*
Nightjar	*Caprimulgus europaeus*
Kingfisher	*Alcedo atthis*
Lesser Spotted Woodpecker	*Dendrocopos minor*
Woodlark	*Lullula arborea*
Swallow	*Hirundo rustica*
Yellow Wagtail	*Motacilla flava*
Grey Wagtail	*M. cinerea*
Dipper	*Cinclus cinclus*
Wren	*Troglodytes troglodytes* (Fair Isle subsp. *fridariensis*)
Nightingale	*Luscinia megarhynchos*
Redstart	*Phoenicurus phoenicurus*
Whinchat	*Saxicola rubetra*
Stonechat	*S. torquata*
Wheatear	*Oenanthe oenanthe*
Ring Ousel	*Turdus torquatus*
Fieldfare	*T. pilaris*
Redwing	*T. iliacus*
Cetti's Warbler	*Cettia cetti*
Grasshopper Warbler	*Locustella naevia*
Savi's Warbler	*L. luscinioides*
Sedge Warbler	*Acrocephalus schoenobaenus*
Reed Warbler	*A. scirpaceus*
Dartford Warbler	*Sylvia undata*

Wood Warbler	*Phylloscopus sibilatrix*
Firecrest	*Regulus ignicapillus*
Pied Flycatcher	*Ficedula hypoleuca*
Bearded Tit	*Panurus biarmicus*
Crested Tit	*Parus cristatus*
Treecreeper	*Certhia familiaris*
Short-toed Treecreeper	*Certhia brachydactyla*
Chough	*Pyrrhocorax pyrrhocorax*
Raven	*Corvus corax*
Starling	*Sturnus vulgaris*
Serin	*Serinus serinus*
Twite	*Carduelis flavirostris*
Crossbill	*Loxia curvirostra*
Scottish Crossbill	*L. scotica*
Hawfinch	*Coccothraustes coccothraustes*
Lapland Bunting	*Calcarius lapponicus*
Snow Bunting	*Plectrophenax nivalis*
Cirl Bunting	*Emberiza cirlus*
Reed Bunting	*E. schoeniclus*

APPENDIX II: PLANT SPECIES MENTIONED IN TEXT

Adder's-tongue	*Ophioglossum vulgatum*
Alder	*Alnus glutinosa*
Alder buckthorn	*Frangula alnus*
Alexanders	*Smyrnium olusatrum*
Alpine bearberry	*Arctostaphylos alpinus*
Alpine bistort	*Polygonum viviparum*
Alpine meadow-grass	*Poa alpina*
Alpine meadow-rue	*Thalictrum alpinum*
Alpine saw-wort	*Saussurea alpina*
Alternate water-milfoil	*Myriophyllum alternifolium*
Amphibious bistort	*Polygonum amphibium*
Annual sea-blite	*Suaeda maritima*
Arctic sandwort	*Arenaria norvegica* subsp. *norvegica*
Arrowhead	*Sagittaria sagittifolia*
Ash	*Fraxinus excelsior*
Aspen	*Populus tremula*
Autumn gentian	*Gentianella amarella*
Baltic rush	*Juncus balticus*
Bastard-toadflax	*Thesium humifusum*
Beaked tasselweed	*Ruppia maritima*
Bearberry	*Arctostaphylos uva-ursi*
Beech	*Fagus sylvatica*
Bell heather	*Erica cinerea*
Bilberry	*Vaccinium myrtillus*
Birch	*Betula* spp.
Biting stonecrop	*Sedum acre*
Black bog-rush	*Schoenus nigricans*
Blackthorn	*Prunus spinosa*
Bladder-sedge	*Carex vesicaria*
Bluebell	*Hyacinthoides non-scripta*
Blunt-flowered rush	*Juncus subnodulosus*
Bog asphodel	*Narthecium ossifragum*
Bogbean	*Menyanthes trifoliata*
Bog bilberry	*Vaccinium uliginosum*
Bog myrtle	*Myrica gale*
Bog orchid	*Hammarbya paludosa*
Bog pondweed	*Potamogeton polygonifolius*
Bog-rosemary	*Andromeda polifolia*
Bottle sedge	*Carex rostrata*
Bracken	*Pteridium aquilinum*
Brackish water-crowfoot	*Ranunculus baudotii*
Bramble	*Rubus fruticosus*
Branched bur-reed	*Sparganium erectum*
Breckland speedwell	*Veronica praecox*
Breckland wild thyme	*Thymus serpyllum*
Bristle bent	*Agrostis curtisii*

Bristly oxtongue	*Picris echioides*
Broad-leaved cottongrass	*Eriophorum latifolium*
Brown beak-sedge	*Rhynchospora fusca*
Buck's-horn plantain	*Plantago coronopus*
Bulbous foxtail	*Alopecurus bulbosus*
Bulrush	*Typha* spp.
Bur medick	*Medicago minima*
Burnet rose	*Rosa pimpinellifolia*
Burnet-saxifrage	*Pimpinella saxifraga*
Canadian waterweed	*Elodea canadensis*
Canary-grass	*Phalaris canariensis*
Carline thistle	*Carlina vulgaris*
Carnation sedge	*Carex panicea*
Cloudberry	*Rubus chamaemorus*
Common bent	*Agrostis capillaris*
Common bird's-foot-trefoil	*Lotus corniculatus*
Common blue-sow-thistle	*Cicerbita macrophylla*
Common butterwort	*Pinguicula vulgaris*
Common club-rush	*Schoenoplectus lacustris*
Common cord-grass	*Spartina anglica*
Common cottongrass	*Eriophilum angustifolium*
Common water-crowfoot	*Ranunculus aquatilis*
Common reed	*Phragmites australis*
Common saltmarsh-grass	*Puccinellia maritima*
Common sallow	*Salix cinerea*
Common scurvygrass	*Cochlearia officinalis*
Common sea-lavender	*Limonium vulgare*
Common sedge	*Carex nigra*
Common spike-rush	*Eleocharis palustris*
Common valerian	*Valeriana officinalis*
Cord-grass	*Spartina* spp.
Corsican pine	*Pinus nigra* subsp. *laricio*
Cowbane	*Cicuta virosa*
Cowberry	*Vaccinium vitis-idaea*
Cowslip	*Primula veris*
Cranberry	*Vaccinium oxycoccos*
Creeping bent	*Agrostis stolonifera*
Creeping lady's-tresses	*Goodyera repens*
Creeping willow	*Salix repens*
Crested dog's-tail	*Cynosurus cristatus*
Cross-leaved heath	*Erica tetralix*
Crowberry	*Empetrum nigrum* subsp. *nigrum*
Cuckooflower	*Cardamine pratensis*
Curved sedge	*Carex maritima*
Deergrass	*Scirpus cespitosus*
Devil's-bit scabious	*Succisa pratensis*
Dorset heath	*Erica ciliaris*
Downy birch	*Betula pubescens*
Dune fescue	*Vulpia fasciculata*
Dune gentian	*Gentianella uliginosa*

Dwarf birch	*Betula nana*
Dwarf eelgrass	*Zostera noltii*
Dwarf gorse	*Ulex minor*
Dwarf pansy	*Viola kitaibeliana*
Dwarf sedge	*Carex humilis*
Dwarf thistle	*Cirsium acaulon*
Dwarf willow	*Salix herbacea*
Eared willow	*Salix aurita*
Early forget-me-not	*Myosotis ramosissima*
Early gentian	*Gentianella anglica*
Early marsh-orchid	*Dactylorhiza incarnata*
Early-purple orchid	*Orchis mascula*
Eelgrass	*Zostera marina*
Elder	*Sambucus nigra*
Elm	*Ulmus* spp.
English scurvygrass	*Cochlearia anglica*
English stonecrop	*Sedum anglicum*
Fairy flax	*Linum catharticum*
False oat-grass	*Arrhenatherum elatius*
Fen orchid	*Liparis loeselii*
Fen pondweed	*Potamogeton coloratus*
Fennel pondweed	*Potamogeton pectinatus*
Field fleawort	*Senecio integrifolius*
Field maple	*Acer campestre*
Field wormwood	*Artemisia campestris*
Fine-leaved water-dropwort	*Oenanthe aquatica*
Fingered speedwell	*Veronica triphyllos*
Fir clubmoss	*Huperzia selago*
Flat-stalked pondweed	*Potamogeton friesii*
Floating sweet-grass	*Glyceria fluitans*
Flowering-rush	*Butomus umbellatus*
Fringed water-lily	*Nymphoides peltata*
Frogbit	*Hydrocharis morsus-ranae*
Glasswort	*Salicornia* agg.
Globeflower	*Trollius europaeus*
Golden dock	*Rumex maritimus*
Golden-samphire	*Inula crithmoides*
Gorse	*Ulex europaeus*
Great fen-sedge	*Cladium mariscus*
Great wood-rush	*Luzula sylvatica*
Greater bladderwort	*Utricularia australis*
Greater pond-sedge	*Carex riparia*
Greater sea-spurrey	*Spergularia media*
Greater spearwort	*Ranunculus lingua*
Greater tussock-sedge	*Carex paniculata*
Greater water-parsnip	*Sium latifolium*
Green spleenwort	*Asplenium viride*
Green-winged orchid	*Orchis morio*
Grey club-rush	*Schoenoplectus tabernaemontani*
Grey hair-grass	*Corynephorus canescens*

Guelder-rose	*Viburnum opulus*
Hairlike pondweed	*Potamogeton trichoides*
Hare's-tail cottongrass	*Eriophorum vaginatum*
Hawthorn	*Crataegus monogyna*
Hay-scented buckler-fern	*Dryopteris aemula*
Hazel	*Corylus avellana*
Heath bedstraw	*Galium saxatile*
Heath dog-violet	*Viola canina*
Heath rush	*Juncus squarrosus*
Heather	*Calluna vulgaris*
Hemlock water-dropwort	*Oenanthe crocata*
Hoary stock	*Matthiola incana*
Holly	*Ilex aquifolium*
Holly fern	*Polystichum lonchitis*
Holy-grass	*Hierochloe odorata*
Irish lady's-tresses	*Spiranthes romanzoffiana*
Jointed rush	*Juncus articulatus*
Juniper	*Juniperus communis*
Kidney vetch	*Anthyllis vulneraria*
Knotted hedge-parsley	*Torilis nodosa*
Labrador-tea	*Ledum groenlandicum*
Lady's bedstraw	*Galium verum*
Large-flowered hemp-nettle	*Galeopsis speciosa*
Lax-flowered sea-lavender	*Limonium humile*
Least adder's-tongue	*Ophioglossum lusitanicum*
Lesser bladderwort	*Utricularia minor*
Lesser bulrush	*Typha angustifolia*
Lesser butterfly-orchid	*Platanthera bifolia*
Lesser clubmoss	*Selaginella selaginoides*
Lesser meadow-rue	*Thalictrum minus*
Lesser pondweed	*Potamogeton pusillus*
Lesser sea-spurrey	*Spergularia marina*
Lesser spearwort	*Ranunculus flammula*
Lesser tussock-sedge	*Carex diandra*
Lesser twayblade	*Listera cordata*
Lesser water-parsnip	*Berula erecta*
Limestone bedstraw	*Galium sterneri*
Little-robin	*Geranium purpureum*
Long-bracted sedge	*Carex extensa*
Long-stalked pondweed	*Potamogeton praelongus*
Lousewort	*Pedicularis sylvatica*
Lyme-grass	*Leymus arenarius*
Many-stalked spike-rush	*Eleocharis multicaulis*
Mare's-tail	*Hippuris vulgaris*
Maritime pine	*Pinus pinaster*
Marram	*Ammophila arenaria*
Marsh arrowgrass	*Triglochin palustris*
Marsh cinquefoil	*Potentilla palustris*
Marsh clubmoss	*Lycopodiella inundata*
Marsh fern	*Thelypteris palustris*

Marsh foxtail	*Alopecurus geniculatus*
Marsh gentian	*Gentiana pneumonanthe*
Marsh-mallow	*Althaea officinalis*
Marsh-marigold	*Caltha palustris*
Marsh-orchids	*Dactylorhiza* spp.
Marsh pea	*Lathyrus palustris*
Marsh pennywort	*Hydrocotyle vulgaris*
Marsh ragwort	*Senecio aquaticus*
Marsh sow-thistle	*Sonchus palustris*
Mat-grass	*Nardus stricta*
Meadow barley	*Hordeum secalinum*
Meadow fescue	*Festuca pratensis*
Meadow thistle	*Cirsium dissectum*
Meadowsweet	*Filipendula ulmaria*
Melancholy thistle	*Cirsium helenioides*
Milk-parsley	*Peucedanum palustre*
Moss campion	*Silene acaulis*
Mossy saxifrage	*Saxifraga hypnoides*
Mountain avens	*Dryas octopetala*
Mountain everlasting	*Antennaria dioica*
Mudwort	*Limosella aquatica*
Narrow-leaved bird's-foot-trefoil	*Lotus tenuis*
Narrow-leaved eelgrass	*Zostera angustifolia*
Nettle	*Urtica* spp.
Oak	*Quercus* spp.
Oak-leaved goosefoot	*Chenopodium glaucum*
Opposite-leaved pondweed	*Groenlandia densa*
Orange bird's-foot	*Ornithopus pinnatus*
Oysterplant	*Mertensia maritima*
Pale forget-me-not	*Myosotis stolonifera*
Parsley water-dropwort	*Oenanthe lachenalii*
Pepper-saxifrage	*Silaum silaus*
Perennial glasswort	*Salicornia perennis*
Perennial knawel	*Scleranthus perennis*
Perennial rye-grass	*Lolium perenne*
Perfoliate pondweed	*Potamogeton perfoliatus*
Petty whin	*Genista anglica*
Portland spurge	*Euphorbia portlandica*
Prickly saltwort	*Salsola kali*
Primrose	*Primula vulgaris*
Purple moor-grass	*Molinia caerulea*
Purple saxifrage	*Saxifraga oppositifolia*
Pyramidal bugle	*Ajuga pyramidalis*
Ragged-robin	*Lychnis flos-cuculi*
Red fescue	*Festuca rubra*
Reed canary-grass	*Phalaris arundinacea*
Reed sweet grass	*Glyceria maxima*
Reedmace	*Typha* spp.
Reflexed saltmarsh-grass	*Puccinellia distans*
Rhododendron	*Rhododendron ponticum*

Rigid hornwort	*Ceratophyllum demersum*
River water–dropwort	*Oenanthe fluviatilis*
Rock sea-lavender	*Limonium binervosum*
Rosebay willowherb	*Epilobium angustifolium*
Roseroot	*Sedum rosea*
Round-leaved sundew	*Drosera rotundifolia*
Rowan	*Sorbus aucuparia*
Royal fern	*Osmunda regalis*
Salad burnet	*Sanguisorba minor* subsp. *minor*
Sallow	*Salix* spp.
Saltmarsh flat-sedge	*Blysmus rufus*
Saltmarsh rush	*Juncus gerardii*
Sand catchfly	*Silene conica*
Sand couch	*Elymus farctus*
Sand leek	*Allium scorodoprasum*
Sand sedge	*Carex arenaria*
Saw-wort	*Serratula tinctoria*
Scentless mayweed	*Tripleurospermum inodorum*
Scottish primrose	*Primula scotica*
Scots lovage	*Ligusticum scoticum*
Scots pine	*Pinus sylvestris*
Sea arrowgrass	*Triglochin maritima*
Sea aster	*Aster tripolium*
Sea beet	*Beta vulgaris* subsp. *maritima*
Sea-buckthorn	*Hippophae rhamnoides*
Sea campion	*Silene maritima*
Sea club-rush	*Scirpus maritimus*
Sea couch	*Elymus pycnanthus*
Sea-heath	*Frankenia laevis*
Sea-holly	*Eryngium maritimum*
Sea-kale	*Crambe maritima*
Sea lettuce	*Ulva lactuca*
Sea mayweed	*Tripleurospermum maritimum*
Sea milkwort	*Glaux maritima*
Sea pea	*Lathyrus japonicus*
Sea pearlwort	*Sagina maritima*
Sea plantain	*Plantago maritima*
Sea purslane	*Halimione portulacoides*
Sea radish	*Raphanus maritimus*
Sea rocket	*Cakile maritima*
Sea rush	*Juncus maritimus*
Sea sandwort	*Honkenya peploides*
Sea spleenwort	*Asplenium marinum*
Sea spurge	*Euphorbia paralias*
Sea stock	*Matthiola incana*
Sea wormwood	*Artemisia maritima*
Serrated wintergreen	*Orthilia secunda*
Shady horsetail	*Equisetum pratense*
Sheep's-fescue	*Festuca ovina*
Shoreweed	*Littorella uniflora*

Short-leaved water-starwort	*Callitriche truncata*
Shrubby sea-blite	*Suaeda vera*
Silver birch	*Betula pendula*
Silverweed	*Potentilla anserina*
Six-stamened waterwort	*Elatine hexandra*
Slender-leaved pondweed	*Potamogeton filiformis*
Slender naiad	*Najas flexilis*
Slender sedge	*Carex lasiocarpa*
Slender spike-rush	*Eleocharis uniglumis*
Slender tufted-sedge	*Carex acuta*
Small adder's-tongue	*Ophioglossum azoricum*
Small cord-grass	*Spartina maritima*
Sneezewort	*Achillea ptarmica*
Soft hornwort	*Ceratophyllum submersum*
Soft-rush	*Juncus effusus*
Southern marsh-orchid	*Dactylorhiza praetermissa*
Spanish catchfly	*Silene otites*
Spear-leaved orache	*Atriplex prostrata*
Spiked speedwell	*Veronica spicata*
Spiked water-milfoil	*Myriophyllum spicatum*
Spiral tasselweed	*Ruppia spiralis*
Spotted rock-rose	*Tuberaria guttata*
Spring speedwell	*Veronica verna*
Spring squill	*Scilla verna*
Star sedge	*Carex echinata*
Starry saxifrage	*Saxifraga stellaris*
Stiff sedge	*Carex bigelowii*
Stone bramble	*Rubus saxatilis*
Strawberry clover	*Trifolium fragiferum*
Sundews	*Drosera* spp.
Swamp meadow-grass	*Poa palustris*
Sweet chestnut	*Castanea sativa*
Sweet vernal grass	*Anthoxanthum odoratum*
Sycamore	*Acer pseudoplatanus*
Tall ramping-fumitory	*Fumaria bastardii*
Three-leaved rush	*Juncus trifidus*
Thrift	*Armeria maritima*
Timothy	*Phleum pratense* subsp. *pratense*
Trailing azalea	*Loiseleuria procumbens*
Tree-mallow	*Lavatera arborea*
Triangular club-rush	*Schoenoplectus triqueter*
Tubular water-dropwort	*Oenanthe fistulosa*
Tufted hair-grass	*Deschampsia cespitosa*
Twinflower	*Linnaea borealis*
Water lobelia	*Lobelia dortmanna*
Water-pepper	*Polygonum hydropiper*
Water sedge	*Carex aquatilis*
Water soldier	*Stratiotes aloides*
Water-violet	*Hottonia palustris*
Wavy hair-grass	*Deschampsia flexuosa*

Western gorse	*Ulex gallii*
White beak-sedge	*Rhynchospora alba*
White water-lily	*Nymphaea alba*
Whorled caraway	*Carum verticillatum*
Wild grape hyacinth	*Muscari neglectum*
Wild cabbage	*Brassica oleracea*
Wild pansy	*Viola tricolor*
Wild privet	*Ligustrum vulgare*
Wild service tree	*Sorbus torminalis*
Wild thyme	*Thymus praecox* subsp. *arcticus*
Willow	*Salix* spp.
Wilson's filmy-fern	*Hymenophyllum wilsonii*
Yellow horned-poppy	*Glaucium flavum*
Yellow iris	*Iris pseudacorus*
Yellow saxifrage	*Saxifraga aizoides*
Yellow water-lily	*Nuphar lutea*
Yellow-wort	*Blackstonia perfoliata*
Yew	*Taxus baccata*
Yorkshire fog	*Holcus lanatus*

APPENDIX III: EC WILD BIRDS DIRECTIVE

25.4.79   Official   Journal   of   the   European   Communities   No   L   103

II

(Acts whose publication is not obligatory)

COUNCIL

COUNCIL DIRECTIVE

of 2 April 1979

on the conservation of wild birds

(79/409/EEC)

THE COUNCIL OF THE EUROPEAN COMMUNITIES,

Having regard to the Treaty establishing the European Economic Community, and in particular Article 235 thereof,

Having regard to the proposal from the Commission,[1]

Having regard to the opinion of the European Parliament,[2]

Having regard to the opinion of the Economic and Social Committee,[3]

Whereas the Council declaration of 22 November 1973 on the programme of action of the European Communities on the environment[4] calls for specific action to protect birds, supplemented by the resolution of the Council of the European Communities and of the representatives of the Governments of the Member States meeting within the Council of 17 May 1977 on the continuation and implementation of a European Community policy and action programme on the environment;[5]

Whereas a large number of species of wild birds naturally occurring in the European territory of the member States are declining in number, very rapidly in some cases; whereas this decline represents a serious threat to the conservation of the natural environment, particularly because of the biological balances threatened thereby;

---

[1]OJ No C24, 1.2.1977, po. 3; OJ No C201, 23.8.1977, p. 2.
[2]OJ No C163, 11.7.1977, p. 28.
[3]OJ No C152, 29.6.1977, p. 3.
[4]OJ No C112, 20.12.1973, p. 40.
[5]OJ No C139, 13.6.1977, p. 1.

Whereas the species of wild birds naturally occurring in the European territory of the Member States are mainly migratory species; whereas such species constitute a common heritage and whereas effective bird protection is typically a trans-frontier environment problem entailing common responsibilities;

Whereas the conditions of life for birds in Greenland are fundamentally different from those in the other regions of the European territory of the member States on account of the general circumstances and in particular the climate, the low density of population and the exceptional size and geographical situation of the island;

Whereas therefore this Directive should not apply to Greenland;

Whereas the conservation of the species of wild birds naturally occurring in the European territory of the Member States is necessary to attain, within the operation of the common market, of the Community's objectives regarding the improvement of living conditions, a harmonious development of economic activities throughout the Community and a continuous and balanced expansion, but the necessary specific powers to act have not been provided for in the Treaty;

Whereas the measures to be taken must apply to the various factors which may affect the numbers of birds, namely the repercussions of man's activities and in particular the destruction and pollution of their habitats, capture and killing by man and the trade resulting from such practices; whereas the stringency of such measures should be adapted to the particular situation of the various species within the framework of a conservation policy;

Whereas conservation is aimed at the long-term protection and management of natural resources as an integral part of the heritage of the peoples of Europe; whereas it makes it possible to control natural resources and governs their use on the basis of the measures necessary for the maintenance and adjustment of the natural balances between species as far as is reasonably possible;

Whereas the preservation, maintenance or restoration of a sufficient diversity and area of habitats is essential to the conservation of all species of birds; whereas certain species of birds should be the subject of special conservation measures concerning their habitats in order to ensure their survival and reproduction in their area of distribution; whereas such measures must also take account of migratory species and be coordinated with a view to setting up a coherent whole;

Whereas, in order to prevent commercial interests from exerting a possible harmful pressure on exploitation levels it is necessary to impose a general ban on marketing and to restrict all derogation to those species whose biological status so permits, account being taken of the specific conditions obtaining in the different regions;

Whereas, because of their high population level, geographical distribution and reproductive rate in the Community as a whole, certain species may be hunted, which constitutes acceptable exploitation; where certain limits are established and respected, such hunting must be compatible with maintenance of the population of these species at a satisfactory level;

Whereas the various means, devices or methods of large-scale or non-selective capture or killing and hunting with certain forms of transport must be banned because of the excessive pressure which they exert or may exert on the numbers of the species concerned;

Whereas, because of the importance which may be attached to certain specific situations, provision should be made for the possibility of derogations on certain conditions and subject to monitoring by the Commission;

Whereas the conservation of birds and, in particular, migratory problems which call for scientific research; whereas such research will also make it possible to assess the effectiveness of the measures taken;

Whereas care should be taken in consultation with the Commission to see that the introduction of any species of wild bird not naturally occurring in the European territory of the Member States does not cause harm to local flora and fauna;

Whereas the Commission will every three years prepare and transmit to the Member States a composite report based on information submitted by the Member States on the application of national provisions introduced pursuant to this Directive;

Whereas it is necessary to adapt certain Annexes rapidly in the light of technical and scientific progress; whereas, to facilitate the implementation of the measures needed for this purpose, provision should be made for a procedure establishing close cooperation between the Member States and the Commission in a Committee for Adaptation to Technical and Scientific Progress,

HAS ADOPTED THIS DIRECTIVE:

Article 1

1. This Directive relates to the conservation of all species of naturally occurring birds in the wild state in the European territory of the Member States to which the Treaty applies. It covers the protection, management and control of these species and lays down rules for their exploitation.

2. It shall apply to birds, their eggs, nests and habitats.

3. This Directive shall not apply to Greenland.

Article 2

Member States shall take the requisite measures to maintain the population of the species referred to in Article 1 at a level which corresponds in particular to ecological, scientific and cultural requirements, while taking account of economic and recreational requirements, or to adapt the population of these species to that level.

Article 3

1. In the light of the requirements referred to in Article 2, Member States shall take the requisite measures to preserve, maintain or re-establish a sufficient diversity and area of habitats for all the species of birds referred to in Article 1.

2. The preservation, maintenance and re-establishment of biotopes and habitats shall include primarily the following measures:

(a) creation of protected areas;

(b) upkeep and management in accordance with the ecological needs of habitats inside and outside the protected zones;

(c) re-establishment of destroyed biotopes;

(d) creation of biotopes.

Article 4

1. The species mentioned in Annex I shall be the subject of special conservation measures concerning their habitat in order to ensure their survival and reproduction in their area of distribution.

In this connection, account shall be taken of:

(a) species in danger of extinction;

(b) species vulnerable to specific changes in their habitat;

(c) species considered rare because of small populations or restricted local distribution;

(d) other species requiring particular attention for reasons for the specific nature of their habitat.

Trends and variations in population levels shall be taken into account as a background for evaluations.

Member States shall classify in particular the most suitable territories in number and size as special protection areas for the conservation of these species, taking into account their protection requirements in the geographical sea and land area where this Directive applies.

2. Member States shall take similar measures for regularly occurring migratory species not listed in Annex I, bearing in mind their need for protection in the geographical sea and land area where this Directive applies, as regards their breeding, moulting and wintering areas and staging posts along their migration routes. To this end, Member States shall pay particular attention to the protection of wetlands and particularly to wetlands of international importance.

3. Member States shall send the Commission all relevant information so that it may take appropriate initiatives with a view to the coordination necessary to ensure that the areas provided for in paragraphs 1 and 2 above form a coherent whole which meets the protection requirements of these species in the geographical sea and land area where this Directive applies.

4. In respect of the protection areas referred to in paragraphs 1 and 2 above, Member States shall take appropriate steps to avoid pollution or deterioration of habitats or any disturbances affecting the birds, in so far as these would be significant having regard to the objectives of this Article. Outside these protection areas, Member States shall also strive to avoid pollution or deterioration of habitats.

Article 5

Without prejudice to Articles 7 and 9, Member States shall take the requisite measures to establish a general system of protection for all species of birds referred to in Article 1, prohibiting in particular:

(a) deliberate killing or capture by any method;

(b) deliberate destruction of, or damage to, their nests and eggs or removal of their nests;

(c) taking their eggs in the wild and keeping these eggs even if empty;

(d) deliberate disturbance of these birds particularly during the period of breeding and rearing, in so far as disturbance would be significant having regard to the objectives of this Directive;

(e) keeping birds of species the hunting and capture of which is prohibited.

Article 6

1. Without prejudice to the provisions of paragraphs 2 and 3, Member States shall prohibit, for all the bird species referred to in Article 1, the sale, transport for sale, keeping for sale and the offering for sale of live or dead birds and of any readily recognizable parts or derivatives of such birds.

2. The activities referred to in paragraph 1 shall not be prohibited in respect of the species referred to in Annex III/1, provided that the birds have been legally killed or captured or otherwise legally acquired.

3. Member States may, for the species listed in Annex III/2, allow within their territory the activities referred to in paragraph 1, making provision for certain restrictions, provided the birds have been legally killed or captured or otherwise legally acquired.

Member States wishing to grant such authorization shall first of all consult the Commission with a view to examining jointly with the latter whether the marketing of specimens of such species would result or could reasonably be expected to result in the population levels, geographical distribution or reproductive rate of the species being endangered throughout the Community. Should this examination prove that the intended authorization will, in the view of the Commission, result in any one of the aforementioned species being thus endangered or in the possibility of their being thus endangered, the Commission shall forward a reasoned recommendation to the Member State concerned stating its opposition to the marketing of the species in question. Should the Commission consider that no such risk exists, it will inform the Member State concerned accordingly.

503

The Commission's recommendation shall be published in the Official Journal of the European Communities.

Member States granting authorization pursuant to this paragraph shall verify at regular intervals that the conditions governing the granting of such authorization continue to be fulfilled.

4. The Commission shall carry out studies on the biological status of the species listed in Annex III/3 and on the effects of marketing on such status.

It shall submit, at the latest four months before the time limit referred to in Article 18(1) of this Directive, a report and its proposals to the Committee referred to in Article 16, with a view to a decision on the entry of such species in Annex III/2.

Pending this decision, the Member States may apply existing national rules to such species without prejudice to paragraph 3 hereof.

Article 7

1. Owing to their population level, geographical distribution and reproductive rate throughout the Community, the species listed in Annex II may be hunted under national legislation. Member States shall ensure that the hunting of these species does not jeopardize conservation efforts in their distribution area.

2. The species referred to in Annex II/1 may be hunted in the geographical sea and land area where this Directive applies.

3. The species referred to in Annex II/2 may be hunted only in the Member States in respect of which they are indicated.

4. Member States shall ensure that the practice of hunting, including falconry if practised, as carried on in accordance with the national measures in force, complies with the principles of wise use and ecologically balanced control of the species of birds concerned and that this practice is compatible as regards the population of these species, in particular migratory species, with the measures resulting from Article 2. They shall see in particular that the species to which hunting laws apply are not hunted during the rearing season nor during the various stages of reproduction. In the case of migratory species, they shall see in particular that the species to which hunting regulations apply are not hunted during their period of reproduction or during their return to their rearing grounds. Member States shall send the Commission all relevant information on the practical application of their hunting regulations.

Article 8

1. In respect of the hunting, capture or killing of birds under this Directive, Member States shall prohibit the use of all means, arrangements or methods used for the large-scale or non-selective capture or killing of birds or capable of causing the local disappearance of a species, in particular the use of those listed in Annex IV(a).

2. Moreover, Member States shall prohibit any hunting from the modes of transport and under the conditions mentioned in Annex IV(b).

Article 9

1. Member States may derogate from the provisions of Article 5, 6, 7 and 8, where there is no other satisfactory solution, for the following reasons:

    (a) – in the interests of public health and safety,

        – in the interests of air safety,

        – to prevent serious damage to crops, livestock, forests, fisheries and water,

        – for the protection of flora and fauna;

    (b) for the purposes of research and teaching, of re-population, of re-introduction and for the breeding necessary for these purposes;

    (c) to permit, under strictly supervised conditions and on a selective basis, the capture, keeping or other judicious use of, certain birds in small numbers.

2. The derogations must specify:

    – the species which are subject to the derogations,

    – the means, arrangements or methods authorized for capture or killing,

    – the conditions of risk and the circumstances of time and place under which such derogations may be granted,

    – the authority empowered to declare that the required conditions obtain and to decide what means, arrangements or methods may be used, within what limits and by whom,

    – the controls which will be carried out.

3. Each year the Member States shall send a report to the Commission on the implementation of this Article.

4. On the basis of the information available to it, and in particular the information communicated to it pursuant to paragraph 3, the Commission shall at all times ensure that the consequences of these derogations are not incompatible with this Directive. It shall take appropriate steps to this end.

Article 10

1. Member States shall encourage research and any work required as a basis for the protection, management and use of the population of all species of bird referred to in Article 1.

2. Particular attention shall be paid to research and work on the subjects listed in Annex V. Member States shall send the Commission any information required to enable it to take appropriate measures for the coordination of the research and work referred to in this Article.

Article 11

Member States shall see that any introduction of species of bird which do not occur naturally in the wild state in the European territory of the Member States does not prejudice the local flora and fauna. In this connection they shall consult the Commission.

Article 12

1. Member States shall forward to the Commission every three years, starting from the date of expiry of the time limit referred to in Article 18(1), a report on the implementation of national provisions taken thereunder.

2. The Commission shall prepare every three years a composite report based on the information referred to in paragraph 1. That part of the draft report covering the information supplied by a Member State shall be forwarded to the authorities of the Member State in question for verification. The final version of the report shall be forwarded to the Member States.

Article 13

Application of the measures taken pursuant to this Directive may not lead to deterioration in the present situation as regards the conservation of species of birds referred to in Article 1.

Article 14

Member States may introduce stricter protective measures than those provided for under this Directive.

Article 15

Such amendments as are necessary for adapting Annexes I to V to this Directive to technical and scientific progress and the amendments referred to in the second paragraph of Article 6(4) shall be adopted in accordance with the procedure laid down in Article 17.

Article 16

1. For the purposes of the amendments referred to in Article 15 of this Directive, a Committee for the Adaptation to Technical and Scientific Progress (hereinafter called 'the Committee'), consisting of representatives of the Member States and chaired by a representative of the Commission, is hereby set up.

2. The Committee shall draw up its rules of procedure.

Article 17

1. Where the procedure laid down in this Article is to be followed, matters shall be referred to the Committee by its chairman, either on his own initiative or at the request of the representative of a Member State.

2. The Commission representative shall submit to the Committee a draft of the measures to be taken. The Committee shall deliver its opinion on the draft within a time limit set by the chairman having regard to the urgency of the matter. It shall act by a majority of 41 votes, the votes of the Member States being weighted as provided in Article 148 (2) of this Treaty. The chairman shall not vote.

3. (a) The Commission shall adopt the measures envisaged where they are in accordance with the opinion of the Committee.

   (b) Where the measures envisaged are not in accordance with the opinion of the Committee, or if no opinion is delivered, the Commission shall without delay submit a proposal to the Council concerning the measures to be adopted. The Council shall act by a qualified majority.

   (c) If, within three months of the proposal being submitted to it, the Council has not acted, the proposed measures shall be adopted by the Commission.

Article 18

1. Member States shall bring into force the laws, regulations and administrative provisions necessary to comply with this Directive within two years of its notification. They shall forthwith inform the Commission thereof.

2. Member States shall communicate to the Commission the texts of the main provisions of national law which they adopt in the field governed by this Directive.

Article 19

This Directive is addressed to the Member States.

Done at Luxembourg, 2 April 1979.

For the Council
The President

J FRANCOIS-PONCET

Annex I (as amended on several occasions, most recently by directive 91/224/EEC of 6 March 1991)

Red-throated Diver	*Gavia stellata*
Black-throated Diver	*Gavia arctica*
Great Northern Diver	*Gavia immer*
Slavonian Grebe	*Podiceps auritus*
Freira	*Pterodroma madeira*
Gon-gon	*Petrodroma feae*
Bulwer's Petrel	*Bulweria bulwerii*
Cory's Shearwater	*Calonectris diomedea*
Manx Shearwater (Balearic subspecies)	*Puffinus puffinus mauretanicus*
Little Shearwater	*Puffinus assimilis*
Frigate Petrel	*Pelagodroma marina*
Storm Petrel	*Hydrobates pelagicus*
Leach's Storm-petrel	*Oceanodroma leucorhoa*
Madeiran Storm-petrel	*Oceanodroma castro*
Cormorant (continental subspecies)	*Phalacrocorax carbo sinensis*
Shag (Mediterranean subspecies)	*Phalacrocorax aristotelis desmarestii*
Pygmy Cormorant	*Phalacrocorax pygmeus*
White Pelican	*Pelecanus onocrotalus*
Dalmatian Pelican	*Pelecanus crispus*
Bittern	*Botaurus stellaris*
Little Bittern	*Ixobrychus minutus*
Night Heron	*Nycticorax nycticorax*
Squacco Heron	*Ardeola ralloides*
Little Egret	*Egretta garzetta*
Great White Egret	*Egretta alba*
Purple Heron	*Ardea purpurea*
Black Stork	*Ciconia nigra*
White Stork	*Ciconia ciconia*
Glossy Ibis	*Plegadis falcinellus*
Spoonbill	*Platalea leucorodia*
Greater Flamingo	*Phoenicopterus ruber*
Bewick's Swan	*Cygnus bewickii (Cygnus columbianus bewickii)*
Whooper Swan	*Cygnus cygnus*
White-fronted Goose (Greenland subspecies)	*Anser albifrons flavirostris*
Lesser White-fronted Goose	*Anser erythropus*
Barnacle Goose	*Branta leucopsis*
Red-breasted Goose	*Branta ruficollis*
Ruddy Shelduck	*Tadorna ferruginea*
Marbled Teal	*Marmaronetta angustirostris*
White-eyed Pochard	*Aythya nyroca*
White-headed Duck	*Oxyura leucocephala*
Honey Buzzard	*Pernis apivorus*
Black-shouldered Kite	*Elanus caeruleus*
Black Kite	*Milvus migrans*
Red Kite	*Milvus milvus*

White-tailed Eagle	*Haliaeetus albicilla*
Bearded Vulture	*Gypaetus barbatus*
Egyptian Vulture	*Neophron percnopterus*
Griffon Vulture	*Gyps fulvus*
Black Vulture	*Aegypius monachus*
Short-toed Eagle	*Circaetus gallicus*
Marsh Harrier	*Circus aeruginosus*
Hen Harrier	*Circus cyaneus*
Pallid Harrier	*Circus macrourus*
Montagu's Harrier	*Circus pygargus*
Goshawk (Corsican-Sardinian subspecies)	*Accipiter gentilis arrigonii*
Sparrowhawk (Canarian-Madeirian subspecies)	*Accipiter nisus granti*
Levant Sparrowhawk	*Accipiter brevipes*
Long-legged Buzzard	*Buteo rufinus*
Lesser Spotted Eagle	*Aquila pomarina*
Spotted Eagle	*Aquila clanga*
Imperial Eagle	*Aquila heliaca*
Spanish Imperial Eagle	*Aquila adalberti*
Golden Eagle	*Aquila chrysaetos*
Booted Eagle	*Hieraaetus pennatus*
Bonelli's Eagle	*Hieraaetus fasciatus*
Osprey	*Pandion haliaetus*
Lesser Kestrel	*Falco naumanni*
Merlin	*Falco columbarius*
Eleonora's Falcon	*Falco eleonorae*
Lanner Falcon	*Falco biarmicus*
Peregrine	*Falco peregrinus*
Hazel Grouse	*Bonasia bonasia*
Ptarmigan (Pyrenean subspecies)	*Lagopus mutus pyrenaicus*
Ptarmigan (Alpine subspecies)	*Lagopus mutus helveticus*
Black Grouse (continental subspecies)	*Tetrao tetrix tetrix*
Capercaillie	*Tetrao urogallus*
Rock Partridge (Alpine subspecies)	*Alectoris graeca saxatilis*
Rock Partridge (Sicilian subspecies)	*Alectoris graeca whitaken*
Barbary Partridge	*Alectoris barbara*
Partridge (Italian subspecies)	*Perdix perdix italica*
Partridge (Iberian subspecies)	*Perdix perdix hispaniensis*
Spotted Crake	*Porzana porzana*
Little Crake	*Porzana parva*
Baillon's Crake	*Porzana pusilla*
Corncrake	*Crex crex*
Purple Gallinule	*Porphyrio porphyrio*
Crested Coot	*Fulica cristata*
Andalusian Hemipode	*Turnix sylvatica*
Crane	*Grus grus*
Little Bustard	*Tetrax tetrax*
Houbara	*Chlamydotis undulata*
Great Bustard	*Otis tarda*
Black-winged Stilt	*Himantopus himantopus*

509

Avocet	*Recurvirostra avosetta*
Stone Curlew	*Burhinus oedicnemus*
Cream-coloured Courser	*Cursorius cursor*
Collared Pratincole	*Glareola pratincola*
Dotterel	*Charadrius morinellus (Eudromias morinellus)*
Golden Plover	*Pluvialis apricaria*
Spur-winged Plover	*Hoplopterus spinosus*
Ruff	*Philomachus pugnax*
Great Snipe	*Gallinago media*
Slender-billed Curlew	*Numenius tenuirostris*
Wood Sandpiper	*Tringa glareola*
Red-necked Phalarope	*Phalaropus lobatus*
Mediterranean Gull	*Larus melanocephalus*
Slender-billed Gull	*Larus genei*
Audouin's Gull	*Larus audouinii*
Gull-billed Tern	*Gelochelidon nilotica*
Caspian Tern	*Sterna caspia*
Sandwich Tern	*Sterna sandvicensis*
Roseate Tern	*Sterna dougallii*
Common Tern	*Sterna hirundo*
Arctic Tern	*Sterna paradisaea*
Little Tern	*Sterna albifrons*
Whiskered Tern	*Chlidonias hybridus*
Black Tern	*Chlidonias niger*
Guillemot (Iberian subspecies)	*Uria aalge ibericus*
Black-bellied Sandgrouse	*Pterocles orientalis*
Pin-tailed Sandgrouse	*Pterocles alchata*
Woodpigeon (Azores subspecies)	*Columba palumbus azorica*
Long-toed Pigeon	*Columba trocaz*
Bolle's Laurel Pigeon	*Columba bollii*
Laurel Pigeon	*Columba junoniae*
Eagle Owl	*Bubo bubo*
Snowy Owl	*Nyctea scandiaca*
Pygmy Owl	*Glaucidium passerinum*
Short-eared Owl	*Asio flammeus*
Tengmalm's Owl	*Aegolius funereus*
Nightjar	*Caprimulgus europaeus*
White-rumped Swift	*Apus caffer*
Kingfisher	*Alcedo atthis*
Roller	*Coracias garrulus*
Grey-headed Woodpecker	*Picus canus*
Black Woodpecker	*Dryocopus martius*
Great Spotted Woodpecker (Tenerife subspecies)	*Dendrocopos major canariensis*
Great Spotted Woodpecker (Gran Canaria subspecies)	*Dendrocopos major thanneri*
Syrian Woodpecker	*Dendrocopos syriacus*
Middle Spotted Woodpecker	*Dendrocopos medius*
White-backed Woodpecker	*Dendrocopos leucotos*

Three-toed Woodpecker	*Picoides tridactylus*
Dupont's Lark	*Chersophilus duponti*
Calandra Lark	*Melanocorypha calandra*
Short-toed Lark	*Calandrella brachydactyla*
Thekla Lark	*Galerida theklae*
Woodlark	*Lullula arborea*
Tawny Pipit	*Anthus campestris*
Wren (Fair Isle subspecies)	*Troglodytes troglodytes fridariensis*
Bluethroat	*Luscinia svuecica*
Canary Islands Stonechat	*Saxicola dacotiae*
Black Wheatear	*Oenanthe leucura*
Moustached Warbler	*Acrocephalus melanopogon*
Aquatic Warbler	*Acrocephalus paludicola*
Olive-tree Warbler	*Hippolais olivetorum*
Marmora's Warbler	*Sylvia sarda*
Dartford Warbler	*Sylvia undata*
Rüppell's Warbler	*Sylvia rüppelli*
Barred Warbler	*Sylvia nisoria*
Red-breasted Flycatcher	*Ficedula parva*
Semi-collared Flycatcher	*Ficedula semitorquata*
Collared Flycatcher	*Ficedula albicollis*
Krüper's Nuthatch	*Sitta krueperi*
Corsican Nuthatch	*Sitta whiteheadi*
Red-backed Shrike	*Lanius collurio*
Lesser Grey Shrike	*Lanius minor*
Chough	*Pyrrhocorax pyrrhocorax*
Chaffinch (Hierro subspecies)	*Fringilla coelebs ombriosa*
Canary Island Chaffinch	*Fringilla teydea*
Scottish Crossbill	*Loxia scotica*
Trumpeter Finch	*Bucanetes githagineus*
Azores Bullfinch	*Pyrrhula murina*
Cinereous Bunting	*Emberiza cineracea*
Ortolan Bunting	*Emberiza hortulana*
Cretzschmar's Bunting	*Emberiza caesia*

Annex II/1

Anseriformes

Bean Goose	*Anser fabalis*
Greylag Goose	*Anser anser*
Canada Goose	*Branta canadensis*
Wigeon	*Anas penelope*
Gadwall	*Anas strepera*
Teal	*Anas crecca*
Mallard	*Anas platyrhynchos*
Pintail	*Anas acuta*
Garganey	*Anas querquedula*
Shoveler	*Anas clypeata*
Pochard	*Aythya ferina*

Tufted Duck   *Aythya fuligula*

Galliformes
Red Grouse	*Lagopus lagopus scoticus et hibernicus*
Ptarmigan	*Lagopus mutus*
Rock Partridge	*Alectoris graeca*
Red-legged Partridge	*Alectoris rufa*
Partridge	*Perdix perdix*
Pheasant	*Phasianus colchicus*

Gruiformes
Coot   *Fulica atra*

Charadriiformes
Jack Snipe	*Lymnocryptes minimus*
Snipe	*Gallinago gallinago*
Woodcock	*Scolopax rusticola*

Columbiformes
Rock Dove	*Columba livia*
Wood Pigeon	*Columba palumbus*

Annex II/2

		United Kingdom
Mute Swan	*Cygnus olor*	
Pink-footed Goose	*Anser brachyrhynchus*	+
White-fronted Goose	*Anser albifrons*	+
Brent Goose	*Branta bernicla*	
Red-crested Pochard	*Netta rufina*	
Scaup	*Aythya marila*	+
Eider	*Somateria mollissima*	
Long-tailed Duck	*Clangula hyemalis*	+
Common Scoter	*Melanitta nigra*	+
Velvet Scoter	*Melanitta fusca*	+
Goldeneye	*Bucephala clangula*	+
Red-breasted merganser	*Mergus serrator*	
Goosander	*Mergus merganser*	
Hazel hen	*Bonasia bonasia (Tetrastes bonasia)*	
Black Grouse	*Tetrao tetrix (Lyrurus tetrix)*	+
Capercaillie	*Tetrao urogallus*	+
Barbary Partridge	*Alectoris barbara*	
Quail	*Coturnix coturnix*	
Wild Turkey	*Meleagris gallopavo*	
Water Rail	*Rallus aquaticus*	
Moorhen	*Gallinula chloropus*	+
Oystercatcher	*Haematopus ostralegus*	
Golden Plover	*Pluvialis apricaria*	+
Grey Plover	*Pluvialis squatarola*	+

Lapwing	*Vanellus vanellus*	
Knot	*Calidris canutus*	
Ruff Reeve	*Philomachus pugnax*	
Black-tailed Godwit	*Limosa limosa*	
Bar-tailed Godwit	*Limosa lapponica*	+
Whimbrel	*Numenius phaeopus*	+
Curlew	*Numenius arquata*	+
Spotted Redshank	*Tringa erythropus*	
Redshank	*Tringa totanus*	+
Greenshank	*Tringa nebularia*	
Black-headed Gull	*Larus ridibundus*	
Common Gull	*Larus canus*	
Lesser black-backed Gull	*Larus fuscus*	
Herring Gull	*Larus argentatus*	
Greater black-backed Gull	*Larus marinus*	
Stock Dove	*Columba oenas*	
Collared Turtle Dove	*Streptopelia decaocto*	
Turtle Dove	*Streptopelia turtur*	
Skylark	*Alauda arvensis*	
Blackbird	*Turdus merula*	
Fieldfare	*Turdus pilaris*	
Song Thrush	*Turdus philomelos*	
Redwing	*Turdus iliacus*	
Mistle Thrush	*Turdus viscivorus*	

+ = Hunting may be authorised under Article 7(3) in the Member State concerned

Annex III/1 (as amended by Directive 91/244/EEC; 6 March 1991)

Mallard	*Anas platyrhynchos*
Red Grouse	*Lagopus lagopus scoticus et hibernicus*
Red-legged Partridge	*Alectoris rufa*
Barbary Partridge	*Alectoris barbara*
Partridge	*Perdix perdix*
Pheasant	*Phasianus colchicus*
Wood Pigeon	*Columba palumbus*

Annex III/2 (as amended by Directive 91/244/EEC; 6 March 1991)

White-fronted Goose (Continental race)	*Anser albifrons albifrons*
Greylag Goose	*Anser anser*
Wigeon	*Anas penelope*
Teal	*Anas crecca*
Pintail	*Anas acuta*
Shoveler	*Anas clypeata*
Pochard	*Aythya ferina*
Tufted Duck	*Aythya fuligula*
Scaup	*Aythya marila*

Eider	*Somateria mollissima*
Common Scoter	*Melanitta nigra*
Ptarmigan	*Lagopus mutus*
Black Grouse (British population)	*Tetrao tetrix britannicus*
Capercaillie	*Tetrao urogallus*
Coot	*Fulica atra*
Golden Plover	*Pluvialis apricaria*
Jack Snipe	*Lymnocryptes minimus*
Snipe	*Gallinago gallinago*
Woodcock	*Scolopax rusticola*

Annex III/3

White-fronted Goose	*Anser albifrons*
Shoveler	*Anas clypeata*
Scaup	*Aythya marila*
Common Scoter	*Melanitta nigra*
Black Grouse	*Tetrao tetrix (Lyrurus tetris)*
Golden Plover	*Pluvialis apricaria*
Jack Snipe	*Lymnocryptes minimus*
Snipe	*Gallinago gallinago*
Woodcock	*Scolopax rusticola*

Annex IV

(a) – Snares, limes, hooks, live birds which are blind or mutilated used as decoys, tape recorders, electrocuting devices.

– Artificial light sources, mirrors, devices for illuminating targets, sighting devices for night shooting comprising an electronic image magnifier or image converter.

– Explosives.

– Nets, traps, poisoned or anaesthetic bait.

– Semi-automatic or automatic weapons with a magazine capable of holding more than two rounds of ammunition.

(b) – Aircraft, motor vehicles.

– Boats driven at a speed exceeding five kilometres per hour. On the open sea, Member States may, for safety reasons, authorize the use of motor-boats with a maximum speed of 18 kilometres per hour. Member States shall inform the Commission of any authorizations granted.

Annex V

(a) National lists of species in danger of extinction or particularly endangered species, taking into account their geographical distribution.

(b) Listing and ecological description of areas particularly important to migratory species on their migratory routes and as wintering and nesting grounds.

(c) Listing of data on the population levels of migratory species as shown by ringing.

(d) Assessing the influence of methods of taking wild birds on population levels.

(e) Developing or refining ecological methods for preventing the type of damage caused by birds.

(f) Determining the role of certain species as indicators of pollution.

(g) Studying the adverse effect of chemical pollution on population levels of bird species.

COUNCIL RESOLUTION

of 2 April 1979

concerning Directive 79/409/EEC on the conservation of wild birds

I

1. The Council calls upon the Member States to notify the Commission within 24 months following adoption of Directive 79/409/EEC on the conservation of wild birds of:

(a) the special protection areas which they have classified under Article 4,

(b) the areas which they have or intend to have designated as wetlands of international importance,

(c) the areas other than wetlands already classified according to national legislation, similar to those described in Article 4 and subject to comparable protection measures.

2. In the designation of these areas, account shall be taken of the need to protect biotopes and flora and fauna without, however, delaying the action of primary importance for bird conservation, particularly in wetlands, to be taken under the Programme of Action of the European Communities on the Environment.

II

1. The Council requests the Commission to draw up a list of the areas notified by the Member States pursuant to point I above.

2. This list shall be drawn up within six months following the transmission of the information and shall be kept up to date. The Council calls upon the Commission to take the necessary coordinating steps to see that the network thereby established fulfils the objectives of the Directive and can be integrated into a larger network, should the need arise.

III

The Council takes note of the Commission's intention of submitting appropriate proposals regarding the criteria for the determination, selection, organization and methods of administration of the special protection areas, and invites the Commission to take into consideration in particular in those proposals the parts of the areas selected which are to be given intensive protection, a minimum threshold for those parts, which will enable the objectives of Article 4 to be attained, and the measures to be taken to prohibit hunting and to control other specific activities likely to disturb the birds.

APPENDIX IV: RAMSAR CONVENTION, CRITERIA AND 'WISE USE' GUIDELINES

(a) Text of Convention on Wetlands of International Importance Especially as Waterfowl Habitat

Ramsar, 2.2. 1971 as amended by the Paris Protocol of 3.12. 1982

The Contracting Parties,

Recognising the interdependence of man and his environment;

Considering the fundamental ecological functions of wetlands as regulators of water regimes and as habitats supporting a characteristic flora and fauna, especially waterfowl;

Being convinced that wetlands constitute a resource of great economic, cultural, scientific and recreational value, the loss of which would be irreparable;

Desiring to stem the progressive encroachment on and loss of wetlands now and in the future;

Recognising that waterfowl in their seasonal migrations may transcend frontiers and so should be regarded as an international resource;

Being confident that the conservation of wetlands and their flora and fauna can be ensured by combining far-sighted national policies with co-ordinated international action;

Have agreed as follows:

Article 1
1. For the purpose of this Convention wetlands are areas of marsh, fen, peatland or water, whether natural of artificial, permanent or temporary, with water that is static or flowing, fresh, brackish or salt, including areas of marine water the depth of which at low tide does not exceed six metres.

2. For the purpose of this Convention waterfowl are birds ecologically dependent on wetlands.

Article 2
1. Each Contracting Party shall designate suitable wetlands within its territory for inclusion in a List of Wetlands of International Importance, hereinafter referred to as 'the List' which is maintained by the bureau established under Article 8. The boundaries of each wetland shall be precisely described and also delimited on a map and they may incorporate riparian and coastal zones adjacent to the wetlands, and islands or bodies of marine water deeper than six metres at low tide lying within the wetlands, especially where these have importance as waterfowl habitat.

2. Wetlands should be selected for the List on account of their international significance in terms of ecology, botany, zoology, limnology or hydrology. In the first instance wetlands of international importance to waterfowl at any season should be included.

517

3. The inclusion of a wetland in the List does not prejudice the exclusive sovereign rights of the Contracting Party in whose territory the wetland is situated.

4. Each Contracting Party shall designate at least one wetland to be included in the List when signing this Convention or when depositing its instrument of ratification or accession, as provided in Article 9.

5. Any Contracting Party shall have the right to add to the List further wetlands situated within its territory, to extend the boundaries of those wetlands already included by it in the List, or, because of its urgent national interests, to delete or restrict the boundaries of wetlands already included by it in the List and shall, at the earliest possible time, inform the organisation or government responsible for the continuing bureau duties specified in Article 8 of any such changes.

6. Each Contracting Party shall consider its international responsibilities for the conservation, management and wise use of migratory stocks of waterfowl, both when designating entries for the List and when exercising its right to change entries in the List relating to wetlands within its territory.

Article 3
1. The Contracting Parties shall formulate and implement their planning so as to promote the conservation of wetlands included in the List, and as far as possible the wise use of wetlands in their territory.

2. Each Contracting Party shall arrange to be informed at the earliest possible time if the ecological character of any wetland in its territory and included in the List has changed, is changing or is likely to change as the result of technological developments, pollution or other human interference. Information on such changes shall be passed without delay to the organisation or government responsible for the continuing bureau duties specified in Article 8.

Article 4
1. Each Contracting Party shall promote the conservation of wetlands and waterfowl by establishing nature reserves on wetlands, whether they are included in the List or not, and provide adequately for their wardening.

2. Where a Contracting Party in its urgent national interest, deletes or restricts the boundaries of a wetland included in the List, it should as far as possible compensate for any loss of wetland resources, and in particular it should create additional nature reserves for waterfowl and for the protection, either in the same area or elsewhere, of an adequate portion of the original habitat.

3. The Contracting Parties shall encourage research and the exchange of data and publications regarding wetlands and their flora and fauna.

4. The Contracting Parties shall endeavour through management to increase waterfowl populations on appropriate wetlands.

5. The Contracting Parties shall promote the training of personnel competent in the fields of wetland research, management and wardening.

Article 5

The Contracting Parties shall consult with each other about implementing obligations arising from the Convention especially in the case of a wetland extending over the territories of more than one Contracting Party or where a water system is shared by Contracting Parties. They shall at the same time endeavour to co-ordinate and support present and future policies and regulations concerning the conservation of wetlands and their flora and fauna.

Article 6

1. The Contracting Parties shall, as the necessity arises, convene Conferences on the Conservation of Wetlands and Waterfowl.

2. The Conferences shall have an advisory character and shall be competent, *inter alia*:

    (a) to discuss the implementation of this Convention;

    (b) to discuss additions to and changes in the List;

    (c) to consider information regarding changes in the ecological character of wetlands included in the List provided in accordance with paragraph 2 of Article 3;

    (d) to make general or specific recommendations to the Contracting Parties regarding the conservation, management and wise use of wetlands and their flora and fauna;

    (e) to request relevant international bodies to prepare reports and statistics on matters which are essentially international in character affecting wetlands.

3. The Contracting Parties shall ensure that those responsible at all levels for wetlands management shall be informed of, and take into consideration, recommendations of such Conferences concerning the conservation, management and wise use of wetlands and their flora and fauna.

Article 7

1. The representatives of the Contracting Parties at such Conferences should include persons who are experts on wetlands or waterfowl by reason of knowledge and experience gained in scientific, administrative or other appropriate capacities.

2. Each of the Contracting Parties represented at a Conference shall have one vote, recommendations being adopted by a simple majority of the votes cast, provided that not less than half the Contracting Parties cast votes.

Article 8

1. The International Union for Conservation of Nature and Natural Resources shall perform the continuing bureau duties under this Convention until such time as another organisation or government is appointed by a majority of two thirds of all Contracting Parties.

2. The continuing bureau duties shall be, *inter alia*:

    (a) to assist in the convening and organising of Conferences specified in Article 6;

    (b) to maintain the List of Wetlands of International Importance and to be informed by the Contracting Parties of any additions, extensions, deletions or restrictions concerning wetlands included in the List provided in accordance with paragraph 5 of Article 2;

(c) to be informed by the Contracting Parties of any changes in the ecological character of wetlands in the List provided in accordance with paragraph 2 of Article 3;

(d) to forward notification of any alterations to the List, or changes in character of wetlands included therein, to all Contracting Parties and to arrange for these matters to be discussed at the next Conference;

(e) to make known to the Contracting Party concerned, the recommendations of the Conferences in respect of such alterations to the List or of changes in the character of wetlands included therein.

Article 9

1. This Convention shall remain open for signature indefinitely.

2. Any member of the United Nations or of one of the Specialised Agencies or of the International Atomic Energy Agency or Party to the Statute of the International Court of Justice may become a Party to this Convention by;

(a) signature without reservation as to ratification;

(b) signature subject to ratification followed by ratification;

(c) accession.

3. Ratification or accession shall be effected by the deposit of an instrument of ratification or accession with the Director General of the United Nations Educational, Scientific and Cultural Organisation (hereinafter referred to as 'the Depositary').

Article 10

1. This Convention shall enter into force four months after seven States have become Parties to this Convention in accordance with paragraph 2 of Article 9.

2. Thereafter this Convention shall enter into force for each Contracting Party four months after the day of its signature without reservation as to ratification, or its deposit of an instrument of ratification or accession.

Article 10 bis

1. This Convention may be amended at a meeting of the Contracting Parties convened for that purpose in accordance with this article.

2. Proposals for amendment may be made by any Contracting Party.

3. The text of any proposed amendment and the reasons for it shall be communicated to the organisation or government performing the continuing bureau duties under the Convention (hereinafter referred to as 'the Bureau') and shall promptly be communicated by the Bureau to all Contracting Parties. Any comments on the text by the Contracting Parties shall be communicated to the Bureau within three months of the

date on which the amendments were communicated to the Contracting Parties by the Bureau. The Bureau shall, immediately after the last day for submission of comments, communicate to the Contracting Parties all comments submitted by that day.

4. A meeting of Contracting Parties to consider an amendment communicated in accordance with paragraph 3 shall be convened by the Bureau upon the written request of one third of the Contracting Parties. The Bureau shall consult the Parties concerning the time and venue of the meeting.

5. Amendments shall be adopted by a two thirds majority of the Contracting Parties present and voting.

6. An amendment adopted shall enter into force for the Contracting Parties which have accepted it on the first day of the fourth month following the date on which two thirds of the Contracting Parties have deposited an instrument of acceptance with the Depositary. For each Contracting Party which deposits an instrument of acceptance after the date on which two thirds of the Contracting Parties have deposited an instrument of acceptance, the amendment shall enter into force on the first day of the fourth month following the date of the deposit of its instrument of acceptance.

Article 11

1. This Convention shall continue in force for an indefinite period.

2. Any Contracting Party may denounce this Convention after a period of five years from the date on which it entered into force for that Party by giving written notice thereof to the Depositary. Denunciation shall take effect four months after the day on which notice thereof is received by the Depositary.

Article 12

1. The Depositary shall inform all States that have signed and acceded to this Convention as soon as possible of:

   (a) signatures to the Convention;

   (b) deposits of instruments of ratification of this Convention;

   (c) deposits of instruments of accession to this Convention;

   (d) the date of entry into force of this Convention;

   (e) notifications of denunciation of this Convention.

2. When this Convention has entered into force, the Depositary shall have it registered with the Secretariat of the United Nations in accordance with Article 102 of the Charter.

   IN WITNESS WHEREOF, the undersigned, being duly authorised to that effect, have signed this Convention.

   DONE at Ramsar this 2nd day of February 1971, in a single original in the English, French, German and Russian languages, all texts being equally authentic which shall be deposited with the Depositary which shall send true copies thereof to all Contracting Parties.

Articles 6 and 7 of the Convention on Wetlands of International Importance especially as Waterfowl Habitat as amended by the Conference of the Parties on 28.5.1987 (Amendments are reproduced below in italics).

Article 6

1. *There shall be established a Conference of the Contracting Parties to review and promote the implementation of this Convention. The Bureau referred to in Article 8, paragraph 1, shall convene ordinary meetings of the Conference of the Contracting Parties at intervals of not more than three years, unless the Conference decides otherwise, and extraordinary meetings at the written request of at least one third of the Contracting Parties. Each ordinary meeting of the Conference of the Contracting Parties shall determine the time and venue of the next ordinary meeting.*

2. *The Conference of the Contracting Parties shall be competent:*

   (a) to discuss the implementation of this Convention;

   (b) to discuss additions to and changes in the List;

   (c) to consider information regarding changes in the ecological character of wetlands included in the List provided in accordance with paragraph 2 of Article 3;

   (d) to make general or specific recommendations to the Contracting Parties regarding the conservation, management and wise use of wetlands and their flora and fauna;

   (e) to request relevant international bodies to prepare reports and statistics on matters which are essentially international in character affecting wetlands;

   (f) to adopt other recommendations, or resolutions, to promote the functioning of this Convention.

3. The Contracting Parties shall ensure that those responsible at all levels for wetland management shall be informed of, and take into consideration, recommendations of such Conferences concerning the conservation, management and wise use of wetlands and their flora and fauna.

4. *The Conference of the Contracting Parties shall adopt rules of procedure for each of its meetings.*

5. *The Conference of the Contracting Parties shall establish and keep under review the financial regulations of this Convention. At each of its ordinary meetings, it shall adopt the budget for the next financial period by a two-third majority of Contracting Parties present and voting.*

6. *Each Contracting Party shall contribute to the budget according to a scale of contributions adopted by unanimity of the Contracting Parties present and voting at a meeting of the ordinary Conference of the Contracting Parties.*

Article 7

1. The representatives of the Contracting Parties at such Conferences should include persons who are experts on wetlands or waterfowl by reason of knowledge and experience gained in scientific, administrative or other appropriate capacities.

2. Each of the Contracting Parties represented at a Conference shall have one vote, recommendations, resolutions and decisions being adopted by a simple majority of the Contracting Parties present and voting, unless otherwise provided for in this Convention.

(b) Criteria for Identifying Wetlands of International Importance

(As amended by the Regina and Montreux Conferences 1987 and 1990)

Introduction

Article 2.1 of the Convention states that 'Each Contracting Party shall designate suitable wetlands within its territory for inclusion in a List of Wetlands of International Importance'. The guidance provided by the Convention text on identification of 'wetlands of international importance' is in Article 2.2, which refers to 'international significance in terms of ecology, botany, zoology, limnology or hydrology' and indicates that 'In the first instance, wetlands of international importance to waterfowl at any season should be included'. The Criteria set out below, which have been approved by meetings of the Conference of the Contracting Parties, are for identifying wetlands of international importance.

Criteria

A wetland is identified as being of international importance if it meets at least one of the criteria set out below:

1. Criteria for representative or unique wetlands

A wetland should be considered internationally important if:

(a) it is a particularly good representative example of a natural or near-natural wetland, characteristic of the appropriate biogeographical region;

or (b) it is a particularly good representative example of a natural or near-natural wetland, common to more than one biogeographical region;

or (c) it is a particularly good representative example of a wetland, which plays a substantial hydrological, biological or ecological role in the natural functioning of a major river basin or coastal system, especially where it is located in a transborder position;

or (d) it is an example of a specific type of wetland, rare or unusual in the appropriate biogeographical region.

2. General criteria based on plants or animals

A wetland should be considered internationally important if:

(a) it supports an appreciable assemblage of rare, vulnerable or endangered species or subspecies of plant or animal, or an appreciable number of individuals of any one or more of these species;

or (b) it is of special value for maintaining the genetic and ecological diversity of a region because of the quality and peculiarities of its flora and fauna;

or (c) it is of special value as the habitat of plants or animals at a critical stage of their biological cycle;

or (d) it is of special value for one or more endemic plant or animal species of communities.

3. Specific criteria based on waterfowl

A wetland should be considered internationally important if:

(a) it regularly supports 20,000 waterfowl;

or (b) it regularly supports substantial numbers of individuals from particular groups of waterfowl, indicative of wetland values, productivity or diversity;

or (c) where data on populations are available, it regularly supports 1% of the individuals in a population of one species or subspecies of waterfowl.

Guidelines for application of the criteria

To assist Contracting Parties in assessing the suitability of wetlands for inclusion on the List of Wetlands of International Importance, the Conference of the Contracting Parties has formulated the following guidelines for application of the Criteria:

(a) A wetland could be considered of international importance under Criterion 1 if, because of its outstanding role in natural, biological, ecological or hydrological systems, it is of substantial value in supporting human communities dependent on the wetland. In this context, such support would include:

– provision of food, fibre or fuel;
– or maintenance of cultural values;
– or support of food chains, water quality, flood control or climatic stability.

The support, in all its aspects, should remain within the framework of sustainable use and habitat conservation, and should not change the ecological character of the wetland.

or (b) A wetland could be considered of international importance under Criterion 1, 2 or 3 if it conforms to additional guidelines developed at regional (eg Scandinavian or West African) or national level. Elaboration of such regional or national guidelines may be especially appropriate:

– where particular groups of animals (other than waterfowl) or plants are considered more suitable as a basis for evaluation;
– or where waterfowl and other animals do not occur in large concentrations (particularly in northern latitudes);
– or where collection of data is difficult (particularly in very large countries).

or (c) The 'particular groups of waterfowl, indicative of wetland values, productivity or diversity' in Criterion 3(b) include any of the following:

- loons or divers: Gaviidae;
- grebes: Podicipedidae;
- cormorants: Phalacrocoracidae;
- pelicans: Pelicanidae;
- herons and bitterns: Ardeidae;
- ibises, storks and spoonbills: Threskiorniformes;
- swans, geese and ducks (wildfowl): Anatidae;
- wetland related raptors: Falconiformes;
- cranes: Gruiformes;
- shorebirds or waders: Charadrii; and
- terns: Sternidae.

or (d) The specific criteria based on waterfowl numbers will apply to wetlands of varying size in different Contracting Parties. While it is impossible to give precise guidance on the size of an area in which these numbers may occur, wetlands identified as being of international importance under Criterion 3 should form an ecological unit, and may thus be made up of one big area or a group of smaller wetlands. Consideration may also be given to turnover of waterfowl at migration periods, so that a cumulative total is reached, if such data are available.

(c) Guidelines for Implementation of the Wise Use Concept of the Convention

(As adopted by the Regina Conference 1987 and amended by the Montreux Conference 1990)

Introduction

Article 3.1 of the Convention states that the Contracting Parties 'shall formulate and implement their planning so as to promote the conservation of the wetlands included in the List, and as far as possible the wise use of wetlands in their territory'.

The third meeting of the Conference of the Contracting Parties in Regina, Canada from 27 May to 5 June 1987, adopted the following definition of wise use of wetlands:

'The wise use of wetlands is their sustainable utilisation for the benefit of humankind in a way compatible with the maintenance of the natural properties of the ecosystem'.

Sustainable utilisation is defined as 'human use of a wetland so that it may yield the greatest continuous benefit to present generations while maintaining its potential to meet the needs and aspirations of future generations'.

Natural properties of the ecosystem are defined as 'those physical, biological or chemical components, such as soil, water, plants, animals and nutrients, and the interactions between them'.

The wise use provisions apply to all wetlands and their support systems within the territory of a Contracting Party, both those wetlands designated for the List, and all other wetlands. The concept of wise use seeks both the formulation and implementation of general wetland policies, and wise use of specific wetlands. These activities are integral parts of sustainable development.

It is desirable in the long term that all Contracting Parties should have comprehensive national wetland policies, formulated in whatever manner is appropriate to its national institutions. However as recognised by the report of the Workshop on Wise Use of the Regina Meeting, elaboration of national wetland policies will be a long-term process, and immediate action should be taken to stimulate wise use. The guidelines presented below therefore include both elements for comprehensive national wetland policies and priority actions.

Establishment of national wetland policies

National wetland policies should as far as possible address all problems and activities related to wetlands within a national context. These may be grouped in different sections:

1. Actions to improve institutional and organisational arrangements including:

    (a) establishment of institutional arrangements which will allow those concerned to identify how wetland conservation can be achieved, and how wetland priorities can be fully integrated into the planning process;

    (b) establishment of mechanisms and procedures for incorporating an integrated multidisciplinary approach into planning and execution of projects concerning wetlands and their support systems, in order to secure wetland conservation and sustainable development.

2. Actions to address legislation and government policies, including:

    (a) review of existing legislation and policies (including subsidies and incentives) which affect wetland conservation;

    (b) application, where appropriate, of existing legislation and policies of importance for the conservation of wetlands;

    (c) adoption, as required, of new legislation and policies;

    (d) use of development funds for projects which permit conservation and sustainable utilisation of wetland resources.

3. Actions to increase knowledge and awareness of wetlands and their values, including;

    (a) interchange of experience and information on wetland policy, conservation and wise use between countries preparing and/or implementing national wetland policies, or pursuing wetland conservation;

    (b) increasing the awareness and understanding of decision-makers and the public of the full benefits and values, within the terms of wise use, of wetlands. Among these benefits and values, which can occur on or off the wetland itself, are:

    – sediment and erosion control,

- flood control,
- maintenance of water quality and abatement of pollution,
- maintenance of surface and underground water supply,
- support for fisheries, grazing and agriculture,
- outdoor recreation and education for human society,
- provision of habitat for wildlife, especially waterfowl,
- contribution to climatic stability.

(c) Review of traditional techniques of wise use, and elaboration of pilot projects which demonstrate wise use of representative wetland types.

(d) Training of appropriate staff in the disciplines which will assist in implementation of wetland conservation action and policies.

4. Actions to review the status of, and identify priorities for, all wetlands in a national context, including:

(a) execution of a national inventory of wetlands including classification of the sites;

(b) identification and evaluation of the benefits and values of each site (see 3b above);

(c) definition of the conservation and management priorities for each site, in accordance with the needs and conditions of each Contracting Party.

5. Actions to address problems at particular wetland sites, including:

(a) integration from the outset of environmental considerations in planning of projects which might affect the wetland (including full assessment of their environmental impact before approval, continuing evaluation during the execution, and full implementation of necessary environmental measures). The planning, assessment and evaluation should cover projects upstream of the wetland, those in the wetland itself, and other projects which may affect the wetland, and should pay particular attention to maintaining the benefits and values listed in 3b above;

(b) regulated utilisation of the natural elements of wetland systems such that they are not over-exploited;

(c) establishment, implementation and, as necessary, periodic revision of management plans which involve local people and take account of their requirements;

(d) designation for the Ramsar List of wetlands identified as being of international importance;

(e) establishment of nature reserves at wetlands, whether or not they are included in the List;

(f) serious consideration of restoration of wetlands whose benefits and values have been diminished or degraded.

Priority actions at national level

Whether or not national wetland policies are being prepared, several actions should receive immediate attention at national level in order to facilitate the preparation of national wetland policies, and to avoid delay in practical implementation of wetland conservation and wise use.

Contracting Parties will naturally select actions, according to their own national priorities and requirements, from those listed above under 'Establishment of national wetland policies'. They may wish to carry on institutional, legislative or educational measures (such as those listed under Sections 1, 2 and 3 above) and at the same time initiate inventories or scientific work (such as those listed under Section 4); in this way the institutional, legislative and educational instruments will be available in time to deal with scientific results.

Equally, Contracting Parties wishing to promote wise use of wetlands without waiting until national wetland policies have been developed, may, based on their situation and needs, wish to:

    (i) identify the issues which require the most urgent attention;
   (ii) take action on one or more of these issues;
  (iii) identify the wetland sites which require the most urgent action;
  (iv) take action at one or more of these wetlands, along the lines set out under 'Priority actions at particular wetland sites' below.

Priority actions at particular wetland sites

As at national level, immediate action may be required in order to avoid destruction or degradation of important wetland values at particular wetland sites. These actions will undoubtedly include some elements listed in Section 5 above, and Contracting Parties will select those appropriate to their own national priorities and requirements.

Whenever planning is initiated for projects which might affect important wetlands, the following actions should be taken in order to promote wise use of the wetland:

– integration from the outset of environmental considerations in planning of projects which might affect wetlands (including full assessment of their environmental impact before approval);

– continuing evaluation during their execution; and

– full implementation of necessary environmental measures.

The planning, assessment and evaluation should cover projects upstream of the wetland, those in the wetland itself, and other projects which may affect the wetland, and should pay particular attention to maintaining the benefits and values listed in 3b above.

Appendix V: Population levels for breeding and wintering birds in Great Britain and other appropriate geographical areas.

	BREEDING			WINTERING		
	Great Britain	Biogeographical population		Great Britain	Biogeographical population	
		Area	Number		Area	Number
Red-throated Diver	1,350	NW	–	6,500	WE	–
Black-throated Diver	150	NW	–	1,200	WE	–
Great Northern Diver	0	NW	–	2,750	WE	5,000
Red-necked Grebe	0	NW	–	135	WE	–
Slavonian Grebe	62	NW	5,125	400	WE	15,000
Black-necked Grebe	28	NW	–	100	WE	–
Fulmar	531,400	WE	11,568,000	–	EAF	–
Manx Shearwater	235,000	WE	–	–	EAF	–
Storm Petrel	60,000	W	257,000	–	–	–
Leach's Petrel	10,000	WE	–	–	–	–
Gannet	158,700	WE	222,200	–	EAF	–
Cormorant	7,000	WC	40,700	17,500	EAF	–
Shag	36,100	WE	120,800	97,500	EAF	–
Bittern	20	WC	2,600	110	NW	–
Mute Swan	3,150	NW	–	18,000	NW+C	180,000
Bewick's Swan	–	–	–	7,000	WC	17,000
Whooper Swan	2	W	–	6,000	W	17,000
Bean Goose	0	NW	–	450	NW	80,000
Pink-footed Goose (Icelandic/Greenland)	0	NW	–	110,000	W	110,000
European White-fronted Goose	–	–	–	6,000	NW	300,000
Greenland White-fronted Goose	–	–	–	10,000	W	22,000
Greylag Goose (N Scottish)	2,000	W	2,000	2,000	W	2,000
Greylag Goose (Icelandic)	0	W	–	100,000	W	100,000

	BREEDING			WINTERING		
	Great Britain	Biogeographical population		Great Britain	Biogeographical population	
		Area	Number		Area	Number
Greenland Barnacle Goose	—	—	—	27,000	W	32,000
Svalbard Barnacle Goose	—	—	—	10,000	W	10,000
Light-bellied Brent Goose (Svalbard)	—	—	—	3,000	W	4,000
Light-bellied Brent Goose (Canada/Greenland)	—	—	—	—	NW	20,000
Dark-bellied Brent Goose	—	—	—	90,000	W	170,000
Shelduck	15,000	NW	—	75,000	NW	250,000
Wigeon	400	NW	—	250,000	NW	750,000
Gadwall	550	NW	—	6,000	NW	12,000
Teal	4,750	NW	—	100,000	NW	400,000
Mallard	40,000	NW	—	500,000	NW	5,000,000
Pintail	40	NW	—	25,000	NW	70,000
Garganey	50	NW	—	—	–	–
Shoveler	1,250	NW	—	9,000	NW	40,000
Pochard	380	NW	—	50,000	NW	350,000
Tufted Duck	7,000	NW	—	60,000	NW	750,000
Scaup	2	NW	—	4,000	NW	150,000
Eider	20,000	NW	—	50,000	WP	3,000,000
Long-tailed Duck	0	NW	—	20,000	NW	2,000,000
Common Scoter	110	NW	—	35,000	WP	800,000
Velvet Scoter	0	NW	—	3,000	WP	250,000
Goldeneye	87	NW	—	15,000	NW	300,000
Smew	0	NW	—	50	NW	15,000
Red-breasted Merganser	1,500	NW	—	10,000	NW	100,000
Goosander	1,100	NW	—	5,500	NW	125,000
Honey Buzzard	30	NW	19,000	—	NW	–
Red Kite	47	NW	4,750	125	WE	–

	BREEDING			WINTERING		
	Great Britain	Biogeographical population		Great Britain	Biogeographical population	
		Area	Number		Area	Number
White-tailed Eagle	10	NW	950	50	WE	–
Marsh Harrier	75	NW	3,110	–	WE	–
Hen Harrier	630	NW	6,820	750	WE	–
Montagu's Harrier	12	NW	585	–	–	–
Golden Eagle (nominate race)	424	NW	1,560	1,100	NW	–
Osprey	52	NW	2,940	–	–	–
Merlin (*aesalon* race)	600	NW	9,000	2,000	NW	–
Hobby	1,000	NW	9,000	–	–	–
Peregrine (nominate race)	850	NW	1,585	3,000	WE	–
Ptarmigan	10,000	NW	–	12,500	NW	–
Capercaillie	1,100	NW		–	NW	–
Spotted Crake	7	NW		–	–	–
Corncrake	575	WE	5,400	–	–	–
Oystercatcher	38,000	NW+C	218,000	279,500	EAF	874,000
Avocet	385	NW+C	19,300	1,000	EAF	67,000
Stone-Curlew	145	NW+C	13,500	–	–	–
Little Ringed Plover	608	NW+C	22,500	–	–	–
Ringed Plover (nominate race)	8,400	NW+C	13,100	23,040	EAF	48,000
Kentish Plover	1	NW+C	8,000	–	EAF	67,000
Dotterel	860	NW+C	36,500	–	–	–
Golden Plover	23,000	NW+C	609,000	200,000	EAF	1,000,000
Grey Plover	–	–	–	21,250	EAF	168,000
Lapwing	215,000	NW+C	869,000	1,000,000	EAF	2,000,000
Knot (*islandica* race)	–	–	–	222,830	EAF	345,000
Sanderling	–	–	–	13,710	EAF	123,000

	BREEDING			WINTERING		
	Great Britain	Biogeographical population		Great Britain	Biogeographical population	
		Area	Number		Area	Number
Little Stint	0	NW+C	205	20	EAF	211,000
Temminck's Stint	6	NW+C	25,400	–	–	–
Purple Sandpiper	2	NW+C	54,000	16,140	EAF	50,000
Dunlin (temperate *schinzii*)	9,150	W	11,100	–	EAF	21,000
Dunlin (*alpina* race)	0	NW	55,000	433,000	EAF	1,373,000
Ruff	11	NW+C	247,000	1,500	EAF	1,000,000
Jack Snipe	0	NW+C	28,100	15,000	EAF	–
Snipe	30,000	NW+C	841,000	–	EAF	1,000,000
Woodcock	21,500	NW+C	347,000	–	EAF	–
Black-tailed Godwit (*islandica*)	54	NW+C	133,000	4,770	EAF	66,000
Bar-tailed Godwit (nominate)	0	NW+C	1,500	60,810	EAF	115,000
Whimbrel (nominate race)	465	NW+C	203,000	0	EAF	69,000
Curlew (nominate race)	35,500	NW+C	125,000	91,200	EAF	348,000
Spotted Redshank	–	–	–	200	EAF	6,500
Redshank	32,500	NW+C	268,000	75,400	EAF	109,000
Greenshank	1,545	NW+C	109,000	400	EAF	19,000
Green Sandpiper	–	–	–	300	EAF	–
Wood Sandpiper	7	NW+C	577,000	–	–	–
Common Sandpiper	18,500	NW+C	882,000	40	EAF	39,000
Turnstone	1	NW	–	44,480	EAF	67,000
Red-necked Phalarope	19	NW+C	150,000	–	–	–
Arctic Skua	3,350	WE	17,300	–	–	–
Great Skua	7,900	WE	13,500	–	–	–
Mediterranean Gull	4	WE	–	100	NW	–
Common Gull	47,000	WC	461,000	635,000	NW	–

	BREEDING			WINTERING		
	Great Britain	Biogeographical population		Great Britain	Biogeographical population	
		Area	Number		Area	Number
Lesser black-backed gull	81,600	WC	177,200	60,000	NW	—
Herring gull	149,700	WC	940,000	—	NW	—
Great black-backed gull	17,900	WE	83,600	—	NW	—
Kittiwake	486,900	WE	2,109,000	—	EAF	—
Sandwich Tern	15,000	WE	44,500	—	—	—
Roseate Tern	85	EC	1,600	—	—	—
Common Tern	12,700	WC	92,500	—	—	—
Arctic Tern	83,000	WC	270,000	—	—	—
Little Tern	2,350	WE	12,600	—		—
Guillemot	1,044,000	WE	3,617,000	—	EAF	—
Razorbill	144,500	WE	1,067,000	—	EAF	—
Black Guillemot	35,100	WE	213,900	45,000	EAF	—
Puffin	720,000	WE	22,613,000	—	EAF	—
Snowy Owl	0	NW	—	3	NW	—
Short-eared Owl	1,000	NW	—	22,000	NW	—
Nightjar	2,000	NW	—	—	—	—
Kingfisher	5,000	NW	—	8,000	NW	—
Woodlark	220	NW	—	175	NW	—
Shore Lark	0	NW	—	900	NW	—
Wren (Fair Isle race)	33	W	33	80	W	80
Redwing	36	NW	—	800,000	NW	—
Dartford Warbler	500	NW	—	1,150	NW	—
Red-backed Shrike	1	NW	—	—	—	—
Chough	262	NW	—	742	NW	—
Brambling	2	NW	—	920,000	NW	—

	BREEDING			WINTERING		
	Great Britain	Biogeographical population		Great Britain	Biogeographical population	
		Area	Number		Area	Number
Twite	22,500	NW	–	100,000	NW	–
Scottish Crossbill	350	W	350	1,500	W	1,500
Snow Bunting	50	NW	–	10,000	NW	–

These population levels are subject to periodic review as new information becomes available. The above figures were used in this book to set the national and international contexts for each species in each IBA.

– = not applicable or no population estimate available; where entered under a 'biogeographical area' this indicates that there are no birds in NW Europe in the relevant season.

Biogeographical areas :
EAF – east Atlantic flyway; EC – European Community; NW – north-west Europe; NW + C – north-west & central Europe; W – world population of the species or race; WC – western & central Europe; WE – western Europe; WP – western Palearctic;

The information contained in this Appendix comes from a variety of sources. The main ones are :
Batten *et al* 1990; Gensbøl 1984; Lack 1986; Lloyd *et al* 1991; Moser 1987; Nature Conservancy Council 1989; Owen *et al* 1986; Piersma 1986; Pirot *et al* 1989; Prater 1981; Smit and Piersma 1989; Stroud *et al* 1990. (Details of these references can be found at the ends of chapters 1 and 2).

Population units used are pairs (for breeding numbers) or individuals (for wintering numbers). A few exceptions to this are described on page 18.

APPENDIX VI: ADDRESSES OF PRINCIPAL OFFICES OF THE PUBLISHING ORGANISATIONS

The Royal Society for the Protection of Birds

Headquarters: The Lodge, Sandy, Bedfordshire SG19 2DL Tel: 0767 680551

Northern Ireland Office: Belvoir Park Forest, Belfast BT8 4QT Tel: 0232 491547

Scottish Headquarters: 17 Regent Terrace, Edinburgh EH7 5BN Tel: 031-557 3136

Wales Office: Bryn Aderyn, The Bank, Newtown, Powys SY16 2AB Tel: 0686 626678

East Anglia Office: 97 Yarmouth Road, Thorpe St Andrew, Norwich NR7 OHF Tel: 0603 700880

East Midlands Office: The Lawn, Union Road, Lincoln LN1 3BU Tel: 0522 535596

East Scotland Office: 10 Albyn Terrace, Aberdeen AB1 1YB Tel: 0224 624824

Midlands Office: 44 Friar Street, Droitwich Spa, Worcestershire WR9 8ED Tel: 0905 770581

North of England Office: 'E' Floor, Milburn House, Dean Street, Newcastle upon Tyne NE1 1LE Tel: 091-232 4148

North Scotland Office: Units C1-C2, Beechwood Office Park, Inverness, Highland

North-West England Office: Brookfoot House, Elland Road, Brighouse, West Yorkshire HD6 2RW Tel: 0484 401112

South and West Scotland Office: Unit 3.1, West of Scotland Science Park, Kelvin Campus, Glasgow G20 OSP Tel: 041-945 5224

South-East England Office: 8 Church Street, Shoreham-by-Sea, West Sussex BN43 5DQ Tel: 0273 463642

South-West England Office: 10 Richmond Road, Exeter, Devon EX4 4JA Tel: 0392 432691

Thames and Chiltern Office: The Lodge, Sandy, Bedfordshire SG19 2DL Tel: 0767 680551

Joint Nature Conservation Committee

Headquarters: Monkstone House, City Road, Peterborough PE1 1JY Tel: 0733 62626

Ramsar/SPA Sites Unit: Battleby, Redgorton, Perth PH1 3EW Tel: 0738 27921

535

Seabirds Team: Wynne Edwards House, 17 Rubislaw Terrace, Aberdeen AB1 1XF
Tel: 0224 642863

Scottish Natural Heritage

Headquarters: 12 Hope Terrace, Edinburgh EH9 2AS Tel: 031-447 4784
2 Anderson Place, Edinburgh EH6 5NP Tel: 031-554 9797
Battleby, Redgorton, Perth PH1 3EW Tel: 0738 27921

North-East Region: Wynne Edwards House, 16/17 Rubislaw Terrace, Aberdeen AB1
1XE Tel: 0224 642863

North-West Region: Fraser Darling House, 9 Culduthel Road, Inverness IV2 4AG Tel:
0463 239431

South-East Region: Research Park (Avenue 1), Ricarton, Edinburgh EH14 4AP Tel:
031-449 4933

South-West Region: The Castle, Balloch Castle Country Park, Balloch, Strathclyde
G83 8LX Tel: 0389 58511

Countryside Council for Wales

Headquarters: Plas Penrhos, Ffordd Penrhos, Bangor, Gwynedd LL57 2LQ Tel: 0248
370444

Dyfed and Mid Wales Region: Plas Gogerddan, Aberystwyth, Dyfed SY23 3EE Tel:
0970 828551

North Wales Region: Hafod Elfyn, Ffordd Penrhos, Bangor, Gwynedd LL57 2LQ Tel:
0248 370444

South Wales Region: 43 The Parade, Roath, Cardiff CF2 3UH Tel: 0222 485111

English Nature

Headquarters: Northminster House, Peterborough PE1 1UA Tel: 0733 340345

North-West Region: Blackwell, Bowness-on-Windermere, Windermere, Cumbria
LA23 3JR Tel: 05394 45286

North-East Region: Archbold House, Archbold Terrace, Newcastle upon Tyne NE2
1EG Tel: 091-281 6316/7

East Region: Northminster House, Peterborough PE1 1UA Tel: 0733 340345

West Midlands Region: Attingham Park, Shrewsbury, Shropshire SY4 4TW Tel:
074377 611

South-East Region: The Countryside Management Centre, Coldharbour Farm, Wy Ashford, Kent TN25 5DB Tel: 0233 812525

South Region: Foxhold House, Crookham Common, Newbury, Berkshire RG15 8EL Tel: 0635 268881

South-West Region: Roughmoor, Bishop's Hull, Taunton, Somerset TA1 5AA Tel: 0823 283211

INDEX TO SITES

England